Test Bank

Precalculus
Functions and Graphs
ELEVENTH EDITION

Earl W. Swokowski

Jeffery A. Cole
Anoka-Ramsey Community College

Prepared by

Jay Domnitch
Palm Beach Community College

THOMSON

BROOKS/COLE

Australia • Brazil • Canada • Mexico • Singapore • Spain • United Kingdom • United States

ISBN-13: 978-0-495-38291-1
ISBN-10: 0-495-38291-4

Thomson Higher Education
10 Davis Drive
Belmont, CA 94002-3098
USA

For more information about our products, contact us at:
Thomson Learning Academic Resource Center
1-800-423-0563

For permission to use material from this text or product, submit a request online at **http://www.thomsonrights.com.**
Any additional questions about permissions can be submitted by email to **thomsonrights@thomson.com.**

Table of Contents

Chapter 9

Chapter 10

Final Exams

1. O'Carroll's formula is used to handicap weight lifters. If a lifter who weighs b kilograms lifts w kilograms of weight, then the handicapped weight W is given by:

$$W = \frac{w}{\sqrt[3]{b} - 35}$$

Suppose two lifters weighing 108 kilograms and 104 kilograms lift weights of 160 kilograms and 264 kilograms, respectively. Use O'Carroll's formula to determine the superior weight lifter.

2. Factor the polynomial: $28x^6 y^3 + 7 x^3 y^4$

3. Factor the polynomial: $36 x^3 + 12 x^2 + x$

4. Solve the formula for p: $\dfrac{1}{f} = \dfrac{1}{r} + \dfrac{1}{p}$

5. Solve the equation by factoring: $8x^2 + 2x - 15 = 0$

6. Solve the equation by factoring: $\dfrac{x}{x - 6} + \dfrac{7}{x + 6} = \dfrac{72}{x^2 - 36}$

7. Solve by using the quadratic formula: $20\,x^2 + 55 = 69\,x$

8. Two surveyors with two-way radios leave the same point at 9:00 A.M., one walking due south at 3 mi/hr and the other due west at 2 mi/hr. How long can they communicate with one another if each radio has a maximum range of 1.80 miles?

9. Write the expression

$$i^{26}$$

in the form $a + bi$, where a and b are real numbers.

10. Write the expression

$$\frac{-\,4 + 6i}{2 + 9i}$$

in the form $a + bi$, where a and b are real numbers.

11. Find the solutions of the equation

$$5\,x^2 - 40\,x + 160 = 0$$

12. Find the solutions of the equation

$$x^3 - 12\,x^2 + 117\,x = 0$$

13. Solve the equation

$$2\sqrt{x} - \sqrt{x-8} = \sqrt{x+11}$$

14. Solve the equation

$$x^{3/4} = 8$$

15. Solve the inequality :

$$|\,7x + 1\,| < 3$$

16. A construction firm is trying to decide which of two models of a crane to purchase. Model A costs $60000 and requires $4000 per year to maintain. Model B has an initial cost of $58500 and a maintenance cost of $4500 per year. For how many years must model A be used before it becomes more economical than B?

17. Solve the inequality

$x^2 - x - 30 < 0$

Express the answer in terms of intervals, if possible.

18. Solve the inequality

$$\frac{1}{x - 2} \geq \frac{8}{x + 34}$$

19. The braking distance d (in feet) of a certain car traveling v mi/hr is given by the equation $d = v + (v^2/20)$ Determine the velocities that result in braking distances of less than 40 feet. Express the answer in terms of intervals, if possible.

20. The population dynamics of many fish are characterized by extremely high fertility rates among adults and very low survival rates among the young. A mature halibut may lay as many as 2.3 million eggs, but only 0.00035% of the offspring survive to the age of 3 years. Use scientific form to approximate the number of offspring (in millions) that live to age 3.

21. Simplify the expression:

$$\frac{(7x^2)(9x^7)}{(x^2)^7}$$

22. Simplify the expression:

$$(4u^4v^3)(7u^5v^{-7})$$

23. Simplify the expression:

$$(6a^6b^7)^4 \left(\frac{-a^7}{3b^2} \right)^2$$

24. Simplify the expression, and rationalize the denominator when appropriate.

$$\sqrt[5]{\frac{2x^6y^3}{81x^5}}$$

25. Simplify the expression.

$$\frac{7x}{5x+3} - \frac{6}{5x^2+3x} + \frac{2}{x}$$

1. O'Carroll's formula is used to handicap weight lifters. If a lifter who weighs b kilograms lifts w kilograms of weight, then the handicapped weight W is given by:

$$W = \frac{w}{\sqrt[3]{b - 35}}$$

Suppose two lifters weighing 119 kilograms and 89 kilograms lift weights of 239 kilograms and 162 kilograms, respectively. Use O'Carroll's formula to determine the superior weight lifter.

2. Factor the polynomial: $25\,x^6 y^5 + 5\,x^4 y^6$

3. Factor the polynomial: $100\,x^3 + 20\,x^2 + x$

4. Solve the formula for q.
$$\frac{1}{h} = \frac{1}{r} + \frac{1}{q}$$

5. Solve the equation by factoring.

$$24x^2 + 14x - 49 = 0$$

6. Solve the equation by factoring.

$$\frac{x}{x - 6} + \frac{6}{x + 6} - \frac{72}{x^2 - 36}$$

7. Solve by using the quadratic formula.

$$24\,x^2 + 169 = 143\,x$$

8. Two surveyors with two-way radios leave the same point at 9:00 A.M., one walking due south at 2 mi/hr and the other due west at 4 mi/hr. How long can they communicate with one another if each radio has a maximum range of 2.98 miles?

9. Write the expression

$$i^{54}$$

in the form $a + bi$, where a and b are real numbers.

10. Write the expression

$$\frac{-\,4 + 6i}{2 + 7i}$$

in the form $a + bi$, where a and b are real numbers.

11. Find the solutions of the equation

$$9\,x^2 - 126\,x + 522 = 0$$

12. Find the solutions of the equation

$$x^3 - 18x^2 + 145x = 0$$

13. Solve the equation

$$2\sqrt{x} - \sqrt{x-2} = \sqrt{x+5}$$

14. Solve the equation

$$x^{3/4} = 64$$

15. Solve the inequality :

$$|13x + 4| < 7$$

16. A construction firm is trying to decide which of two models of a crane to purchase. Model A costs $50000 and requires $3500 per year to maintain. Model B has an initial cost of $48500 and a maintenance cost of $4000 per year. For how many years must model A be used before it becomes more economical than B?

17. Solve the inequality

$$x^2 - x - 2 < 0$$

Express the answer in terms of intervals, if possible.

18. Solve the inequality

$$\frac{1}{x - 1} \geq \frac{7}{x + 24}$$

19. The braking distance d (in feet) of a certain car traveling v mi/hr is given by the equation $d = v + (v^2/10)$
Determine the velocities that result in braking distances of less than 200 feet.
Express the answer in terms of intervals, if possible.

20. The population dynamics of many fish are characterized by extremely high fertility rates among adults and very low survival rates among the young. A mature halibut may lay as many as 2.5 million eggs, but only 0.00035% of the offspring survive to the age of 3 years. Use scientific form to approximate the number of offspring (in millions) that live to age 3.

21. Simplify the expression:

$$\frac{(3x^7)(8x^9)}{(x^7)^9}$$

22. Simplify the expression:

$$(4u^2v^2)(9u^6v^{-8})$$

23. Simplify the expression:

$$(8a^6b^8)^4 \left(\frac{-a^7}{4b^2} \right)^2$$

24. Simplify the expression, and rationalize the denominator when appropriate.

$$\sqrt[5]{\frac{2x^6y^2}{25x^3}}$$

25. Simplify the expression.

$$\frac{7x}{5x + 2} - \frac{6}{5x^2 + 2x} + \frac{3}{x}$$

1. Simplify the expression:

$$(10a^4b^5)^4 \left(\frac{-a^5}{5b^4} \right)^2$$

    a. $10a^4b^5$

    b. $-400a^{26}b^{12}$

    c. $-10a^4b^5$

    d. $-400a^4b^5$

    e. $400a^{26}b^{12}$

2. The length-weight relationship for Pacific halibut can be approximated by the formula:

$$L = 0.46 \sqrt[3]{W} ,$$

where W is in kilograms and L is in meters. The largest documented halibut weighed 202 kilograms. Estimate its length.

    a.   2.72 m

    b.   2.60 m

    c.   2.70 m

    d.   3.94 m

    e.   5.03 m

3. Express as a polynomial :

$$(6\,x + 10\,y)^3$$

a. $216x^3 + 1080x^2y + 600xy^2 + 6000y^3$

b. $216x^3 + 360x^2y + 1800xy^2 + 3600y^3$

c. $216x^3 + 360x^2y + 600xy^2 + 1000y^3$

d. $216x^3 + 1080x^2y + 1800xy^2 + 1000y^3$

4. Factor the polynomial :

$$4\,x^8y^3 + 2\,x^4y^4$$

a. $2x^4y^3(x^4 + y^4)$

b. $4x^4y^3(2x^4 + y^2)$

c. $2x^4y^3(x^4 + y)$

d. $2x^4y^3(2x^4 + y)$

5. Factor the polynomial :

$$16\,x^2 + 86\,x + 63$$

a. $(9x + 2)\,(8x + 7)$

b. $(2x + 7)\,(8x + 9)$

c. $(2x + 9)\,(8x + 7)$

d. $(2x + 9)\,(7x + 8)$

6. Factor the polynomial :

$$12\,x^2 - 75\,y^2$$

    a. $3(2x - 11y)\,(2x + 11y)$

    b. $3(2x - 5y)\,(2x + 5y)$

    c. $2(2x - 5y)\,(3x + 5y)$

    d. $2(3x - 5y)\,(3x + 11y)$

7. The basal energy requirement for an individual indicates the minimum number of calories necessary to maintain essential life-sustaining processes such as circulation, body temperature, and respiration. Given a person's sex, weight w (in kilograms), height h (in centimeters), and age y (in years), we can estimate the basal energy requirement in calories using the following formulas, where C_f and C_m are the calories necessary for females and males, respectively:

$$C_f = 66.5 + 13.8w + 5h - 6.8y$$
$$C_m = 655 + 9.6w + 1.9h - 4.7y$$

Determine the basal energy requirements for a 30-year-old female weighing 60 kilograms and 159 centimeters tall.

    a.   1560.7 calories

    b.   1392.1 calories

    c.   1485.5 calories

    d.   1316.9 calories

8. Simplify the expression

$$\frac{9x}{5x - 9} + \frac{27}{5x^2 - 9x} + \frac{3}{x}$$

    a. $\dfrac{2(2x + 5)}{5x - 9}$

    b. $\dfrac{3(3x + 5)}{5x - 2}$

    c. $\dfrac{3(3x + 5)}{5x - 9}$

    d. $\dfrac{3(3x + 2)}{2x - 9}$

9. Simplify the expression

$$\frac{\dfrac{8}{x + 2} + \dfrac{7x}{x + 3}}{\dfrac{x}{x + 2} + \dfrac{8}{x + 3}}$$

    a. $\dfrac{x^2 + 22x + 24}{x^2 + 11x + 16}$

    b. $\dfrac{7x^2 + 22x + 24}{x^2 + 16x + 11}$

    c. $\dfrac{7x^2 + 22x + 24}{x^2 + 11x + 16}$

    d. $\dfrac{7x^2 + 22x + 24}{x^2 + 11x + 13}$

10. Rationalize the denominator.

$$\dfrac{\sqrt{t} + 2}{\sqrt{t} - 2}$$

a. $\dfrac{t - 2\sqrt{t} + 2}{t - 2}$

b. $\dfrac{t^2 + 4t + 4}{t - 4}$

c. $\dfrac{t + 4\sqrt{t} + 4}{t - 4}$

d. $\dfrac{t + 4}{t - 4}$

11. Solve the formula for p.

$$S = \dfrac{b}{p + b(1 - p)}$$

a. $p = \dfrac{b(1 + S)}{S(1 - b)}$

b. $p = \dfrac{b(1 - S)}{S(1 + b)}$

c. $p = \dfrac{b(1 - S)}{S(1 - b)}$

d. $p = \dfrac{b(1 + S)}{S(1 + b)}$

12. A runner starts at the beginning of a runners' path and runs at a constant rate of 6 mi/hr. Five minutes later a second runner begins at the same point, running at a rate of 8 mi/hr and following the same course. How long will it take the second runner to reach the first?

    a.   24 minutes

    b.   25 minutes

    c.   20 minutes

    d.   17 minutes

13. It takes a boy 90 minutes to mow the lawn, but his sister can mow it in 60 minutes. How long would it take them to mow the lawn if they worked together, using two lawn mowers?

    a.   36 minutes

    b.   18 minutes

    c.   40 minutes

    d.   28 minutes

14. Solve the equation by factoring.

$$6x^2 + 11x - 35 = 0$$

    a. $x = \dfrac{5}{3}, \; x = -\dfrac{7}{2}$

    b. $x = \dfrac{7}{3}, \; x = -\dfrac{5}{2}$

    c. $x = 5, \; x = -7$

    d. $x = 3, \; x = -2$

15. Solve the equation by factoring.

$$\frac{x}{x-9} + \frac{1}{x+9} = \frac{162}{x^2-81}$$

     a. $x = -19,\ x = 9$

     b. $x = 81$

     c. $x = -9$

     d. $x = -19$

16. Solve by using the quadratic formula.

$$72\,x^2 + 169 = 234\,x$$

     a. $x = \dfrac{13}{12},\ x = \dfrac{13}{6}$

     b. $x = \dfrac{13}{11},\ x = \dfrac{13}{5}$

     c. $x = \dfrac{169}{12},\ x = \dfrac{169}{6}$

17. Two surveyors with two-way radios leave the same point at 9:00 A.M., one walking due south at 3 mi/hr and the other due west at 2 mi/hr. How long can they communicate with one another if each radio has a maximum range of 1.20 miles? Round the answer to the nearest minute.

     a.   20 minutes

     b.   16 minutes

     c.   58 minutes

     d.   42 minutes

18. Write the expression

$$i^{34}$$

in the form $a + bi$, where a and b are real numbers.

    a. i

    b.   1

    c.   -1

    d. $-i$

19. Write the expression

$$\frac{-4 + 6i}{2 + 9i}$$

in the form $a + bi$, where a and b are real numbers.

    a. $\dfrac{46}{85} + \dfrac{48i}{85}$

    b. $\dfrac{48i}{85}$

    c. $\dfrac{46}{85}$

    d. $\dfrac{46}{85} - \dfrac{48i}{85}$

20. Find the solutions of the equation

$$4x^2 - 24x + 136 = 0$$

    a. $6 + 6i, 6 - 6i$

    b. $3 + 5i, 3 - 5i$

    c. $-6 + 6i, -6 - 6i$

    d. $-3 + 5i, -3 - 5i$

21. Find the solutions of the equation: $x^3 - 10x^2 + 61x = 0$

    a.   0

    b. $0, -5 + 6i, -5 - 6i$

    c.   no solutions

    d. $0, 5 + 6i, 5 - 6i$

22. Solve the equation: $2\sqrt{x} - \sqrt{x - 2} = \sqrt{x + 11}$

    a. $x = \dfrac{72}{169}$

    b. $x = -\dfrac{72}{169}$

    c. $x = -\dfrac{169}{72}$

    d. $x = \dfrac{169}{72}$

23. Solve the equation: $x^{3/4} = 125$

    a. $x = 5$

    b. $x = 125$

    c. $x = 625$

    d. $x = 25$

24. Solve the inequality: $|7x + 1| < 4$

    a. $\left(-\infty, -\dfrac{4}{7}\right) \cup \left(\dfrac{4}{7}, \infty\right)$

    b. $\left(-\dfrac{5}{7}, \dfrac{3}{7}\right)$

    c. $\left(-\infty, -\dfrac{5}{7}\right) \cup \left(\dfrac{3}{7}, \infty\right)$

    d. $\left(-\dfrac{4}{7}, \dfrac{4}{7}\right)$

25. Solve the inequality

$x^2 - x - 20 < 0$

and express the solution in terms of intervals.

    a. $(-4, 5)$

    b. $(5, \infty)$

    c. $(-\infty, -4)$

    d. $(-\infty, -4) \cup (5, \infty)$

1. Simplify the expression:

$$(4a^5b^9)^4 \left(\frac{-a^7}{2b^7} \right)^2$$

   a. $4a^5b^9$

   b. $-4a^5b^9$

   c. $-64a^{34}b^{22}$

   d. $-64a^5b^9$

   e. $64a^{34}b^{22}$

2. The length-weight relationship for Pacific halibut can be approximated by the formula:

$$L = 0.46\sqrt[3]{W} ,$$

   where W is in kilograms and L is in meters. The largest documented halibut weighed 229 kilograms. Estimate its length.

   a.   2.83 m

   b.   5.14 m

   c.   2.81 m

   d.   4.05 m

   e.   2.71 m

3. Express as a polynomial :

$$(6\,x + 7\,y)^{\,3}$$

a. $216x^3 + 756x^2y + 294xy^2 + 2058y^3$

b. $216x^3 + 252x^2y + 294xy^2 + 343y^3$

c. $216x^3 + 756x^2y + 882xy^2 + 343y^3$

d. $216x^3 + 252x^2y + 882xy^2 + 1764y^3$

4. Factor the polynomial :

$$28\,x^5y^5 + 7\,x^2y^6$$

a. $7x^2y^5(x^3 + y^6)$

b. $28x^2y^5(4x^3 + y^2)$

c. $7x^2y^5(x^3 + y)$

d. $7x^2y^5(4x^3 + y)$

5. Factor the polynomial :

$$16\,x^2 + 74\,x + 63$$

a. $(8x + 9)\,(7x + 2)$

b. $(8x + 9)\,(2x + 7)$

c. $(9x + 8)\,(2x + 7)$

d. $(8x + 7)\,(2x + 9)$

6. Factor the polynomial :

$$36\ x^2 - 100\ y^2$$

a. $4(3x - 7y)\ (3x + 7y)$

b. $3(3x - 5y)\ (4x + 5y)$

c. $3(4x - 5y)\ (4x + 7y)$

d. $4(3x - 5y)\ (3x + 5y)$

7. The basal energy requirement for an individual indicates the minimum number of calories necessary to maintain essential life-sustaining processes such as circulation, body temperature, and respiration. Given a person's sex, weight w (in kilograms), height h (in centimeters), and age y (in years), we can estimate the basal energy requirement in calories using the following formulas, where C_f and C_m are the calories necessary for females and males, respectively:

$$C_f = 66.5 + 13.8w + 5h - 6.8y$$

$$C_m = 655 + 9.6w + 1.9h - 4.7y$$

Determine the basal energy requirements for a 29-year-old male weighing 74 kilograms and 176 centimeters tall.

a.   1770.5 calories

b.   1563.5 calories

c.   1638.7 calories

d.   1695.3 calories

8. Simplify the expression

$$\frac{25x}{3x - 25} + \frac{125}{3x^2 - 25x} + \frac{5}{x}$$

    a. $\dfrac{5(5x + 7)}{7x - 25}$

    b. $\dfrac{5(5x + 3)}{3x - 7}$

    c. $\dfrac{7(7x + 3)}{3x - 25}$

    d. $\dfrac{5(5x + 3)}{3x - 25}$

9. Simplify the expression

$$\frac{\dfrac{4}{x + 8} + \dfrac{7x}{x + 3}}{\dfrac{x}{x + 8} + \dfrac{6}{x + 3}}$$

    a. $\dfrac{7x^2 + 60x + 12}{x^2 + 48x + 9}$

    b. $\dfrac{7x^2 + 60x + 12}{x^2 + 9x + 48}$

    c. $\dfrac{x^2 + 60x + 12}{x^2 + 9x + 48}$

    d. $\dfrac{7x^2 + 60x + 12}{x^2 + 9x + 20}$

10. Rationalize the denominator.

$$\frac{\sqrt{t} + 1}{\sqrt{t} - 1}$$

a. $$\frac{t + 2\sqrt{t} + 1}{t - 1}$$

b. $$\frac{t + 1}{t - 1}$$

c. $$\frac{t - 2\sqrt{t} + 1}{t - 1}$$

d. $$\frac{t^2 + 2t + 1}{t - 1}$$

11. Solve the formula for d.

$$S = \frac{c}{d + c(1 - d)}$$

a. $$d = \frac{c(1 + S)}{S(1 - c)}$$

b. $$d = \frac{c(1 - S)}{S(1 + c)}$$

c. $$d = \frac{c(1 + S)}{S(1 + c)}$$

d. $$d = \frac{c(1 - S)}{S(1 - c)}$$

12. A runner starts at the beginning of a runners' path and runs at a constant rate of 4 mi/hr. Five minutes later a second runner begins at the same point, running at a rate of 6 mi/hr and following the same course. How long will it take the second runner to reach the first?

    a.   12 minutes

    b.   19 minutes

    c.   15 minutes

    d.   10 minutes

13. It takes a boy 120 minutes to mow the lawn, but his sister can mow it in 80 minutes. How long would it take them to mow the lawn if they worked together, using two lawn mowers?

    a.   52 minutes

    b.   48 minutes

    c.   40 minutes

    d.   24 minutes

14. Solve the equation by factoring.

$$15 x^2 + 4 x - 35 = 0$$

    a. $x = \dfrac{5}{5}, x = -\dfrac{7}{3}$

    b. $x = 5, x = -3$

    c. $x = 7, x = -5$

    d. $x = \dfrac{7}{5}, x = -\dfrac{5}{3}$

15. Solve the equation by factoring.

$$\frac{x}{x-2} + \frac{16}{x+2} - \frac{8}{x^2-4}$$

   a. $x = 4$

   b. $x = -20$

   c. $x = -20, x = 2$

   d. $x = -2$

16. Solve by using the quadratic formula.

$$18x^2 + 169 = 117x$$

   a. $x = \dfrac{169}{3}, x = \dfrac{169}{6}$

   b. $x = \dfrac{13}{2}, x = \dfrac{13}{5}$

   c. $x = \dfrac{13}{3}, x = \dfrac{13}{6}$

17. Two surveyors with two-way radios leave the same point at 9:00 A.M., one walking due south at 4 mi/hr and the other due west at 2 mi/hr. How long can they communicate with one another if each radio has a maximum range of 2.98 miles? Round the answer to the nearest minute.

   a.   116 minutes

   b.   84 minutes

   c.   36 minutes

   d.   40 minutes

18. Write the expression

$$i^{82}$$

in the form $a + bi$, where a and b are real numbers.

a. $-i$

b. -1

c. i

d. 1

19. Write the expression

$$\frac{-4 + 6i}{2 + 3i}$$

in the form $a + bi$, where a and b are real numbers.

a. $\dfrac{10}{13} + \dfrac{24i}{13}$

b. $\dfrac{10}{13}$

c. $\dfrac{10}{13} - \dfrac{24i}{13}$

d. $\dfrac{24i}{13}$

20. Find the solutions of the equation

$$3x^2 - 12x + 87 = 0$$

a. $-5 + 6i, -5 - 6i$

b. $-2 + 5i, -2 - 5i$

c. $5 + 6i, 5 - 6i$

d. $2 + 5i, 2 - 5i$

21. Find the solutions of the equation

$$x^3 - 6x^2 + 45x = 0$$

a.   no solutions

b. $0, -3 + 6i, -3 - 6i$

c. $0, 3 + 6i, 3 - 6i$

d. 0

22. Solve the equation

$$2\sqrt{x} - \sqrt{x-2} = \sqrt{x+7}$$

a. $x = \dfrac{40}{81}$

b. $x = \dfrac{81}{40}$

c. $x = -\dfrac{40}{81}$

d. $x = -\dfrac{81}{40}$

23. Solve the equation

$$x^{3/4} = 64$$

  a. $x = 4$

  b. $x = 64$

  c. $x = 256$

  d. $x = 16$

24. Solve the inequality :

$$|11x + 4| < 5$$

  a. $\left(-\infty, -\dfrac{9}{11} \right) \cup \left(\dfrac{1}{11}, \infty \right)$

  b. $\left(-\dfrac{5}{11}, \dfrac{5}{11} \right)$

  c. $\left(-\dfrac{9}{11}, \dfrac{1}{11} \right)$

  d. $\left(-\infty, -\dfrac{5}{11} \right) \cup \left(\dfrac{5}{11}, \infty \right)$

25. Solve the inequality

$$x^2 - x - 12 < 0$$

and express the solution in terms of intervals.

  a. $(-3, 4)$

  b. $(-\infty, -3) \cup (4, \infty)$

  c. $(-\infty, -3)$

  d. $(4, \infty)$

1. Rewrite the number without using the absolute value symbol, and simplify the result.

$$\left| \frac{1}{7} - \frac{1}{2} \right|$$

a. $\dfrac{9}{14}$

b. $\dfrac{3}{14}$

c. $-\dfrac{5}{14}$

d. $\dfrac{5}{14}$

2. The length-weight relationship for Pacific halibut can be approximated by the formula:

$$L = 0.46 \sqrt[3]{W} \,,$$

where W is in kilograms and L is in meters. The largest documented halibut weighed 251 kilograms. Estimate its length.

a.   2.80 m

b.   5.23 m

c.   4.14 m

d.   2.92 m

e.   2.90 m

3. Express as a polynomial :

$$(2x + 5y)^3$$

a. $8x^3 + 60x^2y + 50xy^2 + 250y^3$

b. $8x^3 + 60x^2y + 150xy^2 + 125y^3$

c. $8x^3 + 20x^2y + 50xy^2 + 125y^3$

d. $8x^3 + 20x^2y + 150xy^2 + 100y^3$

4. Factor the polynomial :

$$16\, x^2 - 484\, y^2$$

  a. $2(2x - 11y)\,(4x + 11y)$

  b. $4(2x - 5y)\,(2x + 5y)$

  c. $2(4x - 11y)\,(4x + 5y)$

  d. $4(2x - 11y)\,(2x + 11y)$

5. The basal energy requirement for an individual indicates the minimum number of calories necessary to maintain essential life-sustaining processes such as circulation, body temperature, and respiration. Given a person's sex, weight w (in kilograms), height h (in centimeters), and age y (in years), we can estimate the basal energy requirement in calories using the following formulas, where C_f and C_m are the calories necessary for females and males, respectively:

$$C_f = 66.5 + 13.8w + 5h - 6.8y$$
$$C_m = 655 + 9.6w + 1.9h - 4.7y$$

Determine the basal energy requirements for a 40-year-old female weighing 63 kilograms and 172 centimeters tall.

  a. 1398.6 calories

  b. 1599.1 calories

  c. 1323.4 calories

  d. 1523.9 calories

6. Simplify the expression

$$\dfrac{\dfrac{5}{x+4} + \dfrac{3x}{x+2}}{\dfrac{x}{x+4} + \dfrac{8}{x+2}}$$

a. $\dfrac{3x^2 + 17x + 10}{x^2 + 10x + 15}$

b. $\dfrac{x^2 + 17x + 10}{x^2 + 10x + 32}$

c. $\dfrac{3x^2 + 17x + 10}{x^2 + 32x + 10}$

d. $\dfrac{3x^2 + 17x + 10}{x^2 + 10x + 32}$

7. Solve the equation

$$\dfrac{-8}{x+4} + \dfrac{-8x+39}{x^2-16}$$

a. $x = -2$

b. $x = 4$

c. $x = 5$

d. $x = 3$

8. Two surveyors with two-way radios leave the same point at 9:00 A.M., one walking due south at 2 mi/hr and the other due west at 4 mi/hr. How long can they communicate with one another if each radio has a maximum range of 2.98 miles? Round the answer to the nearest minute.

  a.   116 minutes

  b.   40 minutes

  c.   84 minutes

  d.   28 minutes

9. Find the solutions of the equation

$$x^3 - 8\,x^2 + 80\,x = 0$$

  a. $0, -4 + 8i, -4 - 8i$

  b.   0

  c.   no solutions

  d. $0, 4 + 8i, 4 - 8i$

10. Solve the equation

$$3\,x^4 - 102\,x^2 + 675 = 0$$

  a. $6, -6, 2, -2$

  b. $6, 2$

  c. $25, 9$

  d. $5, -5, 3, -3$

11. Solve the inequality :

$$|7x + 1| < 7$$

a. $\left(-\infty, -\dfrac{7}{7}\right) \cup \left(\dfrac{7}{7}, \infty\right)$

b. $\left(-\dfrac{7}{7}, \dfrac{7}{7}\right)$

c. $\left(-\dfrac{8}{7}, \dfrac{6}{7}\right)$

d. $\left(-\infty, -\dfrac{8}{7}\right) \cup \left(\dfrac{6}{7}, \infty\right)$

12. A consumer is trying to decide whether to purchase car A or car B. Car A costs $10000 and has an mpg rating of 30, and insurance is $600 per year. Car B costs $12600 and has an mpg rating of 50, and insurance is $650 per year. Assume that the consumer drives 15,000 miles per year and that the price of gas remains constant at $1.25 per gallon. Based only on these facts, determine how long it will take for the total cost of car B to become less than that of car A.

a.   13 years

b.   14 years

c.   15 years

d.   12 years

13. O'Carroll's formula is used to handicap weight lifters. If a lifter who weighs b kilograms lifts w kilograms of weight, then the handicapped weight W is given by:

$$W = \frac{w}{\sqrt[3]{b} - 35}$$

Suppose two lifters weighing 113 kilograms and 116 kilograms lift weights of 193 kilograms and 226 kilograms, respectively. Use O'Carroll's formula to determine the superior weight lifter.

14. Solve the equation

$$\frac{5}{4} + \frac{-71}{12x + 4} = \frac{6}{3x + 1}$$

15. Solve the formula for d.

$$\frac{1}{g} = \frac{1}{w} + \frac{1}{d}$$

16. The speed of the current in a stream is 2.3 mi/hr. It takes a canoeist 80 minutes longer to paddle 1.2 miles upstream than to paddle the same distance downstream. What is the canoeist's rate in still water?

17. Find the solutions of the equation

$$5x^2 - 90x + 725 = 0$$

18. Find the solutions of the equation

$$x^3 - 8x^2 + 80x = 0$$

19. Solve the inequality :

$$2x(6x + 5) < (3x - 4)(4x + 1)$$

Express the answer in terms of intervals, if possible.

20. A construction firm is trying to decide which of two models of a crane to purchase. Model A costs $45000 and requires $3000 per year to maintain. Model B has an initial cost of $41000 and a maintenance cost of $5000 per year. For how many years must model A be used before it becomes more economical than B?

21. Solve the inequality

$$\frac{1}{x-2} \geq \frac{5}{x+11}$$

22. The braking distance d (in feet) of a certain car traveling v mi/hr is given by the equation $d = v + (v^2/20)$ Determine the velocities that result in braking distances of less than 120 feet. Express the answer in terms of intervals, if possible.

23. Simplify the expression:

$$\frac{(2x^7)(9x^7)}{(x^7)^7}$$

24. Simplify: $\left(27a^9\right)^{-2/3}$

25. Simplify the expression.

$$\frac{5x}{9x+2} - \frac{6}{9x^2+2x} + \frac{3}{x}$$

1. Rewrite the number without using the absolute value symbol, and simplify the result.

$$\left| \frac{1}{7} - \frac{1}{4} \right|$$

    a. $\dfrac{5}{28}$

    b. $-\dfrac{3}{28}$

    c. $\dfrac{3}{28}$

    d. $\dfrac{11}{28}$

2. The length-weight relationship for Pacific halibut can be approximated by the formula:

$$L = 0.46 \sqrt[3]{W},$$

where W is in kilograms and L is in meters. The largest documented halibut weighed 251 kilograms. Estimate its length.

    a.   5.23 m

    b.   2.92 m

    c.   2.80 m

    d.   4.14 m

    e.   2.90 m

3. Express as a polynomial:

$$(2x + 5y)^3$$

a. $8x^3 + 20x^2y + 50xy^2 + 125y^3$

b. $8x^3 + 60x^2y + 50xy^2 + 250y^3$

c. $8x^3 + 20x^2y + 150xy^2 + 100y^3$

d. $8x^3 + 60x^2y + 150xy^2 + 125y^3$

4. Factor the polynomial :

$$18x^2 - 242y^2$$

a. $3(3x - 11y)(2x + 11y)$

b. $2(3x - 5y)(3x + 5y)$

c. $2(3x - 11y)(3x + 11y)$

d. $3(2x - 11y)(2x + 5y)$

5. The basal energy requirement for an individual indicates the minimum number of calories necessary to maintain essential life-sustaining processes such as circulation, body temperature, and respiration. Given a person's sex, weight w (in kilograms), height h (in centimeters), and age y (in years), we can estimate the basal energy requirement in calories using the following formulas, where C_f and C_m are the calories necessary for females and males, respectively:

$$C_f = 66.5 + 13.8w + 5h - 6.8y$$
$$C_m = 655 + 9.6w + 1.9h - 4.7y$$

Determine the basal energy requirements for a 55-year-old female weighing 64 kilograms and 173 centimeters tall.

a.   1515.9 calories

b.   1440.7 calories

c.   1339.6 calories

d.   1264.4 calories

6. Simplify the expression

$$\dfrac{\dfrac{5}{x+8} + \dfrac{7x}{x+1}}{\dfrac{x}{x+8} + \dfrac{9}{x+1}}$$

    a. $\dfrac{x^2 + 61x + 5}{x^2 + 10x + 72}$

    b. $\dfrac{7x^2 + 61x + 5}{x^2 + 10x + 15}$

    c. $\dfrac{7x^2 + 61x + 5}{x^2 + 72x + 10}$

    d. $\dfrac{7x^2 + 61x + 5}{x^2 + 10x + 72}$

7. Solve the equation

$$\dfrac{-4}{x+4} + \qquad\qquad \dfrac{-4x+26}{x^2-16}$$

    a. $x = 4$

    b. $x = -5$

    c. $x = 6$

    d. $x = 8$

8. Two surveyors with two-way radios leave the same point at 9:00 A.M., one walking due south at 3 mi/hr and the other due west at 2 mi/hr. How long can they communicate with one another if each radio has a maximum range of 1.20 miles? Round the answer to the nearest minute.

    a.   20 minutes

    b.   58 minutes

    c.   42 minutes

    d.   14 minutes

9. Find the solutions of the equation

$$x^3 - 16 x^2 + 73 x = 0$$

    a. $0, 8 + 3i, 8 - 3i$

    b.   0

    c.   no solutions

    d. $0, -8 + 3i, -8 - 3i$

10. Solve the equation

$$5 x^4 - 185 x^2 + 180 = 0$$

    a. $2, -2, 5, -5$

    b. $1, 36$

    c. $1, -1, 6, -6$

    d. $2, 5$

11. Solve the inequality :

$$|13x + 1| < 8$$

   a. $\left(-\dfrac{9}{13}, \dfrac{7}{13}\right)$

   b. $\left(-\infty, -\dfrac{9}{13}\right) \cup \left(\dfrac{7}{13}, \infty\right)$

   c. $\left(-\dfrac{8}{13}, \dfrac{8}{13}\right)$

   d. $\left(-\infty, -\dfrac{8}{13}\right) \cup \left(\dfrac{8}{13}, \infty\right)$

12. A consumer is trying to decide whether to purchase car A or car B. Car A costs $10000 and has an mpg rating of 30, and insurance is $500 per year. Car B costs $12200 and has an mpg rating of 50, and insurance is $550 per year. Assume that the consumer drives 15,000 miles per year and that the price of gas remains constant at $1.25 per gallon. Based only on these facts, determine how long it will take for the total cost of car B to become less than that of car A.

   a.   12 years

   b.   11 years

   c.   13 years

   d.   10 years

13. O'Carroll's formula is used to handicap weight lifters. If a lifter who weighs b kilograms lifts w kilograms of weight, then the handicapped weight W is given by:

$$W = \frac{w}{\sqrt[3]{b} - 35}$$

Suppose two lifters weighing 113 kilograms and 88 kilograms lift weights of 182 kilograms and 216 kilograms, respectively. Use O'Carroll's formula to determine the superior weight lifter.

14. Solve the equation

$$\frac{4}{7} + \frac{-3}{21x + 7} - \frac{7}{3x + 1}$$

15. Solve the formula for q.

$$\frac{1}{f} = \frac{1}{r} + \frac{1}{q}$$

16. The speed of the current in a stream is 2.8 mi/hr. It takes a canoeist 85 minutes longer to paddle 1.9 miles upstream than to paddle the same distance downstream. What is the canoeist's rate in still water?

17. Find the solutions of the equation

$$7 x^2 - 56 x + 287 = 0$$

18. Find the solutions of the equation

$$x^3 - 12 x^2 + 117 x = 0$$

19. Solve the inequality :

$$4x(3x + 5) < (6x - 2)(2x + 1)$$

Express the answer in terms of intervals, if possible.

20. A construction firm is trying to decide which of two models of a crane to purchase. Model A costs $45000 and requires $4000 per year to maintain. Model B has an initial cost of $34500 and a maintenance cost of $5500 per year. For how many years must model A be used before it becomes more economical than B?

21. Solve the inequality

$$\frac{1}{x-3} \geq \frac{8}{x+19}$$

22. The braking distance d (in feet) of a certain car traveling v mi/hr is given by the equation $d = v + (v^2/20)$ Determine the velocities that result in braking distances of less than 40 feet. Express the answer in terms of intervals, if possible.

23. Simplify the expression:

$$\frac{(4x^3)(9x^4)}{(x^3)^4}$$

24. Simplify.

$$\left(625a^{16}\right)^{-3/4}$$

25. Simplify the expression.

$$\frac{5x}{7x+3} - \frac{6}{7x^2+3x} + \frac{2}{x}$$

Test Form 1-A

1. 104
2. $7x^3 \cdot y^3 \cdot \left(4x^3 + y\right)$
3. $x \cdot (6x+1)^2$
4. $p = \dfrac{f \cdot r}{(r-f)}$
5. $\dfrac{5}{4}, -\dfrac{3}{2}$
6. -19
7. $\dfrac{11}{5}, \dfrac{5}{4}$
8. 30 min
9. -1

10. $\dfrac{46}{85} + \dfrac{48i}{85}$
11. $4+4i, 4-4i$
12. $0, 6+9i, 6-9i$
13. $\dfrac{361}{24}$
14. 16
15. $\left(-\dfrac{4}{7}, \dfrac{2}{7}\right)$
16. 3
17. $\{-5, 6\}$
18. $(-\infty, -34) \cup \left(2, \dfrac{50}{7}\right]$

19. $(0, 20)$
20. 8.05×10^{-6}
21. $\dfrac{63}{x^5}$
22. $\dfrac{28u^9}{v^4}$
23. $144a^{46} \cdot b^{24}$
24. $\dfrac{1}{3} \cdot \sqrt[5]{6x^3 \cdot y^3}$
25. $\dfrac{7x+10}{5x+3}$

Test Form 1-B

1. 239
2. $5x^4 \cdot y^5 \cdot \left(5x^2 + y\right)$
3. $x \cdot (10x+1)^2$
4. $q = \dfrac{h \cdot r}{(r-h)}$
5. $\dfrac{7}{6}, -\dfrac{7}{4}$
6. -18
7. $\dfrac{13}{3}, \dfrac{13}{8}$
8. 40 min
9. -1

10. $\dfrac{34}{53} + \dfrac{40i}{53}$
11. $7+3i, 7-3i$
12. $0, 9+8i, 9-8i$
13. $\dfrac{49}{24}$
14. 256
15. $\left(-\dfrac{11}{13}, \dfrac{3}{13}\right)$
16. 3
17. $\{-1, 2\}$
18. $(-\infty, -24) \cup \left(1, \dfrac{31}{6}\right]$

19. $(0, 40)$
20. 8.75×10^{-6}
21. $\dfrac{24}{x^{47}}$
22. $\dfrac{36u^8}{v^6}$
23. $256a^{46} \cdot b^{26}$
24. $\dfrac{1}{5} \cdot \sqrt[5]{250x^3 \cdot y^2}$
25. $\dfrac{7x+15}{5x+2}$

Test Form 1-C

1.	e	14.	a
2.	c	15.	d
3.	d	16.	a
4.	d	17.	a
5.	c	18.	c
6.	b	19.	a
7.	c	20.	b
8.	c	21.	d
9.	c	22.	d
10.	c	23.	c
11.	c	24.	b
12.	c	25.	a
13.	a		

Test Form 1-D

1.	e	14.	d
2.	c	15.	b
3.	c	16.	c
4.	d	17.	d
5.	b	18.	b
6.	d	19.	a
7.	b	20.	d
8.	d	21.	c
9.	b	22.	b
10.	a	23.	c
11.	d	24.	c
12.	c	25.	a
13.	b		

Test Form 1-E

1.	d	16.	3, 1	
2.	e	17.	$9+8i, 9-8i$	
3.	b	18.	$0, 4+8i, 4-8i$	
4.	d	19.	$\left(-\infty, -\dfrac{4}{23}\right)$	
5.	d			
6.	d	20.	2	
7.	d	21.	$(-\infty, -11) \cup \left(2, \dfrac{21}{4}\right]$	
8.	b			
9.	d	22.	$(0, 40)$	
10.	d	23.	$\dfrac{18}{x^{35}}$	
11.	c			
12.	a			
13.	116	24.	$\dfrac{1}{9a^6}$	
14.	$x = 6$			
15.	$d = \dfrac{g \cdot w}{(w-g)}$	25.	$\dfrac{5x+27}{9x+2}$	

Test Form 1-F

1.	c	16.	3, 9	
2.	e	17.	$4+5i, 4-5i$	
3.	d	18.	$0, 6+9i, 6-9i$	
4.	c	19.	$\left(-\infty, -\dfrac{1}{9}\right)$	
5.	b			
6.	d	20.	7	
7.	c	21.	$(-\infty, -19) \cup \left(3, \dfrac{43}{7}\right]$	
8.	a			
9.	a	22.	$(0, 20)$	
10.	c	23.	$\dfrac{36}{x^5}$	
11.	a			
12.	b			
13.	88	24.	$\dfrac{1}{125a^{12}}$	
14.	$x = 4$			
15.	$q = \dfrac{f \cdot r}{(r-f)}$	25.	$\dfrac{5x+14}{7x+3}$	

1. Given $A(-2, 6)$, find the coordinates of the point B such that $C(3, -9)$ is the midpoint of segment AB.

2. Find an equation of the circle that satisfies the conditions:

   center $C(6, -4)$, radius 8

3. Find an equation of the circle that satisfies the conditions:

   endpoints of the diameter $A(8, -17)$ and $B(-4, 19)$

4. Find the slope-intercept form of the line with the x-intercept 13 and y-intercept -4.

5. Find the slope-intercept form of the line through the points $A(5, 0)$ and $B(-1, 4)$.

6. Find a general form of an equation for the perpendicular bisector of the segment AB.

$$A(2, -1);\ B(-4, 3)$$

7. Find an equation of the circle that has center $C(2, -3)$ and is tangent to the line $y = 5$.

8. If *a* and *h* are real numbers, find

$$\frac{f(a + h) - f(a)}{h}, \quad h \neq 0 \quad \text{if}$$

$$f(x) = 3x - 1$$

9. Find the domain of *f*.

$$f(x) = \sqrt{x^2 - 9}$$

10. Find the domain of *f*.

$$f(x) = \frac{4}{6x^2 + 24x - 126}$$

11. Find the domain of *f*.

$$f(x) = \frac{\sqrt{6x - 7}}{x^2 - 9}$$

12. Simplify the difference quotient $\dfrac{f(x + h) - f(x)}{h}$, $h \neq 0$ if $f(x) = x^2 + 9$

13. If a linear function *f* satisfies the conditions: $f(-3) = -10$ and $f(3) = 14$, find $f(x)$.

14. Express the function

$$f(x) = -\frac{3}{4}x^2 + 15x - 30$$

in the form $a(x - h)^2 + k$.

15. Use the quadratic formula to find the zeros of the function
$$f(x) = 25x^2 + 60x + 36$$

16. The parabola shown below has a vertex of (3, 9); find the standard equation.

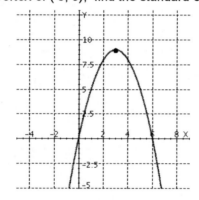

17. Find the standard equation of the parabola shown in the figure.

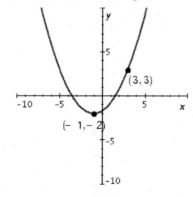

18. An object is projected vertically upward from the top of a building with an initial velocity of 112 ft/sec. Its distance in feet above the ground after t seconds is given by the equation

$s(t) = -16t^2 + 112t + 91$

Find its maximum distance above the ground.

19. A cable television firm presently serves 2400 households and charges $16 per month. A marketing survey indicates that each decrease of $1 in the monthly charge will result in 240 new customers. Let $R(x)$ denote the total monthly revenue when the monthly charge is x dollars. Determine the revenue function R.

20. Let $f(x) = 6x + 3$, $g(x) = x^2$. Find:

$(f + g)(1)$

21. Let $f(x) = 6x - 7$, $g(x) = 4x^2 - x + 2$. Find:

$(g \circ f)(x)$

22. A spherical balloon is being inflated at a rate of $\frac{9}{2}\pi$ cm^3/sec. Express its radius R as a function of time t (in seconds), assuming that $R = 0$ when $t = 0$.

23. Sketch the graph of the circle:

$$(x + 3)^2 + (y - 2)^2 = 9$$

24. Sketch the graph of *f*.

$$f(x) = \begin{cases} x + 2 & \text{if } x \le -1 \\ x^3 & \text{if } |x| < 1 \\ -x + 3 & \text{if } x \ge 1 \end{cases}$$

25. Sketch the graph of the function.

$$f(x) = 2x^2 - 4x - 8$$

1. Given $A(-2, 5)$, find the coordinates of the point B such that $C(4, -8)$ is the midpoint of segment AB.

2. Find an equation of the circle that satisfies the conditions:

    center $C(7, -7)$, radius 7

3. Find an equation of the circle that satisfies the conditions:

    endpoints of the diameter $A(20, -17)$ and $B(-10, 19)$

4. Find the slope-intercept form of the line with the x-intercept 8 and y-intercept - 15.

5. Find the slope-intercept form of the line through the points $A(5, 0)$ and $B(-1, 4)$.

6. Find a general form of an equation for the perpendicular bisector of the segment AB.

    $$A(3, -2); B(-5, 4)$$

7. Find an equation of the circle that has center $C(3, -2)$ and is tangent to the line $y = 6$.

8. If a and h are real numbers, find

$$\frac{f(a + h) - f(a)}{h}, \quad h \neq 0 \quad \text{if}$$

$$f(x) = 7x - 3$$

9. Find the domain of f.

$$f(x) = \sqrt{x^2 - 16}$$

10. Find the domain of f.

$$f(x) = \frac{5}{9x^2 + 45x - 126}$$

11. Find the domain of f.

$$f(x) = \frac{\sqrt{5x - 3}}{x^2 - 9}$$

12. Simplify the difference quotient $\dfrac{f(x + h) - f(x)}{h}, \quad h \neq 0 \quad \text{if}$

$$f(x) = x^2 + 5$$

13. If a linear function f satisfies the conditions : $f(-3) = -13$ and $f(3) = 23$, find $f(x)$.

14. Express the function

$$f(x) = -\frac{3}{4}x^2 + 12x - 40$$

in the form $a(x - h)^2 + k$.

15. Use the quadratic formula to find the zeros of the function
$$f(x) = 9x^2 + 48x + 64$$

16. The parabola shown below has a vertex of (1, 1); find the standard equation.

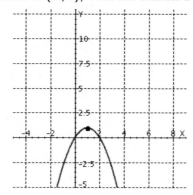

17. Find the standard equation of the parabola shown in the figure.

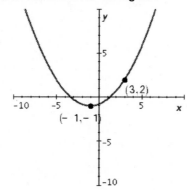

18. An object is projected vertically upward from the top of a building with an initial velocity of 112 ft/sec. Its distance in feet above the ground after t seconds is given by the equation

$$s\,(t) = -16t^2 + 112\,t + 96$$

Find its maximum distance above the ground.

19. A cable television firm presently serves 6500 households and charges $23 per month. A marketing survey indicates that each decrease of $1 in the monthly charge will result in 650 new customers. Let $R(x)$ denote the total monthly revenue when the monthly charge is x dollars. Determine the revenue function R.

20. Let $f\,(x) = 8\,x + 3$, $g\,(x) = x^2$. Find:

$$(f + g)(4)$$

21. Let $f(x) = 9x - 9$, $g(x) = 5x^2 - x + 6$. Find:

$$(g \circ f)(x)$$

22. A spherical balloon is being inflated at a rate of $\frac{9}{2}\pi$ ft^3/min. Express its radius R as a function of time t (in minutes), assuming that $R = 0$ when $t = 0$.

23. Sketch the graph of the circle:

$$(x + 3)^2 + (y - 2)^2 = 9$$

24. Sketch the graph of *f*.

$$f(x) = \begin{cases} x + 2 & \text{if } x \leq -1 \\ x^3 & \text{if } |x| < 1 \\ -x + 3 & \text{if } x \geq 1 \end{cases}$$

25. Sketch the graph of the function.

$$f(x) = 3x^2 - 6x - 7$$

1. Given $A(-5, 7)$, find the coordinates of the point B such that $C(3, -7)$ is the midpoint of segment AB.

    a. $B(16, -28)$

    b. $B(11, -21)$

    c. $B(11, -28)$

    d. $B(16, -21)$

2. Sketch the graph of the equation: $(x + 1)^2 + (y - 4)^2 = 9$

    a.

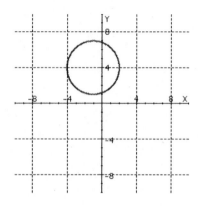

    b.

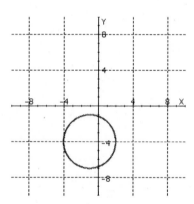

    c.

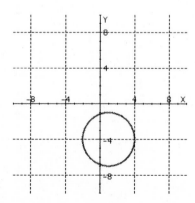

3. Find the equation of the circle that satisfies the conditions:

center C (9, - 3), tangent to the y-axis

    a. $(x + 9)^2 + (y - 3)^2 = 9$

    b. $(x - 9)^2 + (y + 3)^2 = 81$

    c. $(x + 9)^2 - (y + 3)^2 = 81$

    d. $(x - 9)^2 + (y + 3)^2 = 9$

    e. $(x + 9)^2 + (y + 3)^2 = 9$

4. Find the equation of the circle that satisfies the conditions:

endpoints of the diameter A (12, - 1) and B (- 2, 19)

    a. $(x + 5)^2 - (y + 9)^2 = 154$

    b. $(x - 5)^2 + (y - 9)^2 = 149$

    c. $(x + 5)^2 + (y - 9)^2 = 151$

    d. $(x + 5)^2 + (y + 9)^2 = 151$

    e. $(x - 5)^2 + (y + 9)^2 = 149$

5. Find the center and radius for the circle

$x^2 + y^2 + 6x - 18y + 54 = 0$

    a.   center c (- 3, 9), radius 6

    b.   center c (- 2, 11), radius 6

    c.   center c (- 3, - 11), radius 8

    d.   center c (3, - 9), radius 8

    e.   center c (- 3, - 9), radius 8

6. Find a general form of an equation of the line through the points A (2, - 4) and B (- 2, 5).

    a. $4x - 9y = 2$

    b. $4y = 9$

    c. $9x + 4y = 2$

7. Find a general form of an equation of the line through the point A (- 2, 3) with the x-intercept 0

    a. $2x - 3y = 0$

    b. $3x = 2$

    c. $3x + 2y = 0$

8. Find a general form of an equation for the perpendicular bisector of the segment AB.

$$A (8, - 5); B (- 4, 9)$$

    a. $6x + 7y = 2$

    b. $5x - 8y = - 2$

    c. $6x - 7y = - 2$

9. The line below has a slope of $-\frac{7}{4}$. Find a slope-intercept form of an equation of the line shown in the figure.

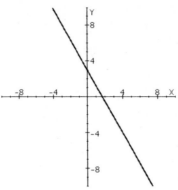

a. $y = \frac{7}{4}x + 8$

b. $y = -\frac{7}{4}x + 3$

c. $y = -6$

10. The growth of a fetus more than 12 weeks old can be approximated by the formula $L = 1.53t - 6.7$, where L is the length (in centimeters) and t is the age (in weeks). Prenatal length can be determined by ultrasound. Approximate the age of a fetus whose length is 25.43 centimeters.

a.   21 weeks

b.   18 weeks

c.   26 weeks

11.
Find the domain of $f(x) = \sqrt{x^2 - 16}$

    a. $[4, \infty)$

    b. $(-4, 4)$

    c. $(-\infty, -4] \cup [4, \infty)$

    d. $[16, \infty)$

12. Find the domain of f.

$$f(x) = \frac{2}{4x^2 + 12x - 72}$$

    a. $(-\infty, -6) \cup (3, \infty)$

    b. $(-\infty, -4) \cup (-4, 2) \cup (2, \infty)$

    c. $(-\infty, -6) \cup (-6, 3) \cup (3, \infty)$

    d. $(-\infty, -4) \cup (2, \infty)$

13.
Simplify the difference quotient $\dfrac{f(x + h) - f(x)}{h}$, $h \neq 0$ if

$$f(x) = x^2 + 8$$

    a. $\dfrac{f(x + h) - f(x)}{h} = 2x + h$

    b. $\dfrac{f(x + h) - f(x)}{h} = 2x + h + 16$

    c. $\dfrac{f(x + h) - f(x)}{h} = x + h$

    d. $\dfrac{f(x + h) - f(x)}{h} = 2x$

14. If a linear function *f* satisfies the conditions : $f(-3) = -7$ and $f(3) = 23$, find $f(x)$.

    a. $f(x) = -7x - 8$

    b. $f(x) = 5x + 8$

    c. $f(x) = 7x + 11$

15. Graph the function: $f(x) = |x| + 2$

    a.

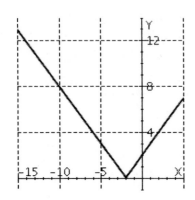

    b.

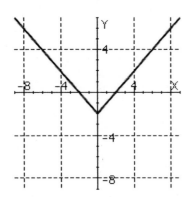

    c.

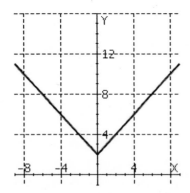

16. Graph the function $f(x) = \sqrt{5x} - 1$

a.

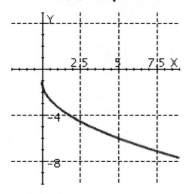

b.

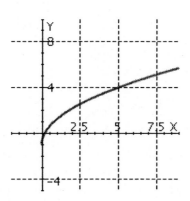

c.

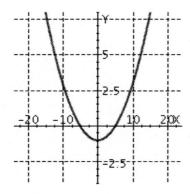

17. Sketch the graph of *f*

$$f(x) = \begin{cases} x + 2 & \text{if } x \le -1 \\ x^3 & \text{if } |x| < 1 \\ -x + 5 & \text{if } x \ge 1 \end{cases}$$

a.

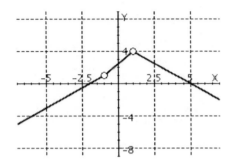

b.

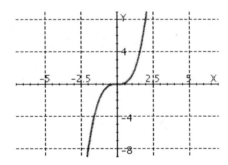

c.

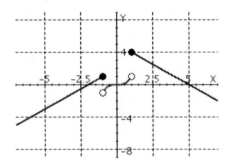

18. Express the function

$$f(x) = -\frac{3}{4}x^2 + 15x - 41$$

in the form $a(x - h)^2 + k$.

   a. $f(x) = -3(\frac{1}{2}x - 5)^2 - 41$

   b. $f(x) = -\frac{3}{4}(x - 10)^2 + 34$

   c. $f(x) = (-\frac{3}{4}x + 10)^2 - 41$

19. Use the quadratic formula to find the zeros of the function

$$f(x) = 49x^2 + 56x + 16$$

   a. $-\dfrac{7}{9}$

   b. $-\dfrac{8}{7}$

   c. $-\dfrac{4}{7}$

   d. $\dfrac{4}{9}$

20. Sketch the graph of the function

$f(x) = 3x^2 - 6x - 8$

a.

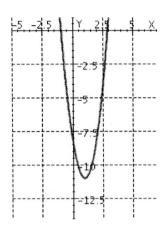

b.

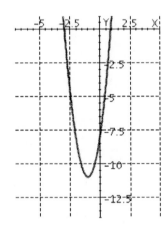

c.

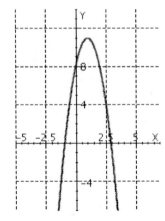

21. An object is projected vertically upward from the top of a building with an initial velocity of 144 ft/sec. Its distance in feet above the ground after t seconds is given by the equation

$s\,(t) = -16t^2 + 144\,t + 93$

Find its maximum distance above the ground.

    a.   444 feet

    b.   424 feet

    c.   403 feet

    d.   417 feet

22. Let $f\,(x) = 2\,x + 4$, $g\,(x) = x^2$. Find:

$(f + g)(1)$

    a. $(f + g)(1) = 12$

    b. $(f + g)(1) = 4$

    c. $(f + g)(1) = 7$

    d. $(f + g)(1) = 6$

    e. $(f + g)(1) = 14$

23. Let $f(x) = 6x - 5$, $g(x) = 6x^2 - x + 7$. Find $(g \circ f)(x)$

    a. $(g \circ f)(x) = 223x^2 - 732x + 162$

    b. $(g \circ f)(x) = 216x^2 - 366x + 162$

    c. $(g \circ f)(x) = -216x^2 + \text{?} \; 178$

    d. $(g \circ f)(x) = -216x^2 + \text{?} \; 162$

    e. $(g \circ f)(x) = -223x^2 + 732x - 178$

24. Several values of two functions T and S are listed in the following tables:

t	0	1	2	3
$T(t)$	2	3	1	0

x	0	1	2	3
$S(x)$	1	0	3	2

Find:

$(S \circ T)(2)$

    a. $(S \circ T)(2) = 0$

    b. $(S \circ T)(2) = 2$

    c. $(S \circ T)(2) = 1$

    d. $(S \circ T)(2) = 3$

25. A 100-foot-long cable of diameter 2 inches is submerged in seawater. Because of corrosion, the surface area of the cable decreases at the rate of 600 in^2 per year. Express the diameter d of the cable as a function of time t (in years). (Disregard corrosion at the ends of the cable.)

    a. $d = 2 - 6\pi t$

    b. $d = 2 + \dfrac{6}{\pi} t$

    c. $d = 2\pi - 6t$

    d. $d = 2\pi t - 6$

    e. $d = 2 - \dfrac{6}{\pi} t$

1. Given $A(-4, 10)$, find the coordinates of the point B such that $C(7, -10)$ is the midpoint of segment AB.

    a. $B(22, -30)$

    b. $B(18, -30)$

    c. $B(22, -40)$

    d. $B(18, -40)$

2. Sketch the graph of the equation: $(x + 1)^2 + (y - 4)^2 = 4$

    a.

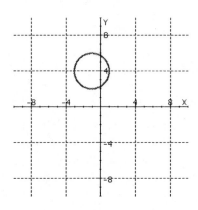

    b.

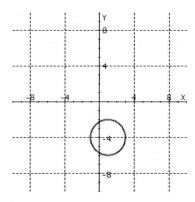

    c.

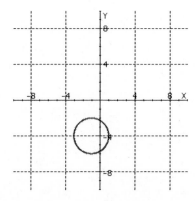

3. Find the equation of the circle that satisfies the conditions:

    center C (5, - 9), tangent to the y-axis

    a. $(x - 5)^2 + (y + 9)^2 = 5$

    b. $(x + 5)^2 + (y + 9)^2 = 5$

    c. $(x + 5)^2 + (y - 9)^2 = 5$

    d. $(x + 5)^2 - (y + 9)^2 = 25$

    e. $(x - 5)^2 + (y + 9)^2 = 25$

4. Find the equation of the circle that satisfies the conditions:

    endpoints of the diameter A (16, - 1) and B (- 8, 17)

    a. $(x + 4)^2 + (y + 8)^2 = 227$

    b. $(x - 4)^2 + (y + 8)^2 = 225$

    c. $(x - 4)^2 + (y - 8)^2 = 225$

    d. $(x + 4)^2 + (y - 8)^2 = 227$

    e. $(x + 4)^2 - (y + 8)^2 = 230$

5. Find the center and radius for the circle

    $x^2 + y^2 + 8x - 18y + 96 = 0$

    a.   center c (4, - 9), radius 3

    b.   center c (- 4, - 9), radius 3

    c.   center c (- 3, 11), radius 1

    d.   center c (- 4, - 11), radius 3

    e.   center c (- 4, 9), radius 1

6. Find a general form of an equation of the line through the points A (2, - 2) and B (- 2, 7).

    a. $4y = 9$

    b. $4x - 9y = 10$

    c. $9x + 4y = 10$

7. Find a general form of an equation of the line through the point A (- 4, 5) with the x-intercept 0

    a. $4x - 5y = 0$

    b. $5x + 4y = 0$

    c. $5x = 4$

8. Find a general form of an equation for the perpendicular bisector of the segment AB.

$$A (6, - 8); B (- 2, 14)$$

    a. $3x - 12y = - 25$

    b. $4x - 11y = - 25$

    c. $4x + 11y = 25$

9. The line below has a slope of $-\dfrac{7}{3}$. Find a slope-intercept form of an equation of the line shown in the figure.

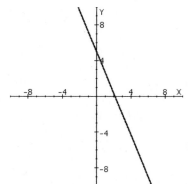

    a. $y = \dfrac{7}{3}x + 10$

    b. $y = - 8$

    c. $y = -\dfrac{7}{3}x + 5$

10. The growth of a fetus more than 12 weeks old can be approximated by the formula $L = 1.53t - 6.7$, where L is the length (in centimeters) and t is the age (in weeks). Prenatal length can be determined by ultrasound. Approximate the age of a fetus whose length is 22.37 centimeters.

    a.   19 weeks

    b.   24 weeks

    c.   16 weeks

11. Find the domain of $ff(x) = \sqrt{x^2 - 36}$

    a. $[6, \infty)$

    b. $[36, \infty)$

    c. $(-\infty, -6] \cup [6, \infty)$

    d. $(-6, 6)$

12. Find the domain of f.

$$f(x) = \frac{7}{4x^2 + 8x - 96}$$

    a. $(-\infty, -6) \cup (4, \infty)$

    b. $(-\infty, -3) \cup (-3, 8) \cup (8, \infty)$

    c. $(-\infty, -3) \cup (8, \infty)$

    d. $(-\infty, -6) \cup (-6, 4) \cup (4, \infty)$

13. Simplify the difference quotient $\dfrac{f(x+h) - f(x)}{h}$, $h \neq 0$ if

$$f(x) = x^2 + 3$$

a. $\dfrac{f(x+h) - f(x)}{h} = 2x + h$

b. $\dfrac{f(x+h) - f(x)}{h} = 2x$

c. $\dfrac{f(x+h) - f(x)}{h} = 2x + h + 6$

d. $\dfrac{f(x+h) - f(x)}{h} = x + h$

14. If a linear function f satisfies the conditions : $f(-3) = -5$ and $f(3) = 19$, find $f(x)$.

a. $f(x) = 6x + 10$

b. $f(x) = 4x + 7$

c. $f(x) = -6x - 7$

15. Graph the function

$f(x) = |x| + 8$

a.

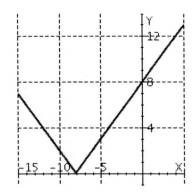

b.

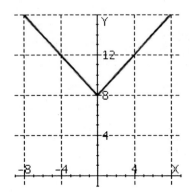

c.

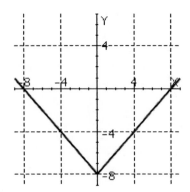

16. Graph the function $f(x) = \sqrt{8x} - 1$

a.

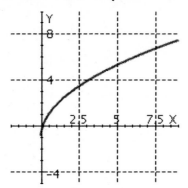

b.

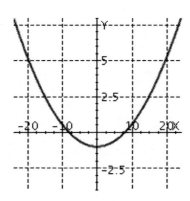

c.

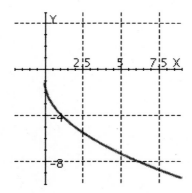

17. Sketch the graph of *f*

$$f(x) = \begin{cases} x + 1 & \text{if } x \le -1 \\ x^3 & \text{if } |x| < 1 \\ -x + 6 & \text{if } x \ge 1 \end{cases}$$

a.

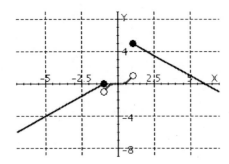

b.

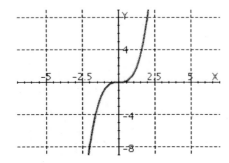

c.

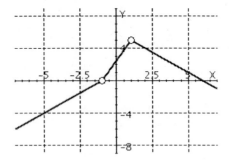

18. Express the function

$$f(x) = -\frac{3}{4}x^2 + 9x - 23$$

in the form $a(x - h)^2 + k$.

    a. $f(x) = -\frac{3}{4}(x - 6)^2 + 4$

    b. $f(x) = -3(\frac{1}{2}x - 3)^2 - 23$

    c. $f(x) = (-\frac{3}{4}x + 6)^2 - 23$

19. Use the quadratic formula to find the zeros of the function

$$f(x) = 9x^2 + 12x + 4$$

    a. $-\frac{3}{5}$

    b. $-\frac{2}{3}$

    c. $\frac{2}{5}$

    d. $-\frac{4}{3}$

20. Sketch the graph of the function

$f(x) = 4\,x^2 - 8\,x - 7$

a.

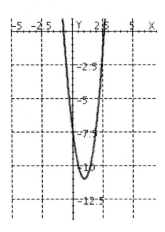

b.

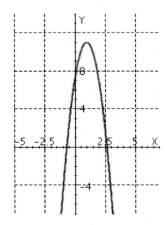

c.

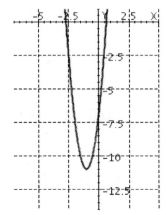

21. An object is projected vertically upward from the top of a building with an initial velocity of 80 ft/sec. Its distance in feet above the ground after t seconds is given by the equation

$s(t) = -16t^2 + 80\,t + 84$

Find its maximum distance above the ground.

    a.   190 feet

    b.   172 feet

    c.   200 feet

    d.   184 feet

22. Let $f(x) = 5x + 8$, $g(x) = x^2$. Find: $(f + g)(7)$

    a. $(f + g)(7) = 97$

    b. $(f + g)(7) = 92$

    c. $(f + g)(7) = 89$

    d. $(f + g)(7) = 184$

    e. $(f + g)(7) = 91$

23. Let $f(x) = 6x - 5$, $g(x) = 6x^2 - x + 7$. Find $(g \circ f)(x)$

    a. $(g \circ f)(x) = -216x^2 + \overline{}\; 162$

    b. $(g \circ f)(x) = -223x^2 + 732x - 178$

    c. $(g \circ f)(x) = 216x^2 - 366x + 162$

    d. $(g \circ f)(x) = 223x^2 - 732x + 162$

    e. $(g \circ f)(x) = -216x^2 + \; 178$

24. Several values of two functions *T* and *S* are listed in the following tables:

t	0	1	2	3
T(t)	2	3	1	0

x	0	1	2	3
S(x)	1	0	3	2

Find:

$(S \circ T)(2)$

   a. $(S \circ T)(2) = 0$

   b. $(S \circ T)(2) = 3$

   c. $(S \circ T)(2) = 1$

   d. $(S \circ T)(2) = 2$

25. A 100-foot-long cable of diameter 3 inches is submerged in seawater. Because of corrosion, the surface area of the cable decreases at the rate of 1000 in^2 per year. Express the diameter *d* of the cable as a function of time *t* (in years). (Disregard corrosion at the ends of the cable.)

   a. $d = 3 + \dfrac{10}{\pi}\, t$

   b. $d = 3 - 10\pi\, t$

   c. $d = 3\pi - 10\, t$

   d. $d = 3 - \dfrac{10}{\pi}\, t$

   e. $d = 3\pi t - 10$

1. Given $A(-5, 8)$, find the coordinates of the point B such that $C(5, -6)$ is the midpoint of segment AB.

    a. $B(20, -20)$

    b. $B(15, -28)$

    c. $B(20, -28)$

    d. $B(15, -20)$

2. Find the equation of the circle that satisfies the conditions:

    center $C(3, -4)$, tangent to the y-axis

    a. $(x + 3)^2 - (y + 4)^2 = 9$

    b. $(x + 3)^2 + (y - 4)^2 = 3$

    c. $(x - 3)^2 + (y + 4)^2 = 9$

    d. $(x + 3)^2 + (y + 4)^2 = 3$

    e. $(x - 3)^2 + (y + 4)^2 = 3$

3. Find the center and radius for the circle

    $x^2 + y^2 + 14x - 6y + 33 = 0$

    a.   center c $(-6, 5)$, radius 5

    b.   center c $(-7, 3)$, radius 5

    c.   center c $(7, -3)$, radius 7

    d.   center c $(-7, -5)$, radius 7

    e.   center c $(-7, -3)$, radius 7

4. Find a general form of an equation of the line through the point A (- 2, 5) with the x-intercept 0

    a.　　$5x = 2$

    b.　　$5x + 2y = 0$

    c.　　$2x - 5y = 0$

5. Find a general form of an equation for the perpendicular bisector of the segment AB.

$$A (10, - 9); B (- 8, 13)$$

    a.　　$9x + 11y = 13$

    b.　　$8x - 12y = - 13$

    c.　　$9x - 11y = - 13$

6. The slope of the figure below is $-\dfrac{3}{2}$. Find a slope-intercept form of an equation of the line shown in the figure..

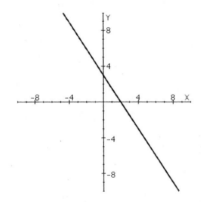

    a.　　$y = \dfrac{3}{2}x + 8$

    b.　　$y = -6$

    c.　　$y = -\dfrac{3}{2}x + 3$

7. The growth of a fetus more than 12 weeks old can be approximated by the formula $L = 1.53t - 6.7$, where L is the length (in centimeters) and t is the age (in weeks). Prenatal length can be determined by ultrasound. Approximate the age of a fetus whose length is 22.37 centimeters.

    a.   24 weeks

    b.   19 weeks

    c.   16 weeks

8. If a linear function f satisfies the conditions : $f(-3) = -12$ and $f(3) = 18$, find $f(x)$.

    a. $f(x) = 7x + 6$

    b. $f(x) = 5x + 3$

    c. $f(x) = -7x - 3$

9. Graph the function $f(x) = \sqrt{7x} - 1$

a.

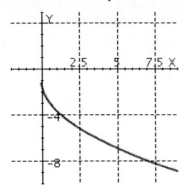

b.

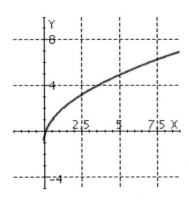

c.

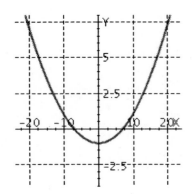

10. Sketch the graph of f

$$f(x) = \begin{cases} x + 2 & \text{if } x \leq -1 \\ x^3 & \text{if } |x| < 1 \\ -x + 1 & \text{if } x \geq 1 \end{cases}$$

a.

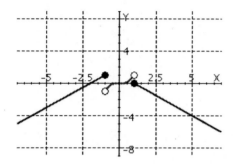

b.

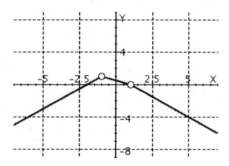

c.

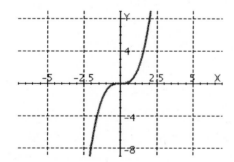

11. Let $f(x) = 4x + 7$, $g(x) = x^2$. Find:

$(f + g)(4)$

    a. $(f + g)(4) = 38$

    b. $(f + g)(4) = 39$

    c. $(f + g)(4) = 78$

    d. $(f + g)(4) = 36$

    e. $(f + g)(4) = 44$

12. Several values of two functions T and S are listed in the following tables:

t	0	1	2	3
$T(t)$	2	3	1	0

x	0	1	2	3
$S(x)$	1	0	3	2

Find: $(T \circ S)(1)$

    a. $(T \circ S)(1) = 1$

    b. $(T \circ S)(1) = 2$

    c. $(T \circ S)(1) = 0$

    d. $(T \circ S)(1) = 3$

13. Find an equation of the circle that satisfies the conditions:

endpoints of the diameter A (18, - 1) and B (- 8, 7)

14. Find the slope-intercept form of the line through the points A (2, 2) and B (- 7, 8).

15. Find the domain of f $f(x) = \sqrt{x^2 - 9}$.

16. Find the domain of f.

$$f(x) = \frac{5}{6x^2 + 6x - 120}$$

17. Simplify the difference quotient $\dfrac{f(x + h) - f(x)}{h}$, $h \neq 0$ if $f(x) = x^2 + 5$

18. Express the function

$$f(x) = -\frac{3}{4}x^2 + 15x - 10$$

in the form $a(x - h)^2 + k$.

19. Use the quadratic formula to find the zeros of the function
$$f(x) = 49\,x^2 + 28\,x + 4$$

20. Find the standard equation of the parabola shown in the figure.

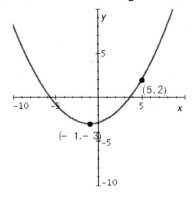

21. An object is projected vertically upward from the top of a building with an initial velocity of 160 ft/sec. Its distance in feet above the ground after t seconds is given by the equation

$s\,(t) = -16t^2 + 160\,t + 83$

Find its maximum distance above the ground.

22. A cable television firm presently serves 2000 households and charges $16 per month. A marketing survey indicates that each decrease of $1 in the monthly charge will result in 200 new customers. Let $R(x)$ denote the total monthly revenue when the monthly charge is x dollars. Determine the revenue function R.

23. Let $f(x) = 5x - 1$, $g(x) = 4x^2 - x + 9$. Find:

$(g \circ f)(x)$

24. Sketch the graph of the circle:

$$(x + 3)^2 + (y - 2)^2 = 9$$

25. Sketch the graph of the function.

$$f(x) = 3x^2 - 6x - 7$$

1. Given $A(-4, 7)$, find the coordinates of the point B such that $C(7, -9)$ is the midpoint of segment AB.

    a. $B(22, -25)$

    b. $B(22, -32)$

    c. $B(18, -32)$

    d. $B(18, -25)$

2. Find the equation of the circle that satisfies the conditions:

center $C(9, -2)$, tangent to the y-axis

    a. $(x + 9)^2 - (y + 2)^2 = 81$

    b. $(x + 9)^2 + (y + 2)^2 = 9$

    c. $(x + 9)^2 + (y - 2)^2 = 9$

    d. $(x - 9)^2 + (y + 2)^2 = 81$

    e. $(x - 9)^2 + (y + 2)^2 = 9$

3. Find the center and radius for the circle

$x^2 + y^2 + 14x - 4y + 52 = 0$

    a.   center c $(7, -2)$, radius 3

    b.   center c $(-6, 4)$, radius 1

    c.   center c $(-7, -2)$, radius 3

    d.   center c $(-7, 2)$, radius 1

    e.   center c $(-7, -4)$, radius 3

4. Find a general form of an equation of the line through the point A (- 2, 7) with the x-intercept 4

    a. $7x = 6$

    b. $6x - 7y = 28$

    c. $7x + 6y = 28$

5. Find a general form of an equation for the perpendicular bisector of the segment AB.

$$A \ (\ 8, - 10 \ ); B \ (- 4, 16 \ )$$

    a. $5x - 14y = - 27$

    b. $6x + 13y = 27$

    c. $6x - 13y = - 27$

6. The slope of the figure below is $- \dfrac{5}{2}$. Find a slope-intercept form of an equation of the line shown in the figure..

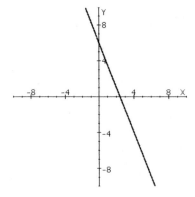

    a. $y = - \dfrac{5}{2}x + 6$

    b. $y = - 9$

    c. $y = \dfrac{5}{2}x + 11$

7. The growth of a fetus more than 12 weeks old can be approximated by the formula $L = 1.53t - 6.7$, where L is the length (in centimeters) and t is the age (in weeks). Prenatal length can be determined by ultrasound. Approximate the age of a fetus whose length is 31.55 centimeters.

     a.   30 weeks

     b.   25 weeks

     c.   22 weeks

8. If a linear function f satisfies the conditions : $f(-3) = -8$ and $f(3) = 22$, find $f(x)$.

     a. $f(x) = 7x + 10$

     b. $f(x) = -7x - 7$

     c. $f(x) = 5x + 7$

9. Graph the function $f(x) = \sqrt{5x} - 1$

a.

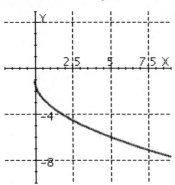

b.

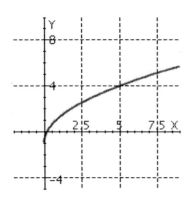

c.

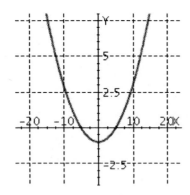

10. Sketch the graph of f

$$f(x) = \begin{cases} x + 6 & \text{if } x \leq -1 \\ x^3 & \text{if } |x| < 1 \\ -x + 3 & \text{if } x \geq 1 \end{cases}$$

a.

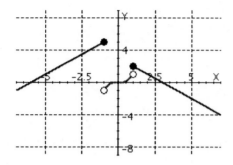

b.

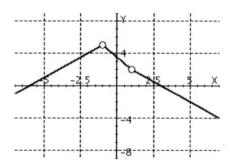

c.

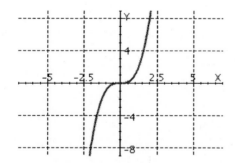

11. Let $f(x) = 3x + 8$, $g(x) = x^2$. Find:

$(f + g)(8)$

    a. $(f + g)(8) = 95$

    b. $(f + g)(8) = 93$

    c. $(f + g)(8) = 96$

    d. $(f + g)(8) = 101$

    e. $(f + g)(8) = 192$

12. Several values of two functions T and S are listed in the following tables:

t	0	1	2	3
$T(t)$	2	3	1	0

x	0	1	2	3
$S(x)$	1	0	3	2

Find: $(S \circ T)(2)$

    a. $(S \circ T)(2) = 0$

    b. $(S \circ T)(2) = 3$

    c. $(S \circ T)(2) = 2$

    d. $(S \circ T)(2) = 1$

13. Find an equation of the circle that satisfies the conditions:

endpoints of the diameter A (10, - 17) and B (- 6, 19)

14. Find the slope-intercept form of the line through the points A (5, 2) and B (- 1, 4).

15. Find the domain of f $f(x) = \sqrt{x^2 - 1}$.

16. Find the domain of f.

$$f(x) = \frac{5}{6x^2 + 18x - 108}$$

17. Simplify the difference quotient $\dfrac{f(x + h) - f(x)}{h}$, $h \ne 0$ if

$$f(x) = x^2 + 7$$

18. Express the function

$$f(x) = -\frac{3}{4}x^2 + 15x - 28$$

in the form $a(x - h)^2 + k$.

19. Use the quadratic formula to find the zeros of the function
$$f(x) = 9x^2 + 12x + 4$$

20. Find the standard equation of the parabola shown in the figure.

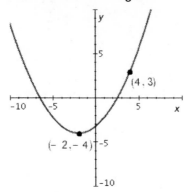

21. An object is projected vertically upward from the top of a building with an initial velocity of 128 ft/sec. Its distance in feet above the ground after t seconds is given by the equation

$$s(t) = -16t^2 + 128\,t + 94$$

Find its maximum distance above the ground.

22. A cable television firm presently serves 5500 households and charges $21 per month. A marketing survey indicates that each decrease of $1 in the monthly charge will result in 550 new customers. Let $R(x)$ denote the total monthly revenue when the monthly charge is x dollars. Determine the revenue function R.

23. Let $f(x) = 7x - 1$, $g(x) = 3x^2 - x + 8$. Find:

$(g \circ f)(x)$

24. Sketch the graph of the circle:

$$(x + 3)^2 + (y - 2)^2 = 9$$

25. Sketch the graph of the function.

$$f(x) = 2x^2 - 4x - 7$$

Test Form 2-A

1. $(8, -24)$

2. $(x-6)^2 + (y+4)^2 = 64$

3. $(x-2)^2 + (y-1)^2 = 360$

4. $y = \frac{4}{13} \cdot x - 4$

5. $y = -\frac{2}{3} \cdot x + \frac{10}{3}$

6. $3x - 2y = -5$

7. $(x-2)^2 + (y+3)^2 = 64$

8. $\dfrac{f(a+h) - f(a)}{h} = 3$

9. $(-\infty, -3] \cup [3, \infty)$

10. $x \in (-\infty, -7) \cup (-7, 3) \cup (3, \infty)$

11. $x \in \left[\frac{7}{6}, 3\right) \cup (3, \infty)$

12. $\dfrac{f(x+h) - f(x)}{h} = 2x + h$

13. $f(x) = 4x + 2$

14. $f(x) = -\frac{3}{4} \cdot (x-10)^2 + 45$

15. $-\frac{6}{5}$

16. $y = -(x-3)^2 + 9$

17. $y = \frac{5}{16} \cdot (x+1)^2 - 2$

18. 287

19. $R(x) = 240x \cdot (26 - x)$

20. 10

21. $4(6x-7)^2 - (6x-7) + 2$

22. $\frac{3}{2} \cdot \sqrt[3]{x}$

23.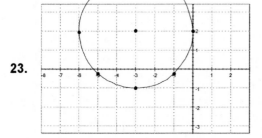

24.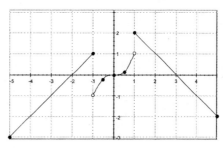

25.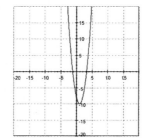

Test Form 2-B

1. $(10,-21)$

2. $(x-7)^2 + (y+7)^2 = 49$

3. $(x-5)^2 + (y-1)^2 = 549$

4. $y = \frac{15}{8} \cdot x - 15$

5. $y = -\frac{2}{3} \cdot x + \frac{10}{3}$

6. $4x - 3y = -7$

7. $(x-3)^2 + (y+2)^2 = 64$

8. $\dfrac{f(a+h) - f(a)}{h} = 7$

9. $(-\infty, -4] \cup [4, \infty)$

10. $x \in (-\infty, -7) \cup (-7, 2) \cup (2, \infty)$

11. $x \in \left[\frac{3}{5}, 3 \right) \cup (3, \infty)$

12. $\dfrac{f(x+h) - f(x)}{h} = 2x + h$

13. $f(x) = 6x + 5$

14. $f(x) = -\frac{3}{4} \cdot (x-8)^2 + 8$

15. $-\frac{8}{3}$

16. $y = -(x-1)^2 + 1$

17. $y = \frac{3}{16} \cdot (x+1)^2 - 1$

18. 292

19. $R(x) = 650x \cdot (33 - x)$

20. 51

21. $5(9x-9)^2 - (9x-9) + 6$

22. $\frac{3}{2} \cdot \sqrt[3]{t}$

23.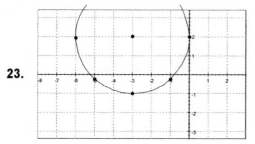

24.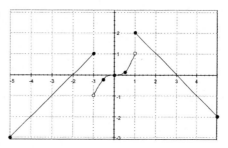

25.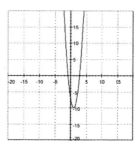

Test Form 2-C

1. b	**2.** a	**3.** b	**4.** b	**5.** a	**6.** c	**7.** c	**8.** c	**9.** b
10. a	**11.** c	**12.** c	**13.** a	**14.** b	**15.** c	**16.** b	**17.** c	**18.** b
19. c	**20.** a	**21.** d	**22.** c	**23.** b	**24.** a	**25.** e		

Test Form 2-D

1. b	**2.** a	**3.** e	**4.** c	**5.** e	**6.** c	**7.** b	**8.** b	**9.** c
10. a	**11.** c	**12.** d	**13.** a	**14.** b	**15.** b	**16.** a	**17.** a	**18.** a
19. b	**20.** a	**21.** d	**22.** b	**23.** c	**24.** a	**25.** d		

Test Form 2-E

1. d
2. c
3. b
4. b
5. c
6. c
7. b
8. b
9. b
10. a
11. b
12. b
13. $(x-5)^2 + (y-3)^2 = 185$
14. $y = -\dfrac{2}{3} \cdot x + \dfrac{10}{3}$
15. $(-\infty, -3] \cup [3, \infty)$
16. $x \in (-\infty, -5) \cup (-5, 4) \cup (4, \infty)$
17. $\dfrac{f(x+h) - f(x)}{h} = 2x + h$
18. $f(x) = -\dfrac{3}{4} \cdot (x-10)^2 + 65$
19. $-\dfrac{2}{7}$
20. $y = \dfrac{5}{36} \cdot (x+1)^2 - 3$
21. 483
22. $R(x) = 200x \cdot (26 - x)$
23. $4(5x-1)^2 - (5x-1) + 9$

24. 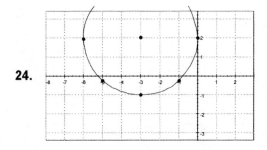   25.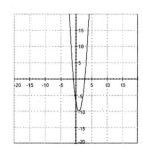

Test Form 2-F

1. d
2. d
3. d
4. c
5. c
6. a
7. b
8. c
9. b
10. a
11. c
12. a
13. $(x-2)^2 + (y-1)^2 = 388$
14. $y = -\dfrac{1}{3} \cdot x + \dfrac{11}{3}$
15. $(-\infty, -1] \cup [1, \infty)$
16. $x \in (-\infty, -6) \cup (-6, 3) \cup (3, \infty)$
17. $\dfrac{f(x+h) - f(x)}{h} = 2x + h$
18. $f(x) = -\dfrac{3}{4} \cdot (x-10)^2 + 47$
19. $-\dfrac{2}{3}$
20. $y = \dfrac{7}{36} \cdot (x+2)^2 - 4$
21. 350
22. $R(x) = 550x \cdot (31 - x)$
23. $3(7x-1)^2 - (7x-1) + 8$

24. 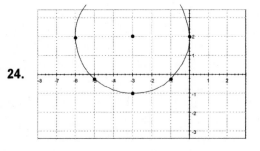   25.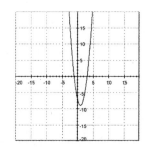

1. Sketch the graph of f for the indicated value of a.

$$f(x) = ax^3 + 3, \quad a = -\frac{1}{3}$$

2. Find all values of x such that $f(x) > 0$.

$$f(x) = \frac{1}{2}(x + 8)(x - 3)(x - 5)$$

3. Find all values of x such that $f(x) < 0$.

$$f(x) = x^3 + 8x^2 - 64x - 512$$

4. A herd of 425 deer is introduced onto a small island. At first the herd increases rapidly, but eventually food resources dwindle and the population declines. Suppose that the number of deer after t years is given by
$N(t) = -t^4 + 8t^2 + 425$, where $t > 0$. When does the population become extinct?

5. Use the remainder theorem to find $f(c)$

$$f(x) = 2x^3 - x^2 + 4x - 7 \quad c = 3$$

6. Use the remainder theorem to find $f(c)$

$$f(x) = x^4 - 4x^2 + 9x - 6 \quad c = -2$$

7. Use synthetic division to find the quotient and remainder if the first polynomial is divided by the second

$$9x^3 - 5x^2 + 7x - 5; \quad x - 2$$

8. Use synthetic division to find $f(c)$

$$f(x) = 3x^3 + 2x^2 - 6x + 2 \quad c = 3$$

9. Find a polynomial $f(x)$ of degree 3 that has the indicated zeros and satisfies the given condition.

$1, -2, 4 ; f(2) = -40$

10. Find the polynomial function of degree 3 whose graph is shown in the figure.

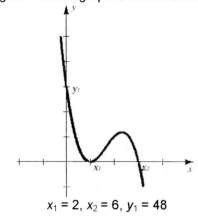

$x_1 = 2, x_2 = 6, y_1 = 48$

11. A polynomial $f(x)$ with real coefficients and leading coefficient 1 has the given zeros and degree. Express $f(x)$ as a product of linear and quadratic polynomials with real coefficients that are irreducible over **R**.

$$9 + 3i, -8 + i; \text{ degree 4}$$

12. A polynomial $f(x)$ with real coefficients and leading coefficient 1 has the given zeros and degree. Express $f(x)$ as a product of linear and quadratic polynomials with real coefficients that are irreducible over **R**.

$$0, -3i, 4-i; \text{ degree } 5$$

13. Find all solutions of the equation.

$$35x^5 + 263x^4 + 121x^3 - 35x^2 = 0$$

14. A storage tank for propane gas is to be constructed in the shape of a right circular cylinder with a hemisphere attached to the top. If the total height of the structure is 35 feet, determine the radius of the cylinder that results in a total volume of $1188\ \pi\ \text{ft}^3$.

15. Sketch the graph of f.

$$f(x) = \frac{3}{x - 4}$$

16. Sketch the graph of f.

$$f(x) = \frac{-3x}{x + 2}$$

17. Simplify $f(x)$, and sketch the graph of f.

$$f(x) = \frac{x^2 + x - 2}{x + 2}$$

18. Find an equation of a rational function f that satisfies the conditions:
vertical asymptote: $x = -1$, $x = 0$
horizontal asymptote: $y = 0$
x-intercept: 7; $f(8) = 1$

19. Find an equation of a rational function f that satisfies the conditions:
vertical asymptotes: $x = -7$, $x = 4$
horizontal asymptote: $y = 0$
x-intercept: -2; $f(0) = -4$
hole at $x = 3$

20. Salt water of concentration 0.1 pound of salt per gallon flows into a large tank that initially contains 48 gallons of pure water. If the flow rate of salt water into the tank is 4 gal/min, find a formula for the salt concentration $f(t)$ (in lb/gal) after t minutes.

21. For a particular salmon population, the relationship between the number S of spawners and the number R of offspring that survive to maturity is given by the formula

$$R = \frac{4600S}{S + 550}$$

Find the number of spawners that would yield 50% of the greatest possible number of offspring that survive to maturity.

22. The pressure P acting at a point in a liquid is directly proportional to the distance d from the surface of the liquid to the point. Express P as a function of d by means of a formula that involves a constant of proportionality k. In a certain oil tank, the pressure at a depth of 8 feet is 472. Find the pressure at a depth of 12 feet for the oil tank.

23. The period P of a simple pendulum - that is, the time required for one complete oscillation - is directly proportional to the square root of its length l. Express P in terms of l and a constant of proportionality k. If a pendulum 3.2 feet long has a period of 2.9 seconds, find the value of k.

24. The speed V at which an automobile was traveling before the brakes were applied can sometimes be estimated from the length L of the skid marks. Assume that V is directly proportional to the square root of L. Express V as a function of L by means of a formula that involves a constant of proportionality k. For a certain automobile on a dry surface, L = 55 ft when V = 43 mi/hr . Estimate the initial speed of the automobile if the skid marks are 179 feet long.

25. The National Football League (NFL) ranks its passers by assigning a passer rating R based on the number of completions C, attempts A, yards Y, touchdowns T, and interceptions I. In a normal situation, it can be shown that the passer rating can be calculated by using the formula

$$R = \frac{25(A + 40C + 2Y + 160T - 200 I)}{12A}$$

During a season, a passer completed 252 of 341 passes, has 36 touchdown passes, and 17 interceptions. How many yards would this passer needed to have completed to obtain a rating of at least 139?

1. Sketch the graph of f for the indicated value of a.

$$f(x) = ax^3 + 3, \quad a = -\frac{1}{3}$$

2. Find all values of x such that $f(x) > 0$.

$$f(x) = \frac{1}{5}(x + 8)(x - 2)(x - 5)$$

3. Find all values of x such that $f(x) < 0$.

$$f(x) = x^3 + 7x^2 - 25x - 175$$

4. A herd of 525 deer is introduced onto a small island. At first the herd increases rapidly, but eventually food resources dwindle and the population declines. Suppose that the number of deer after t years is given by
$N(t) = -t^4 + 4t^2 + 525$, where $t > 0$. When does the population become extinct?

5. Use the remainder theorem to find $f(c)$

$$f(x) = 3x^3 - x^2 + 2x - 1 \quad c = 1$$

6. Use the remainder theorem to find $f(c)$

$$f(x) = x^4 - 3x^2 + 6x - 9 \quad c = -4$$

7. Use synthetic division to find the quotient and remainder if the first polynomial is divided by the second

$$2 x^3 - 3 x^2 + 8 x - 4; \quad x - 2$$

8. Use synthetic division to find $f(c)$

$$f(x) = 3 x^3 + 4 x^2 - 4 x + 3 \quad c = 4$$

9. Find a polynomial $f(x)$ of degree 3 that has the indicated zeros and satisfies the given condition.

$-1, 1, 4 ; f(3) = -40$

10. Find the polynomial function of degree 3 whose graph is shown in the figure.

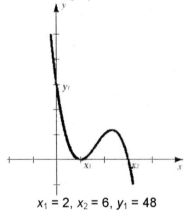

$x_1 = 2, \; x_2 = 6, \; y_1 = 48$

11. A polynomial $f(x)$ with real coefficients and leading coefficient 1 has the given zeros and degree. Express $f(x)$ as a product of linear and quadratic polynomials with real coefficients that are irreducible over **R**.

$3 + 6 i, -7 + i$; degree 4

12. A polynomial $f(x)$ with real coefficients and leading coefficient 1 has the given zeros and degree. Express $f(x)$ as a product of linear and quadratic polynomials with real coefficients that are irreducible over **R**.

$$0, -8i, 4-i \text{ ; degree 5}$$

13. Find all solutions of the equation.

$$66x^5 + 751x^4 + 269x^3 - 66x^2 = 0$$

14. A storage tank for propane gas is to be constructed in the shape of a right circular cylinder with a hemisphere attached to the top. If the total height of the structure is 35 feet, determine the radius of the cylinder that results in a total volume of $1188 \pi \text{ ft}^3$.

15. Sketch the graph of f.

$$f(x) = \frac{3}{x-4}$$

16. Sketch the graph of f.

$$f(x) = \frac{-3x}{x+2}$$

17. Simplify $f(x)$, and sketch the graph of f.

$$f(x) = \frac{x^2 + x - 2}{x+2}$$

18. Find an equation of a rational function f that satisfies the conditions:
vertical asymptote: $x = -5$, $x = 0$
horizontal asymptote: $y = 0$
x-intercept: 7; $f(8) = 1$

19. Find an equation of a rational function f that satisfies the conditions:
vertical asymptotes: $x = -9$, $x = 5$
horizontal asymptote: $y = 0$
x-intercept: -1; $f(0) = -5$
hole at $x = 4$

20. Salt water of concentration 0.5 pound of salt per gallon flows into a large tank that initially contains 275 gallons of pure water. If the flow rate of salt water into the tank is 5 gal/min, find a formula for the salt concentration $f(t)$ (in lb/gal) after t minutes.

21. For a particular salmon population, the relationship between the number S of spawners and the number R of offspring that survive to maturity is given by the formula

$$R = \frac{4200S}{S + 550}$$

Find the number of spawners that would yield 90% of the greatest possible number of offspring that survive to maturity.

22. The pressure P acting at a point in a liquid is directly proportional to the distance d from the surface of the liquid to the point. Express P as a function of d by means of a formula that involves a constant of proportionality k. In a certain oil tank, the pressure at a depth of 3 feet is 177. Find the pressure at a depth of 8 feet for the oil tank.

23. The period *P* of a simple pendulum - that is, the time required for one complete oscillation - is directly proportional to the square root of its length *l*. Express *P* in terms of *l* and a constant of proportionality *k*. If a pendulum 3.6 feet long has a period of 1.5 seconds, find the value of *k*.

24. The speed *V* at which an automobile was traveling before the brakes were applied can sometimes be estimated from the length *L* of the skid marks. Assume that *V* is directly proportional to the square root of *L*. Express *V* as a function of *L* by means of a formula that involves a constant of proportionality *k*. For a certain automobile on a dry surface, *L* = 40 ft when *V* = 38 mi/hr . Estimate the initial speed of the automobile if the skid marks are 171 feet long.

25. The National Football League (NFL) ranks its passers by assigning a passer rating R based on the number of completions C, attempts A, yards Y, touchdowns T, and interceptions I. In a normal situation, it can be shown that the passer rating can be calculated by using the formula

$$R = \frac{25(A + 40C + 2Y + 160T - 200I)}{12A}$$

During a season, a passer completed 265 of 389 passes, has 45 touchdown passes, and 10 interceptions. How many yards would this passer needed to have completed to obtain a rating of at least 105?

1. Sketch the graph of *f* for the indicated value of *a*.

$$f(x) = ax^3 + 1, \quad a = -\frac{3}{5}$$

a.

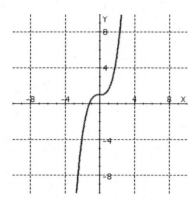

b.

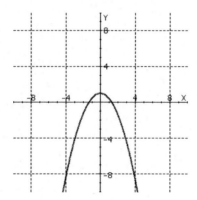

c.

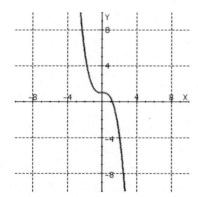

2. Find all values of x such that $f(x) < 0$.

$$f(x) = x^3 + 6x^2 - 9x - 54$$

    a. $(-\infty, -6) \cup (-3, 3)$

    b. $(-\infty, -6] \cup [-3, \infty)$

    c. $(-\infty, \infty)$

3. Find all values of x such that $f(x) < 0$.

$$f(x) = x^4 - 56x^2 + 343$$

    a. $(-7, -\sqrt{7}) \cup (\sqrt{7}, 7)$

    b. $(-343, -\sqrt{343}) \cup (\sqrt{343}, 343)$

    c. $(-\infty, -56) \cup (56, \infty)$

4. Let $f(x)$ be a polynomial such that the coefficient of every even power of x is 0. Is f an even or odd function?

    a.   even

    b.   odd

    c.   neither even nor odd

5. A herd of 575 deer is introduced onto a small island. At first the herd increases rapidly, but eventually food resources dwindle and the population declines. Suppose that the number of deer after t years is given by
$N(t) = -t^4 + 2t^2 + 575$, where $t > 0$. When does the population become extinct?

    a. $t = 10$

    b. $t = 5$

    c. $t = 8$

6. Find the quotient and remainder if $f(x)$ is divided by $p(x)$

$$f(x) = 3x^4 - x^3 - 4x^2 + 8x - 8; \quad p(x) = x^2 - 3$$

    a.   Quotient: $3x^2 - x$
             Remainder: $5x + 7$

    b.   Quotient: $3x^2 - x + 5$
             Remainder: $5x + 7$

    c.   Quotient: $5x + 7$
             Remainder: $3x^2 - x + 5$

7. Use the remainder theorem to find $f(c)$

$$f(x) = x^4 - 6x^2 + 2x - 9 \quad c = -9$$

a. $f(-9) = 6210$

b. $f(-9) = 5870$

c. $f(-9) = 6048$

d. $f(-9) = 6520$

8. Use synthetic division to decide whether c is a zero of

$$f(x) = 2x^4 + 11x^3 - 4x^2 - 62x + 9 \quad c = -4$$

a. c is not a zero

b. c is a zero

9. Find a polynomial $f(x)$ of degree 3 that has the indicated zeros and satisfies the given condition.

$2, 3, -2 ; f(0) = 48$

a. $f(x) = 11x^3 - 8x^2 - 48x + 16$

b. $f(x) = 4x^3 - 12x^2 - 16x + 48$

c. $f(x) = 48x^3 - 16x^2 - 12x + 4$

d. $f(x) = 5x^3 - 15x^2 - 16x + 48$

10. Find the polynomial function of degree 3 whose graph is shown in the figure.

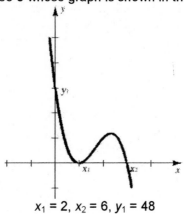

$x_1 = 2$, $x_2 = 6$, $y_1 = 48$

a. $f(x) = -48x^3 + 56x^2 - 20x + 2$

b. $f(x) = -21x^3 + 23x^2 - 56x + 48$

c. $f(x) = -27x^3 + 24x^2 - 48x + 56$

d. $f(x) = -2x^3 + 20x^2 - 56x + 48$

11. Find all solutions of the equation.

$$x^4 + 2x^3 - 18x^2 - 6x + 45 = 0$$

a. $-5, -\sqrt{3}, \sqrt{3}, 3$

b. $-2, -\sqrt{11}, \sqrt{3}, 3$

c. $5, -\sqrt{3}, \sqrt{3}, 3$

d. $-5, -\sqrt{11}, \sqrt{11}, 3$

12. Find a factored form with integer coefficients of the polynomial *f* shown in the figure.

$$f(x) = 10\,x^5 - 41\,x^4 + 52\,x^3 - 17\,x^2 - 8\,x + 4$$

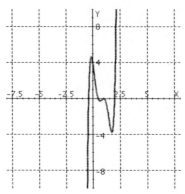

a. $x(5x + 2)(2x - 1)(x - 1)(x - 2)$

b. $(5x + 2)(2x - 1)(x - 1)^2(x - 2)$

c. $(2x + 5)(x^2 - 2)(x - 1)(x - 2)$

d. $(2x + 5)(2x - 1)(x - 1)^2(x - 2)$

13. A storage tank for propane gas is to be constructed in the shape of a right circular cylinder with a hemisphere attached to the top. If the total height of the structure is 15 feet, determine the radius of the cylinder that results in a total volume of $468\,\pi\;\text{ft}^3$.

    a.   8 ft

    b.   7 ft

    c.   6 ft

    d.   5 ft

14. Find the domain D of f.

$$f(x) = \frac{5}{x}$$

a. $(-\infty, 0) \cup (0, \infty)$

b. $(-\infty, 5) \cup (5, \infty)$

c. $(-\infty, \infty)$

15. Find the interval on which f is increasing.

$$f(x) = \frac{1}{x^2}$$

a. $(-\infty, \infty)$

b. $(-\infty, 1)$

c. $(-\infty, 0)$

16. Sketch the graph of *f*.

$$f(x) = \frac{2}{x-1}$$

a.

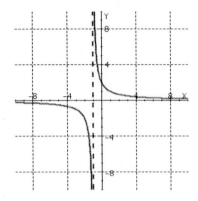

b.

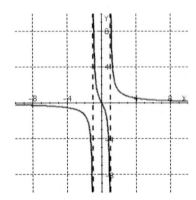

c.

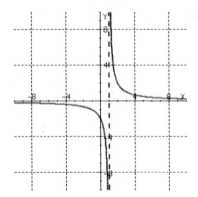

17. Sketch the graph of f. $f(x) = \dfrac{-3x}{x+3}$

a.

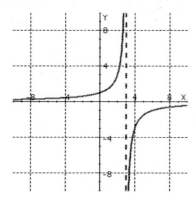

b.

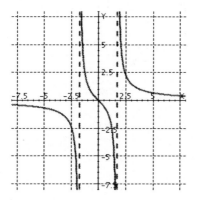

c.

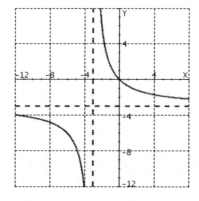

18.
Simplify $f(x)$, and sketch the graph of f. $f(x) = \dfrac{x^2 + x - 12}{x + 4}$

a.

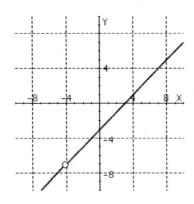

b.

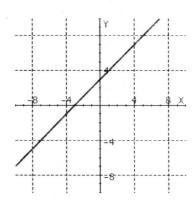

c.

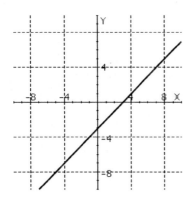

d.

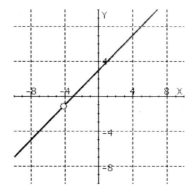

19. Find the oblique asymptote of $f(x)$.

$$f(x) = \dfrac{x^2 - x - 10}{x + 2}$$

a. $y = x + 2$

b. $y = x - 10$

c. $y = x - 3$

20. Find an equation of a rational function f that satisfies the conditions:

vertical asymptotes: $x = -5$, $x = 0$

horizontal asymptote: $y = 0$

x-intercept: 5; $f(6) = 1$

    a.

$$f(x) = \frac{5 - x^2}{x^2 + 66x - 5}$$

    b.

$$f(x) = \frac{66x - 330}{x^2 + 5x}$$

    c.

$$f(x) = \frac{66x - 5}{x^2 + 330x}$$

21. The population density D (in people/mi^2) in a large city is related to the distance x (in miles) from the center of the city by

$$D = \frac{5000x}{x^2 + 24}$$

In what areas of the city does the population density exceed 500 people/mi^2?

    a. $(0, 10)$

    b. $(4, 6)$

    c. $(2, 10)$

22. Express the statement as a formula that involves the variables q, x, y and a constant of proportionality k, and then determine the value of k from the condition : q is inversely proportional to the sum of x and y, if $x = 2.1$ and $y = 2.3$, then $q = 2.8$

    a. $k = 33.264$

    b. $k = 9.856$

    c. $k = 18.48$

    d. $k = 12.32$

23. The pressure P acting at a point in a liquid is directly proportional to the distance d from the surface of the liquid to the point. Express P as a function of d by means of a formula that involves a constant of proportionality k. In a certain oil tank, the pressure at a depth of 8 feet is 472. Find the pressure at a depth of 10 feet for the oil tank.

    a. $p = 590$

    b. $p = 623$

    c. $p = 578$

    d. $p = 567$

24. The speed V at which an automobile was traveling before the brakes were applied can sometimes be estimated from the length L of the skid marks. Assume that V is directly proportional to the square root of L. Express V as a function of L by means of a formula that involves a constant of proportionality k. For a certain automobile on a dry surface, $L = 59$ ft when $V = 28$ mi/hr . Estimate the initial speed of the automobile if the skid marks are 163 feet long.

    a. $v = 35.11$ mi/hr

    b. $v = 38.18$ mi/hr

    c. $v = 46.54$ mi/hr

    d. $v = 41.76$ mi/hr

25. The National Football League (NFL) ranks its passers by assigning a passer rating R based on the number of completions C, attempts A, yards Y, touchdowns T, and interceptions I. In a normal situation, it can be shown that the passer rating can be calculated by using the formula

$$R = \frac{25(A + 40C + 2Y + 160T - 200I)}{12A}$$

During a season, a passer completed 325 of 493 passes, has 42 touchdown passes, and 13 interceptions. How many yards would this passer needed to have completed to obtain a rating of at least 113?

    a.   4576.5 yards

    b.   4554.1 yards

    c.   4550.9 yards

    d.   4563.7 yards

1. Sketch the graph of *f* for the indicated value of *a*.

$$f(x) = ax^3 + 1, \quad a = -\frac{4}{5}$$

a.

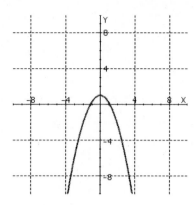

b.

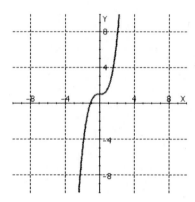

c.

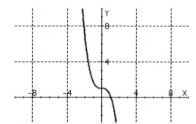

2. Find all values of x such that $f(x) < 0$.

$$f(x) = x^3 + 9x^2 - 9x - 81$$

    a. $(-\infty, \infty)$

    b. $(-\infty, -9] \cup [-3, \infty)$

    c. $(-\infty, -9) \cup (-3, 3)$

3. Find all values of x such that $f(x) < 0$.

$$f(x) = x^4 - 12x^2 + 27$$

    a. $(-3, -\sqrt{3}) \cup (\sqrt{3}, 3)$

    b. $(-\infty, -12) \cup (12, \infty)$

    c. $(-27, -\sqrt{27}) \cup (\sqrt{27}, 27)$

4. Let $f(x)$ be a polynomial such that the coefficient of every even power of x is 0. Is f an even or odd function?

    a.   neither even nor odd

    b.   even

    c.   odd

5. A herd of 550 deer is introduced onto a small island. At first the herd increases rapidly, but eventually food resources dwindle and the population declines. Suppose that the number of deer after t years is given by
$N(t) = -t^4 + 3t^2 + 550$, where $t > 0$. When does the population become extinct?

    a. $t = 8$

    b. $t = 5$

    c. $t = 10$

6. Find the quotient and remainder if $f(x)$ is divided by $p(x)$

$$f(x) = 4x^4 - x^3 - 7x^2 + 7x - 7;$$
$$p(x) = x^2 - 3$$

a.
Quotient: $4x^2 - x + 5$
Remainder: $4x + 8$

b.
Quotient: $4x + 8$
Remainder: $4x^2 - x + 5$

c.
Quotient: $4x^2 - x$
Remainder: $4x + 8$

7. Use the remainder theorem to find $f(c)$

$$f(x) = x^4 - 3x^2 + 6x - 1 \quad c = -2$$

a. $f(-2) = -119$

b. $f(-2) = 418$

c. $f(-2) = 165$

d. $f(-2) = -9$

8. Use synthetic division to decide whether c is a zero of

$$f(x) = 7x^4 + 9x^3 - 10x^2 - 7x + 5 \quad c = -1$$

a. c is a zero

b. c is not a zero

9. Find a polynomial $f(x)$ of degree 3 that has the indicated zeros and satisfies the given condition.

$1, 2, -4$; $f(4) = 192$

a. $\quad f(x) = 11x^3 + 8x^2 - 32x + 40$

b. $\quad f(x) = 4x^3 + 4x^2 - 40x + 32$

c. $\quad f(x) = 32x^3 + 40x^2 - 4x + 4$

d. $\quad f(x) = 5x^3 + 7x^2 - 40x + 32$

10. Find the polynomial function of degree 3 whose graph is shown in the figure.

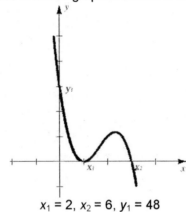

$x_1 = 2,\ x_2 = 6,\ y_1 = 48$

a. $\quad f(x) = -27x^3 + 24x^2 - 48x + 56$

b. $\quad f(x) = -48x^3 + 56x^2 - 20x + 2$

c. $\quad f(x) = -2x^3 + 20x^2 - 56x + 48$

d. $\quad f(x) = -21x^3 + 23x^2 - 56x + 48$

11. Find all solutions of the equation.

$$x^4 + 8x^3 - 12x^2 - 24x + 27 = 0$$

a. $-9, -\sqrt{3}, \sqrt{3}, 1$

b. $-9, -\sqrt{2}, \sqrt{2}, 1$

c. $9, -\sqrt{3}, \sqrt{3}, 1$

d. $-8, -\sqrt{2}, \sqrt{3}, 1$

12. Find a factored form with integer coefficients of the polynomial f shown in the figure.

$$f(x) = 14x^5 - 59x^4 + 80x^3 - 35x^2 - 4x + 4$$

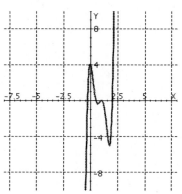

a. $(2x + 7)(2x - 1)(x - 1)^2(x - 2)$

b. $(2x + 7)(x^2 - 2)(x - 1)(x - 2)$

c. $x(7x + 2)(2x - 1)(x - 1)(x - 2)$

d. $(7x + 2)(2x - 1)(x - 1)^2(x - 2)$

13. A storage tank for propane gas is to be constructed in the shape of a right circular cylinder with a hemisphere attached to the top. If the total height of the structure is 25 feet, determine the radius of the cylinder that results in a total volume of $216 \pi \text{ ft}^3$.

    a.   2 ft

    b.   5 ft

    c.   4 ft

    d.   3 ft

14. Find the domain D of f.

$$f(x) = \frac{5}{x}$$

    a. $(-\infty, 5) \cup (5, \infty)$

    b. $(-\infty, 0) \cup (0, \infty)$

    c. $(-\infty, \infty)$

15. Find the interval on which f is increasing.

$$f(x) = \frac{4}{x^2}$$

    a. $(-\infty, 0)$

    b. $(-\infty, \infty)$

    c. $(-\infty, 4)$

16. Sketch the graph of *f*.

$$f(x) = \frac{3}{x - 4}$$

a.

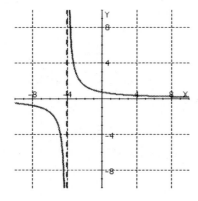

b.

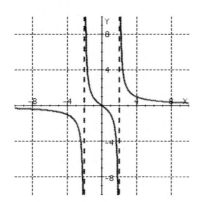

c.

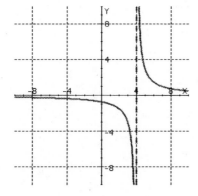

17. Sketch the graph of *f*.

$$f(x) = \frac{-3x}{x + 2}$$

a.

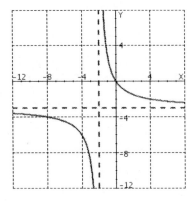

b.

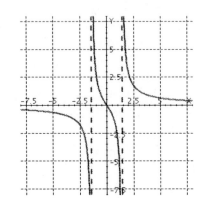

c.

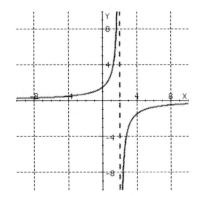

18. Simplify *f* (*x*), and sketch the graph of *f*.

$$f(x) = \frac{x^2 + x - 2}{x + 2}$$

a.

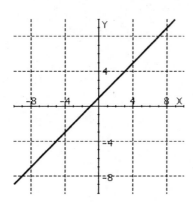

b.

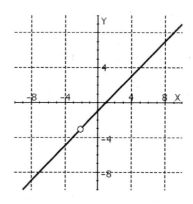

c.

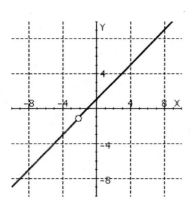

d

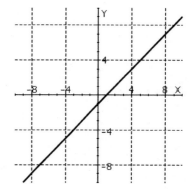

19. Find the oblique asymptote of $f(x)$.

$$f(x) = \frac{x^2 - x - 27}{x + 4}$$

a. $y = x - 5$

b. $y = x - 27$

c. $y = x + 4$

20. Find an equation of a rational function f that satisfies the conditions:
vertical asymptotes: $x = -8$, $x = 0$
horizontal asymptote: $y = 0$
x-intercept: 6; $f(7) = 1$

   a.
$$f(x) = \frac{8 - x^2}{x^2 + 105x - 6}$$

   b.
$$f(x) = \frac{105x - 630}{x^2 + 8x}$$

   c.
$$f(x) = \frac{105x - 6}{x^2 + 630x}$$

21. The population density D (in people/mi^2) in a large city is related to the distance x (in miles) from the center of the city by

$$D = \frac{7500x}{x^2 + 50}$$

In what areas of the city does the population density exceed 500 people/mi^2?

   a.   (5, 15)

   b.   (0, 15)

   c.   (5, 10)

22. Express the statement as a formula that involves the variables q, x, y and a constant of proportionality k, and then determine the value of k from the condition : q is inversely proportional to the sum of x and y, if $x = 2.4$ and $y = 2.3$, then $q = 0.6$

   a. $k = 1.41$

   b. $k = 2.82$

   c. $k = 4.512$

   d. $k = 7.614$

23. The pressure P acting at a point in a liquid is directly proportional to the distance d from the surface of the liquid to the point. Express P as a function of d by means of a formula that involves a constant of proportionality k. In a certain oil tank, the pressure at a depth of 4 feet is 236. Find the pressure at a depth of 7 feet for the oil tank.

    a. $p = 401$

    b. $p = 446$

    c. $p = 390$

    d. $p = 413$

24. The speed V at which an automobile was traveling before the brakes were applied can sometimes be estimated from the length L of the skid marks. Assume that V is directly proportional to the square root of L. Express V as a function of L by means of a formula that involves a constant of proportionality k. For a certain automobile on a dry surface, $L = 45$ ft when $V = 44$ mi/hr . Estimate the initial speed of the automobile if the skid marks are 144 feet long.

    a. $v = 73.93$ mi/hr

    b. $v = 70.35$ mi/hr

    c. $v = 78.71$ mi/hr

    d. $v = 67.28$ mi/hr

25. The National Football League (NFL) ranks its passers by assigning a passer rating R based on the number of completions C, attempts A, yards Y, touchdowns T, and interceptions I. In a normal situation, it can be shown that the passer rating can be calculated by using the formula

$$R = \frac{25(A + 40C + 2Y + 160T - 200\,I)}{12A}$$

During a season, a passer completed 319 of 404 passes, has 15 touchdown passes, and 7 interceptions. How many yards would this passer needed to have completed to obtain a rating of at least 129?

    a.   5438.6 yards

    b.   5425.8 yards

    c.   5413 yards

    d.   5416.2 yards

1. Find the polynomial function of degree 3 whose graph is shown in the figure.

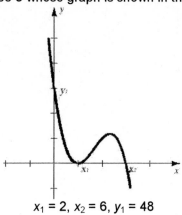

$x_1 = 2$, $x_2 = 6$, $y_1 = 48$

a. $f(x) = -21x^3 + 23x^2 - 56x + 48$

b. $f(x) = -2x^3 + 20x^2 - 56x + 48$

c. $f(x) = -27x^3 + 24x^2 - 48x + 56$

d. $f(x) = -48x^3 + 56x^2 - 20x + 2$

2. Sketch the graph of *f*.

$$f(x) = \frac{-3x}{x + 2}$$

a.

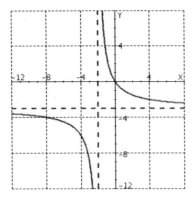

b.

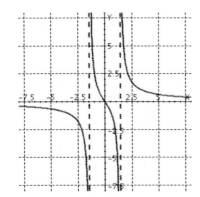

c.

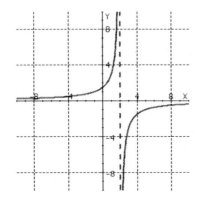

3. Find a factored form with integer coefficients of the polynomial *f* shown in the figure.

$$f(x) = 10\,x^5 - 41\,x^4 + 52\,x^3 - 17\,x^2 - 8\,x + 4$$

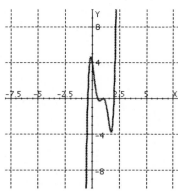

a. $(2x + 5)(x^2 - 2)(x - 1)(x - 2)$

b. $(2x + 5)(2x - 1)(x - 1)^2(x - 2)$

c. $(5x + 2)(2x - 1)(x - 1)^2(x - 2)$

d. $x(5x + 2)(2x - 1)(x - 1)(x - 2)$

4. The National Football League (NFL) ranks its passers by assigning a passer rating R based on the number of completions C, attempts A, yards Y, touchdowns T, and interceptions I. In a normal situation, it can be shown that the passer rating can be calculated by using the formula

$$R = \frac{25(A + 40C + 2Y + 160T - 200I)}{12A}$$

During a season, a passer completed 295 of 393 passes, has 34 touchdown passes, and 9 interceptions. How many yards would this passer needed to have completed to obtain a rating of at least 127?

a.   4049.3 yards

b.   4074.9 yards

c.   4052.5 yards

d.   4062.1 yards

5. Find all values of x such that $f(x) < 0$.

$$f(x) = x^4 - 110\, x^2 + 1000$$

a. $(-\ 10,\ -\ \sqrt{10}\ )\ \cup\ (\ \sqrt{10},\ 10\ )$

b. $(\ -\ \infty,\ -\ 110\ )\ \cup\ (\ 110,\ \infty\ )$

c. $(\ -\ 1000,\ -\ \sqrt{1000}\ )\ \cup\ (\ \sqrt{1000},\ 1000\ )$

6. Let $f(x)$ be a polynomial such that the coefficient of every even power of x is 0. Is f an even or odd function?

a. neither even nor odd

b. even

c. odd

7. Find the quotient and remainder if $f(x)$ is divided by $p(x)$

$$f(x) = 5\, x^4 - x^3 - 9\, x^2 + 9\, x - 10;$$
$$p(x) = x^2 - 3$$

a. Quotient : $5x^2 - x$
Remainder : $6x + 8$

b. Quotient : $6x + 8$
Remainder : $5x^2 - x + 6$

c. Quotient : $5x^2 - x + 6$
Remainder : $6x + 8$

8. Use the remainder theorem to find $f(c)$

$$f(x) = x^4 - 5x^2 + 7x - 8$$
$$c = -2$$

    a. $f(-2) = 110$

    b. $f(-2) = -26$

    c. $f(-2) = -165$

    d. $f(-2) = -408$

9. Use synthetic division to decide whether c is a zero of

$$f(x) = 8x^4 + 26x^3 - 9x^2 - 41x + 13$$
$$c = -3$$

    a. c is not a zero

    b. c is a zero

10. Find the domain D of f.

$$f(x) = \frac{4}{x}$$

    a. $(-\infty, \infty)$

    b. $(-\infty, 4) \cup (4, \infty)$

    c. $(-\infty, 0) \cup (0, \infty)$

11. Find the interval on which f is increasing.

$$f(x) = \frac{2}{x^2}$$

    a. $(-\infty, \infty)$

    b. $(-\infty, 2)$

    c. $(-\infty, 0)$

12. Find the oblique asymptote of $f(x)$.

$$f(x) = \frac{x^2 - x - 5}{x + 1}$$

    a. $y = x - 2$

    b. $y = x - 5$

    c. $y = x + 1$

13. Find all values of x such that $f(x) < 0$.

$$f(x) = x^3 + 8x^2 - 16x - 128$$

14. A herd of 575 deer is introduced onto a small island. At first the herd increases rapidly, but eventually food resources dwindle and the population declines. Suppose that the number of deer after t years is given by
$N(t) = -t^4 + 2t^2 + 575$, where $t > 0$. When does the population become extinct?

15. Use synthetic division to find the quotient and remainder if the first polynomial is divided by the second

$$2x^3 - 3x^2 + 8x - 8;$$
$$x - 2$$

16. Find a polynomial $f(x)$ of degree 3 that has the indicated zeros and satisfies the given condition.

$-4, -2, 2; f(0) = -32$

17. A polynomial $f(x)$ with real coefficients and leading coefficient 1 has the given zeros and degree. Express $f(x)$ as a product of linear and quadratic polynomials with real coefficients that are irreducible over **R**.

$$8 + 3i, -1 + i; \text{ degree 4}$$

18. Find all solutions of the equation.

$$110x^5 + 1299x^4 + 969x^3 - 110x^2 = 0$$

19. Find an equation of a rational function f that satisfies the conditions:
vertical asymptote: $x = -8$, $x = 0$
horizontal asymptote: $y = 0$
x-intercept: 6; $f(7) = 1$

20. The pressure P acting at a point in a liquid is directly proportional to the distance d from the surface of the liquid to the point. Express P as a function of d by means of a formula that involves a constant of proportionality k. In a certain oil tank, the pressure at a depth of 5 feet is 295. Find the pressure at a depth of 9 feet for the oil tank.

21. The speed V at which an automobile was traveling before the brakes were applied can sometimes be estimated from the length L of the skid marks. Assume that V directly proportional to the square root of L. Express V as a function of L by means of a formula that involves a constant of proportionality k. For a certain automobile on a dry surface, $L = 48$ ft when $V = 31$ mi/hr . Estimate the initial speed of the automobile if the skid marks are 147 feet long.

22. A storage tank for propane gas is to be constructed in the shape of a right circular cylinder with a hemisphere attached to the top. If the total height of the structure is 30 feet, determine the radius of the cylinder that results in a total volume of $1008 \; \pi \; \text{ft}^3$.

23. Sketch the graph of f.

$$f(x) = \frac{3}{x - 4}$$

24. Sketch the graph of f for the indicated value of a.

$$f(x) = ax^3 + 2, \quad a = -\frac{1}{3}$$

25. Simplify $f(x)$, and sketch the graph of f.

$$f(x) = \frac{x^2 + x - 2}{x + 2}$$

1. Find the polynomial function of degree 3 whose graph is shown in the figure.

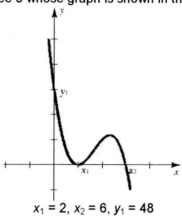

$x_1 = 2$, $x_2 = 6$, $y_1 = 48$

a. $f(x) = -48x^3 + 56x^2 - 20x + 2$

b. $f(x) = -27x^3 + 24x^2 - 48x + 56$

c. $f(x) = -2x^3 + 20x^2 - 56x + 48$

d. $f(x) = -21x^3 + 23x^2 - 56x + 48$

2. Sketch the graph of *f*.

$$f(x) = \frac{-3x}{x+3}$$

a.

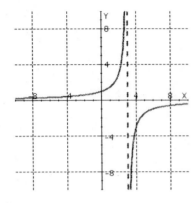

b.

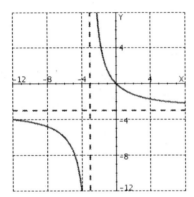

c.

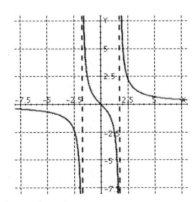

3. Find a factored form with integer coefficients of the polynomial *f* shown in the figure.

$$f(x) = 14x^5 - 59x^4 + 80x^3 - 35x^2 - 4x + 4$$

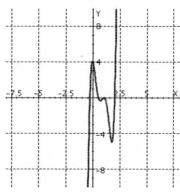

a. $(7x + 2)(2x - 1)(x - 1)^2(x - 2)$

b. $x(7x + 2)(2x - 1)(x - 1)(x - 2)$

c. $(2x + 7)(x^2 - 2)(x - 1)(x - 2)$

d. $(2x + 7)(2x - 1)(x - 1)^2(x - 2)$

4. The National Football League (NFL) ranks its passers by assigning a passer rating R based on the number of completions C, attempts A, yards Y, touchdowns T, and interceptions I. In a normal situation, it can be shown that the passer rating can be calculated by using the formula

$$R = \frac{25(A + 40C + 2Y + 160T - 200I)}{12A}$$

During a season, a passer completed 220 of 338 passes, has 20 touchdown passes, and 8 interceptions. How many yards would this passer needed to have completed to obtain a rating of at least 101?

a.   2824.1 yards

b.   2836.9 yards

c.   2814.5 yards

d.   2811.3 yards

5. Find all values of x such that $f(x) < 0$.

$$f(x) = x^4 - 30x^2 + 125$$

a. $(-125, -\sqrt{125}) \cup (\sqrt{125}, 125)$

b. $(-5, -\sqrt{5}) \cup (\sqrt{5}, 5)$

c. $(-\infty, -30) \cup (30, \infty)$

6. Let $f(x)$ be a polynomial such that the coefficient of every odd power of x is 0. Is f an even or odd function?

a. even

b. neither even nor odd

c. odd

7. Find the quotient and remainder if $f(x)$ is divided by $p(x)$

$$f(x) = 3x^4 - x^3 - 4x^2 + 5x - 12;$$
$$p(x) = x^2 - 3$$

a.
Quotient : $3x^2 - x$
Remainder : $2x + 3$

b.
Quotient : $3x^2 - x + 5$
Remainder : $2x + 3$

c.
Quotient : $2x + 3$
Remainder : $3x^2 - x + 5$

8. Use the remainder theorem to find $f(c)$

$$f(x) = x^4 - 5x^2 + 6x - 2$$
$$c = -9$$

a. $f(-9) = 5976$

b. $f(-9) = 6460$

c. $f(-9) = 6204$

d. $f(-9) = 6100$

9. Use synthetic division to decide whether c is a zero of

$$f(x) = 8x^4 + 18x^3 - 10x^2 - 23x + 10$$
$$c = -2$$

a. c is a zero

b. c is not a zero

10. Find the domain D of f.

$$f(x) = \frac{8}{x}$$

a. $(-\infty, 0) \cup (0, \infty)$

b. $(-\infty, \infty)$

c. $(-\infty, 8) \cup (8, \infty)$

11. Find the interval on which f is increasing.

$$f(x) = \frac{8}{x^2}$$

a. $(-\infty, 8)$

b. $(-\infty, 0)$

c. $(-\infty, \infty)$

12. Find the oblique asymptote of $f(x)$.

$$f(x) = \frac{x^2 - x - 64}{x + 7}$$

a. $y = x + 7$

b. $y = x - 8$

c. $y = x - 64$

13. Find all values of x such that $f(x) < 0$.

$$f(x) = x^3 + 5x^2 - 25x - 125$$

14. A herd of 400 deer is introduced onto a small island. At first the herd increases rapidly, but eventually food resources dwindle and the population declines. Suppose that the number of deer after t years is given by

$N(t) = -t^4 + 9t^2 + 400$, where $t > 0$. When does the population become extinct?

15. Use synthetic division to find the quotient and remainder if the first polynomial is divided by the second

$$6x^3 - 6x^2 + 9x - 9;$$
$$x - 2$$

16. Find a polynomial $f(x)$ of degree 3 that has the indicated zeros and satisfies the given condition.

$-1, 1, 2\,; f(0) = 4$

17. A polynomial $f(x)$ with real coefficients and leading coefficient 1 has the given zeros and degree. Express $f(x)$ as a product of linear and quadratic polynomials with real coefficients that are irreducible over **R**.

$$1 + 7i, -3 + i\,; \text{degree } 4$$

18. Find all solutions of the equation.

$$44x^5 + 489x^4 + 51x^3 - 44x^2 = 0$$

19. Find an equation of a rational function f that satisfies the conditions:
vertical asymptote: $x = -7$, $x = 0$
horizontal asymptote: $y = 0$
x-intercept: 7; $f(8) = 1$

20. The pressure P acting at a point in a liquid is directly proportional to the distance d from the surface of the liquid to the point. Express P as a function of d by means of a formula that involves a constant of proportionality k. In a certain oil tank, the pressure at a depth of 7 feet is 413. Find the pressure at a depth of 10 feet for the oil tank.

21. The speed V at which an automobile was traveling before the brakes were applied can sometimes be estimated from the length L of the skid marks. Assume that V directly proportional to the square root of L. Express V as a function of L by means of a formula that involves a constant of proportionality k. For a certain automobile on a dry surface, $L = 48$ ft when $V = 26$ mi/hr . Estimate the initial speed of the automobile if the skid marks are 101 feet long.

22. A storage tank for propane gas is to be constructed in the shape of a right circular cylinder with a hemisphere attached to the top. If the total height of the structure is 40 feet, determine the radius of the cylinder that results in a total volume of $1368 \div ft^3$.

23. Sketch the graph of f.

$$f(x) = \frac{3}{x - 4}$$

24. Sketch the graph of f for the indicated value of a.

$$f(x) = ax^3 + 2, \quad a = -\frac{1}{4}$$

25. Simplify $f(x)$, and sketch the graph of f.

$$f(x) = \frac{x^2 + x - 2}{x + 2}$$

Test Form 3-A

1.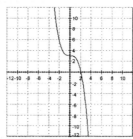

2. $(-8,3) \cup (5,\infty)$
3. $(-\infty,-8) \cup (-8,8)$
4. 5
5. 50
6. -24
7. $9x^2 + 13x + 33,61$
8. 83
9. $5x^3 - 15x^2 - 30x + 40$
10. $-2x^3 + 20x^2 - 56x + 48$
11. $(x^2 - 18x + 90) \cdot (x^2 + 16x + 65)$
12. $x \cdot (x^2 + 9) \cdot (x^2 - 8x + 17)$
13. $-7, -\dfrac{5}{7}, \dfrac{1}{5}, 0, 0$

14. 5.8 ft
15.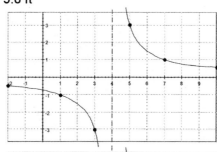

16.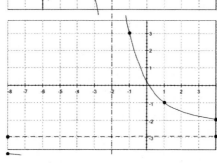

17.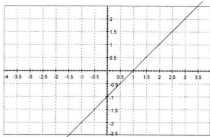

18. $f(x) = \dfrac{72x - 504}{x^2 + x}$

19. $f(x) = \dfrac{56x^2 - 56x - 336}{x^3 - 37x + 84}$

20. $f(t) = \dfrac{t}{10t + 120}$

21. S=550
22. 708
23. 1.62
24. 77.57
25. 4985.3 yards

Test Form 3-B

1.
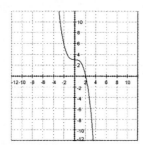

2. $(-8,2) \cup (5,\infty)$

3. $(-\infty,-7) \cup (-5,5)$

4. 5

5. 3

6. 175

7. $2x^2 + x + 10, 16$

8. 243

9. $5x^3 - 20x^2 - 5x + 20$

10. $-2x^3 + 20x^2 - 56x + 48$

11. $(x^2 - 6x + 45) \cdot (x^2 + 14x + 50)$

12. $x \cdot (x^2 + 64) \cdot (x^2 - 8x + 17)$

13. $-11, -\dfrac{6}{11}, \dfrac{1}{6}, 0, 0$

14. 5.8 ft

15.
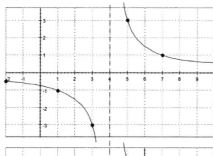

16.
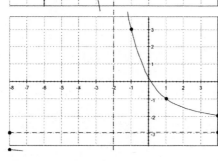

17.
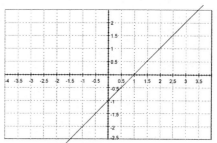

18. $f(x) = \dfrac{104x - 728}{x^2 + 5x}$

19. $f(x) = \dfrac{225x^2 - 675x - 900}{x^3 - 61x + 180}$

20. $f(t) = \dfrac{t}{2t + 110}$

21. $S = 4950$

22. 472

23. 0.79

24. 78.57

25. 1708.3 yards

Test Form 3-C

1. c	**2.** a	**3.** a	**4.** b	**5.** b	**6.** b	**7.** c	**8.** a	**9.** b
10. d	**11.** a	**12.** b	**13.** c	**14.** a	**15.** c	**16.** c	**17.** c	**18.** a
19. c	**20.** b	**21.** b	**22.** d	**23.** a	**24.** c	**25.** d		

Test Form 3-D

1. c	**2.** c	**3.** a	**4.** c	**5.** b	**6.** a	**7.** d	**8.** a	**9.** b
10. c	**11.** a	**12.** d	**13.** d	**14.** b	**15.** a	**16.** c	**17.** a	**18.** b
19. a	**20.** b	**21.** c	**22.** b	**23.** d	**24.** c	**25.** b		

Test Form 3-E

1. b
2. a
3. c
4. d
5. a
6. c
7. c
8. b
9. a
10. c
11. c
12. a
13. $(-\infty, -8) \cup (-4, 4)$
14. 5
15. $2x^2 + x + 10, 12$
16. $2x^3 + 8x^2 - 8x - 32$
17. $(x^2 - 16x + 73) \cdot (x^2 + 2x + 2)$
18. $-11, -\dfrac{10}{11}, \dfrac{1}{10}, 0, 0$
19. $f(x) = \dfrac{105x - 630}{x^2 + 8x}$
20. 531
21. 54.25
22. 5.8 ft

23.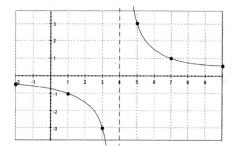

24.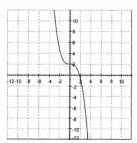

25.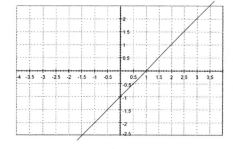

Test Form 3-F

1. c
2. b
3. a
4. a
5. b
6. a
7. b
8. d
9. a
10. a
11. b
12. b
13. $(-\infty, -5) \cup (-5, 5)$
14. 5
15. $6x^2 + 6x + 21, 33$
16. $2x^3 - 4x^2 - 2x + 4$
17. $(x^2 - 2x + 50) \cdot (x^2 + 6x + 10)$
18. $-11, -\dfrac{4}{11}, \dfrac{1}{4}, 0, 0$
19. $f(x) = \dfrac{120x - 840}{x^2 + 7x}$
20. 590
21. 37.71
22. 5.8 ft

23.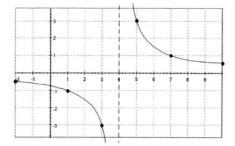

24.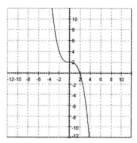

25.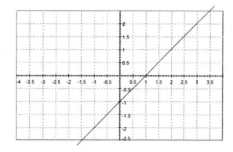

1. Find the inverse function of

$$f(x) = \frac{7x + 4}{4x - 9}$$

2. Determine the domain of f^{-1} for the function without actually finding f^{-1}. *Hint:* First find the domain and range of f.

$$f(x) = \frac{8}{x + 7}$$

3. Find the inverse function of

$$f(x) = 7x^3 - 2$$

4. The number of bacteria in a certain culture increased from 600 to 1800 between 7:00 A.M. and 9:00 A.M. Assuming the growth is exponential, the number $f(t)$ of bacteria t hours after 7:00 A.M. is given by:

$$f(t) = 600(3)^{t/2}$$

Estimate the number of bacteria in the culture at 11:00 A.M.

5. If 10 grams of salt is added to a quantity of water, then the amount that is undissolved after t minutes is given by the function $q(t)$. Sketch a graph that shows the value at any time from $t = 0$ to $t = 10$.

$$q(t) = 10\left(\frac{4}{5}\right)^t$$

6. An economist predicts that the buying power $B(t)$ of a dollar t years from now will be given by:

    $$B(t) = (0.93)^t$$

    Use the graph of B to approximate when the buying power will be half of what it is today.

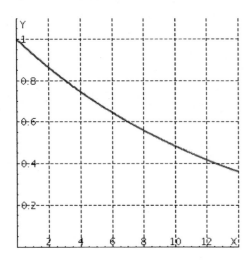

7. In 1974, Johnny Miller won 8 tournaments on the PGA tour and accumulated $311631 in official season earnings. In 1999, Tiger Woods accumulated $6495504 with a similar record. Find the annual interest rate needed for Miller's winnings to be equivalent in value to Woods's winnings.

8. Use the graph of $y = e^x$ to help sketch the graph of
    $$f(x) = e^{x + 4}$$

9. The effective yield (or effective annual interest rate) for an investment is the simple interest rate that would yield at the end of one year the same amount as is yielded by the compounded rate that is actually applied. Approximate, to the nearest 0.01%, the effective yield corresponding to an interest rate of 7% per year compounded quarterly.

10. The population $N(t)$ (in millions) of India t years after 1985 may be approximated by the formula

$$N(t) = 762e^{0.022t}.$$

When will the population reach 1.6 billion?

11. Express in terms of logarithms of x, y, z, or w.

$$\log_a \frac{z^9 x^3}{w^5 y^4}$$

12. Write the expression as one logarithm.

$$3 \log \frac{y^3}{x} - 3 \log y + \frac{1}{2} \log x^6 y^2$$

13. Solve the equation.

$$\log_9 (3x - 19) = \log_9 (8) - \log_9 (4)$$

14. Solve the equation.
$$\ln(8 + x) - \ln x = 2\ln 4$$

15. Solve the equation.

$$\log_6 (x + 5) + \log_6 (x + 10) = 1$$

16. Sketch the graph of

$$f(x) = \log_3(3x)$$

17.

Sketch the graph of $f(x) = \log_3\left(\dfrac{1}{x}\right)$

18. Pareto's law for capitalist countries states that the relationship between annual income y and the number p of individuals whose income exceeds y is where c and w are positive constants. Solve this equation for p.

$$\log p = \log c - w \log y$$

19. Find the exact solution using common logarithms, and a two-decimal-place approximation of the solution of the equation.

$$6^{5-x} = 9$$

20. Find the exact solution, using common logarithms, and a two-decimal-place approximation of the solution of the equation

$$3^{x+4} = 2^{1-5x}$$

21. Find a two-decimal-place approximation of the solution of the equation

$$\log(x^2 + 25) - \log(x + 5) = 2 + \log(x - 5)$$

22. Use natural logarithms to solve for x in terms of y

$$y = \frac{e^x - e^{-x}}{2}$$

23. Use the change of base formula to approximate the x-intercept

$$f(x) = 9^x - 5$$

24. Use the compound interest formula to determine how long it will take for a sum of money to double if it is invested at a rate of 10% per year compounded monthly.

25. If a 100-milligram tablet of an asthma drug is taken orally and if none of the drug is present in the body when the tablet is first taken, the total amount A in the bloodstream after t minutes is predicted to be

$$A = 100[1 - (0.9)^t] \quad \text{for} \quad 0 \leq t \leq 10.$$

Determine the number of minutes needed for 40 milligrams of the drug to have entered the bloodstream.

1. Find the inverse function of

$$f(x) = \frac{3x + 8}{8x - 7}$$

2. Determine the domain of f^{-1} for the function without actually finding f^{-1}. *Hint:* First find the domain and range of f.

$$f(x) = \frac{7}{x + 4}$$

3. Find the inverse function of

$$f(x) = 3x^3 - 7$$

4. The number of bacteria in a certain culture increased from 600 to 1800 between 7:00 A.M. and 9:00 A.M. Assuming the growth is exponential, the number $f(t)$ of bacteria t hours after 7:00 A.M. is given by:

$$f(t) = 600(3)^{t/2}$$

Estimate the number of bacteria in the culture at 9:00 A.M.

5. If 10 grams of salt is added to a quantity of water, then the amount that is undissolved after t minutes is given by the function $q(t)$. Sketch a graph that shows the value at any time from $t = 0$ to $t = 10$.

$$q(t) = 10\left(\frac{4}{5}\right)^t$$

6. An economist predicts that the buying power $B(t)$ of a dollar t years from now will be given by:

$$B(t) = (0.9)^t$$

Use the graph of B to approximate when the buying power will be half of what it is today.

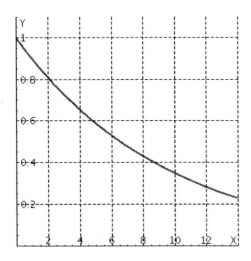

7. In 1974, Johnny Miller won 8 tournaments on the PGA tour and accumulated $365261 in official season earnings. In 1999, Tiger Woods accumulated $6290931 with a similar record. Find the annual interest rate needed for Miller's winnings to be equivalent in value to Woods's winnings.

8. Use the graph of $y = e^x$ to help sketch the graph of
$$f(x) = e^{x+4}$$

9. The effective yield (or effective annual interest rate) for an investment is the simple interest rate that would yield at the end of one year the same amount as is yielded by the compounded rate that is actually applied. Approximate, to the nearest 0.01%, the effective yield corresponding to an interest rate of 8% per year compounded quarterly.

10. The population $N(t)$ (in millions) of India t years after 1985 may be approximated by the formula

$$N(t) = 762e^{0.022t}.$$

When will the population reach 1.1 billion?

11. Express in terms of logarithms of x, y, z, or w.

$$\log_a \frac{w^7 z^5}{x^9 y^3}$$

12. Write the expression as one logarithm.

$$2\log \frac{x^3}{y} - 3\log x + \frac{1}{3}\log y^6 x^3$$

13. Solve the equation.

$$\log_9(4x - 11) = \log_9(15) - \log_9(3)$$

14. Solve the equation.

$$\log(7 + x) - \log x = 2\log 4$$

15. Solve the equation.

$$\log_4(x+6) + \log_4(x+9) = 1$$

16. Sketch the graph of

$$f(x) = \log_3(3x)$$

17.
     Sketch the graph of $f(x) = \log_3\left(\dfrac{1}{x}\right)$

18. Pareto's law for capitalist countries states that the relationship between annual income x and the number p of individuals whose income exceeds x is where c and k are positive constants. Solve this equation for p.

$$\log p = \log c - k \log x$$

19. Find the exact solution using common logarithms, and a two-decimal-place approximation of the solution of the equation.

$$2^{6-x} = 3$$

20. Find the exact solution, using common logarithms, and a two-decimal-place approximation of the solution of the equation

$$9^{x+1} = 4^{1-3x}$$

21. Find a two-decimal-place approximation of the solution of the equation

$\log (x^2 + 25) - \log (x + 5) = 2 + \log (x - 5)$

22. Use natural logarithms to solve for x in terms of y

$$y = \frac{e^x - e^{-x}}{16}$$

23. Use the change of base formula to approximate the x-intercept

$f(x) = 7^x - 6$

24. Use the compound interest formula to determine how long it will take for a sum of money to double if it is invested at a rate of 8% per year compounded monthly.

25. If a 100-milligram tablet of an asthma drug is taken orally and if none of the drug is present in the body when the tablet is first taken, the total amount A in the bloodstream after t minutes is predicted to be

$A = 100[1 - (0.9)^t]$ for $0 \le t \le 10$.

Determine the number of minutes needed for 30 milligrams of the drug to have entered the bloodstream.

1. Find the inverse function of

$$f(x) = \frac{5x + 7}{7x - 11}$$

a. $f^{-1}(x) = \frac{7 + 11x}{5x - 7}$

b. $f^{-1}(x) = \frac{11 + 7x}{7x - 5}$

c. $f^{-1}(x) = \frac{7 + 11x}{7x - 5}$

d. $f^{-1}(x) = \frac{5 + 7x}{5x - 11}$

2. Find the inverse function of

$$f(x) = 7 - 2x^2, \quad x \leq 0$$

a. $f^{-1}(x) = \sqrt{\frac{7 - x}{2}}$

b. $f^{-1}(x) = -\sqrt{\frac{5 - x}{2}}$

c. $f^{-1}(x) = -\sqrt{\frac{7 - x}{5}}$

d. $f^{-1}(x) = -\sqrt{\frac{7 - x}{2}}$

3. The radioactive bismuth isotope ^{210}Bi has a half-life of 5 days. If there is 100 milligrams of present at then the amount remaining after t days is given by:

$$f(t) = 100(2)^{-t/5}$$

How much remains after 5 days?

   a.   59 milligrams

   b.   55 milligrams

   c.   52 milligrams

   d.   50 milligrams

   e.   49 milligrams

4. If $1200 is deposited in a savings account that pays interest at a rate of $10\frac{1}{4}$ % per year compounded continuously, find the balance after 5 years.

   a. $1978.47

   b. $2003.35

   c. $5008.38

   d. $718.80

5. How much money, invested at an interest rate of 10% per year compounded continuously, will amount to $99000 after 17 years?

   a. $36171.34

   b. $5419.21

   c. $109411.92

   d. $18085.67

6. An investment of $929 increased to $10241 in 16 years. If the interest was compounded continuously, find the interest rate.

    a.   15%

    b.   12%

    c.   17%

    d.   30%

7. The 1980 population of the United States was approximately 227 million, and the population has been growing continuously at a rate of 0.7% per year. Predict the population in the year 2040 if this growth trend continues.

    a.   690 million people

    b.   1035 million people

    c.   345 million people

    d.   115 million people

8. The effective yield (or effective annual interest rate) for an investment is the simple interest rate that would yield at the end of one year the same amount as is yielded by the compounded rate that is actually applied. Approximate, to the nearest 0.01%, the effective yield corresponding to an interest rate of 12% per year compounded quarterly.

    a.   25.10%

    b.   4.18%

    c.   37.65%

    d.   12.55%

9. Express in terms of logarithms of x, y, z, w.

$$\log_2 \frac{x^5 w}{y^4 z^3}$$

    a. $5\log_2(x) + \log_2(w) - 3\log_2(y) - 4\log_2(z)$

    b. $5\log_2(x) + \log_2(w) - 4\log_2(y) - 3\log_2(z)$

    c. $\log_2(x) + \log_2(w) - \log_2(y) + \log_2(z)$

    d. $5\log_2(x) + \log_2(w) + 4\log_2(y) + 3\log_2(z)$

10. Write the expression as one logarithm.

$$6\ln(x) - 8\ln(1/y) - 3\ln(xy)$$

    a. $\ln(x^5 y^3)$

    b. $\ln(6x - 8y - 3xy)$

    c. $\ln(x^3 y^5)$

    d. $\ln(x^6 - y^8 - (xy)^3)$

11. Solve the equation.

$$\log_2(4x - 20) = \log_2(8) - \log_2(2)$$

    a. $x = 3$

    b. $x = 11$

    c. $x = 6$

    d. $x = 8$

12. Solve the equation.

$$\log_5 (x + 8) + \log_5 (x +12) = 1$$

a. $x = - 8$

b. $x = - 7$

c. $x = 7$

d. $x = 8$

13. Solve the equation.

$$\ln x = 1 - \ln (x + 2)$$

a. $x = - 1 - \sqrt{1 + e}$

b. $x = - 2 + \sqrt{4 + e}$

c. $x = - 2 - \sqrt{4 + e}$

d. $x = - 1 + \sqrt{1 + e}$

14. Pareto's law for capitalist countries states that the relationship between annual income z and the number m of individuals whose income exceeds z is where a and k are positive constants. Solve this equation for m.

$$\log m = \log a - k \log z$$

a. $\quad m = az^k$

b. $\quad m = \dfrac{a}{kz}$

c. $\quad m = \log \dfrac{a}{z^k}$

d. $\quad m = \dfrac{a}{z^k}$

15. Find the exact solution using common logarithms, and a two-decimal-place approximation of the solution of the equation.

$$6^{2-x} = 11$$

a. $\quad 2 - \dfrac{\log 6}{\log 11} \approx 1.25$

b. $\quad \dfrac{\log 11}{\log 6} \approx 1.34$

c. $\quad 2 - \dfrac{\log 11}{\log 6} \approx 0.66$

d. $\quad \dfrac{\log 6}{\log 11} - 2 \approx -0.83$

16. Find the exact solution, using common logarithms, and a two-decimal-place approximation of the solution of the equation

$$5^{x+6} = 3^{1-4x}$$

    a. $x = \dfrac{\log 405}{\log (3/15625)} \approx -0.70$

    b. $x = \dfrac{\log (3/15625)}{\log 405} \approx -1.43$

    c. $x = \dfrac{\log 15625}{\log 405} \approx 1.61$

17. Find a two-decimal-place approximation of the solution of the equation

$$\log (x^2 + 4) - \log (x + 2) = 2 + \log (x - 2)$$

    a. $x = 5.84$

    b. $x = 0.11$

    c. $x = -3.93$

    d. $x = 2.02$

18. Use common logarithms to solve for x in terms of y

$$y = \frac{10^x + 10^{-x}}{14}$$

a.

$$x = \log\left(7y + \sqrt{14y^2 - 1}\right)$$

b.

$$x = \log\left(14y \pm \sqrt{49y^2 + 1}\right)$$

c.

$$x = \log\left(49y - \sqrt{y^2 - 7}\right)$$

d.

$$x = \log\left(7y \pm \sqrt{49y^2 - 1}\right)$$

19. Use the compound interest formula to determine how long it will take for a sum of money to double if it is invested at a rate of 6% per year compounded monthly.
   a.   13.35 years

   b.   11.81 years

   c.   11.58 years

20. If a 100-milligram tablet of an asthma drug is taken orally and if none of the drug is present in the body when the tablet is first taken, the total amount A in the bloodstream after t minutes is predicted to be

$$A = 100\left[1 - (0.9)^t\right] \quad \text{for} \quad 0 \le t \le 10.$$

Determine the number of minutes needed for 45 milligrams of the drug to have entered the bloodstream.
   a.   8.37 min

   b.   4.32 min

   c.   8.23 min

   d.   5.67 min

21. The graph of a one-to-one function *f* is shown. Use the reflection property to sketch the graph of f^{-1}

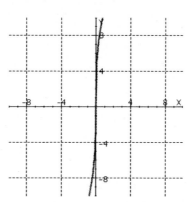

a.

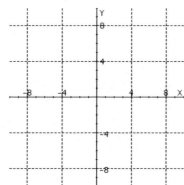

b.

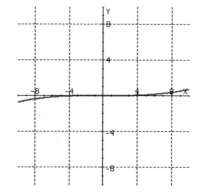

c.

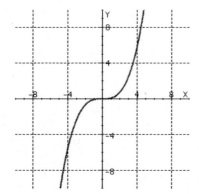

22. Sketch the graph of *f* if:

$$f(x) = 3^{x-3}$$

a.

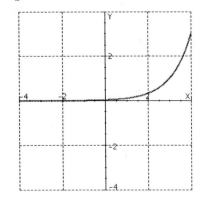

b.

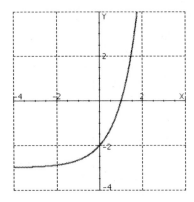

c.

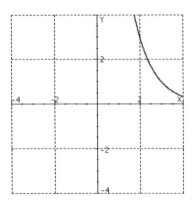

23. Sketch the graph of *f* if:

$$f(x) = \left(\frac{2}{5}\right)^{-x}$$

a.

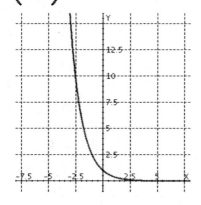

b.

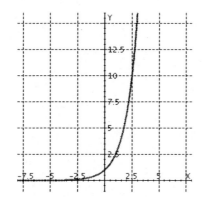

c.

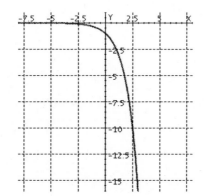

24. If 9 grams of salt is added to a quantity of water, then the amount that is undissolved after t minutes is given by:

$$q(t) = 9\left(\frac{4}{5}\right)^t$$

Sketch a graph that shows the value at any time from $t = 0$ to $t = 10$.

    a.

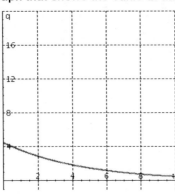

    b.

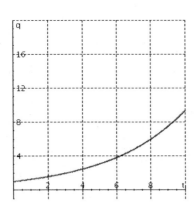

    c.

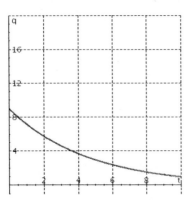

25. Use the graph of $y = e^x$ to help sketch the graph of

$$f(x) = e^{x+5}$$

a.

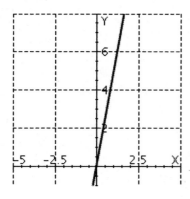

b.

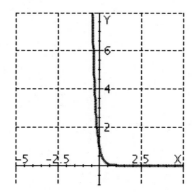

c.

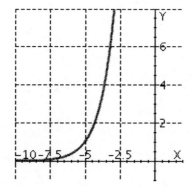

1. Find the inverse function of

$$f(x) = \frac{5x + 11}{11x - 3}$$

a. $f^{-1}(x) = \dfrac{3 + 11x}{11x - 5}$

b. $f^{-1}(x) = \dfrac{11 + 3x}{11x - 5}$

c. $f^{-1}(x) = \dfrac{11 + 3x}{5x - 11}$

d. $f^{-1}(x) = \dfrac{5 + 11x}{5x - 3}$

2. Find the inverse function of

$$f(x) = 3 - 7x^2 , \ x \le 0$$

a. $f^{-1}(x) = \sqrt{\dfrac{3 - x}{7}}$

b. $f^{-1}(x) = - \sqrt{\dfrac{11 - x}{7}}$

c. $f^{-1}(x) = - \sqrt{\dfrac{3 - x}{7}}$

d. $f^{-1}(x) = - \sqrt{\dfrac{3 - x}{11}}$

3. The radioactive bismuth isotope ^{210}Bi has a half-life of 5 days. If there is 100 milligrams of present at then the amount remaining after t days is given by:

    $$f(t) = 100(2)^{-t/5}$$

    How much remains after 15 days?

    a.   11.5 milligrams

    b.   17.5 milligrams

    c.   14.5 milligrams

    d.   21.5 milligrams

    e.   12.5 milligrams

4. If $1100 is deposited in a savings account that pays interest at a rate of $10\frac{1}{4}$ % per year compounded continuously, find the balance after 4 years.

    a. $1657.50

    b. $4143.75

    c. $1641.01

    d. $730.02

5. How much money, invested at an interest rate of 9% per year compounded continuously, will amount to $110000 after 19 years?

    a. $39790.47

    b. $120359.17

    c. $19895.24

    d. $6081.86

6. An investment of $1028 increased to $11332 in 16 years. If the interest was compounded continuously, find the interest rate.

    a.   15%

    b.   12%

    c.   30%

    d.   17%

7. The 1980 population of the United States was approximately 227 million, and the population has been growing continuously at a rate of 0.7% per year. Predict the population in the year 2040 if this growth trend continues.

    a.   690 million people

    b.   345 million people

    c.   1035 million people

    d.   115 million people

8. The effective yield (or effective annual interest rate) for an investment is the simple interest rate that would yield at the end of one year the same amount as is yielded by the compounded rate that is actually applied. Approximate, to the nearest 0.01%, the effective yield corresponding to an interest rate of 11% per year compounded quarterly.

    a.   3.82%

    b.   34.39%

    c.   11.46%

    d.   22.92%

9. Express in terms of logarithms of x, y, z, w.

$$\log_7 \frac{x^5 w}{y^4 z^2}$$

a. $5\log_7(x) + \log_7(w) + 4\log_7(y) + 2\log_7(z)$

b. $\log_7(x) + \log_7(w) - \log_7(y) + \log_7(z)$

c. $5\log_7(x) + \log_7(w) - 4\log_7(y) - 2\log_7(z)$

d. $5\log_7(x) + \log_7(w) - 2\log_7(y) - 4\log_7(z)$

10. Write the expression as one logarithm.

$$7\ln(x) - 8\ln(1/y) - 3\ln(xy)$$

a. $\ln(x^4 y^5)$

b. $\ln(7x - 8y - 3xy)$

c. $\ln(x^5 y^4)$

d. $\ln(x^7 - y^8 - (xy)^3)$

11. Solve the equation.

$$\log_9(3x - 8) = \log_9(8) - \log_9(2)$$

a. $x = 6$

b. $x = 4$

c. $x = 9$

d. $x = 1$

12. Solve the equation.

$$\log_5(x+4) + \log_5(x+8) = 1$$

    a. $x = -3$

    b. $x = 3$

    c. $x = 6$

    d. $x = -6$

13. Solve the equation.

$$\ln x = 1 - \ln(x+8)$$

    a. $x = -4 - \sqrt{16 + e}$

    b. $x = -8 + \sqrt{64 + e}$

    c. $x = -8 - \sqrt{64 + e}$

    d. $x = -4 + \sqrt{16 + e}$

14. Pareto's law for capitalist countries states that the relationship between annual income z and the number m of individuals whose income exceeds z is where c and w are positive constants. Solve this equation for m.

$$\log m = \log c - w \log z$$

a. $m = cz^w$

b. $m = \dfrac{c}{wz}$

c. $m = \log \dfrac{c}{z^w}$

d. $m = \dfrac{c}{z^w}$

15. Find the exact solution using common logarithms, and a two-decimal-place approximation of the solution of the equation.

$$3^{3-x} = 5$$

a. $3 - \dfrac{\log 5}{\log 3} \approx 1.54$

b. $3 - \dfrac{\log 3}{\log 5} \approx 2.32$

c. $\dfrac{\log 5}{\log 3} \approx 1.46$

d. $\dfrac{\log 3}{\log 5} - 3 \approx -2.15$

16. Find the exact solution, using common logarithms, and a two-decimal-place approximation of the solution of the equation

$7^{x+1} = 4^{1-3x}$

   a. $x = \dfrac{\log 7}{\log 448} \approx 0.32$

   b. $x = \dfrac{\log (4/7)}{\log 448} \approx -0.09$

   c. $x = \dfrac{\log 448}{\log (4/7)} \approx -10.91$

17. Find a two-decimal-place approximation of the solution of the equation

$\log (x^2 + 4) - \log (x + 2) = 1 + \log (x - 2)$

   a. $x = -2.91$

   b. $x = 3.61$

   c. $x = 1.51$

   d. $x = 2.21$

18. Use common logarithms to solve for x in terms of y

$$y = \frac{10^x + 10^{-x}}{16}$$

    a.
$$x = \log\left(8y + \sqrt{16y^2 - 1}\right)$$

    b.
$$x = \log\left(16y \pm \sqrt{64y^2 + 1}\right)$$

    c.
$$x = \log\left(64y - \sqrt{y^2 - 8}\right)$$

    d.
$$x = \log\left(8y \pm \sqrt{64y^2 - 1}\right)$$

19. Use the compound interest formula to determine how long it will take for a sum of money to double if it is invested at a rate of 8% per year compounded monthly.

    a.   8.69 years

    b.   9.65 years

    c.   9.73 years

20. If a 100-milligram tablet of an asthma drug is taken orally and if none of the drug is present in the body when the tablet is first taken, the total amount A in the bloodstream after t minutes is predicted to be

$$A = 100\left[1 - (0.9)^t\right] \quad \text{for} \quad 0 \le t \le 10.$$

Determine the number of minutes needed for 55 milligrams of the drug to have entered the bloodstream.

    a.   8.04 min

    b.   10.04 min

    c.   7.35 min

    d.   7.58 min

21. The graph of a one-to-one function f is shown. Use the reflection property to sketch the graph of f^{-1}

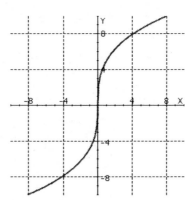

a.

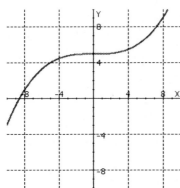

b.

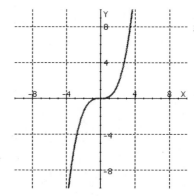

c.

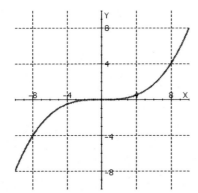

22. Sketch the graph of *f* if:

$$f(x) = 2^{x-3}$$

a.

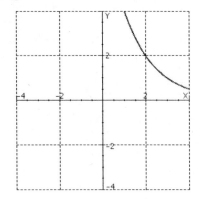

b.

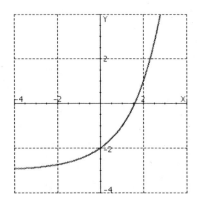

c.

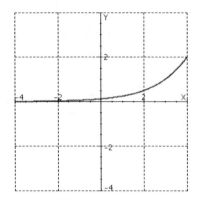

23. Sketch the graph of *f* if:

$$f(x) = \left(\frac{2}{9} \right)^{-x}$$

a.

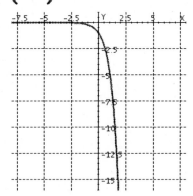

b.

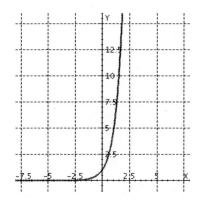

c.

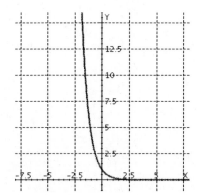

24. If 9 grams of salt is added to a quantity of water, then the amount that is undissolved after t minutes is given by:

$$q(t) = 9\left(\frac{4}{5}\right)^t$$

Sketch a graph that shows the value at any time from $t = 0$ to $t = 10$.

a.

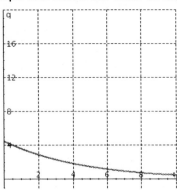

b.

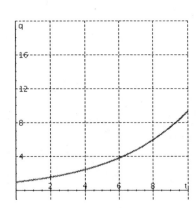

c.

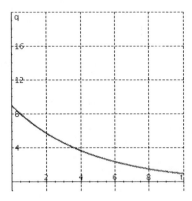

25. Use the graph of $y = e^x$ to help sketch the graph of

$$f(x) = e^{x+2}$$

a.

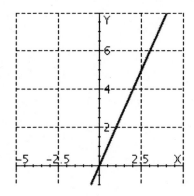

b.

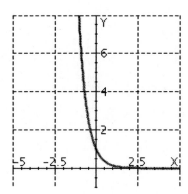

c.

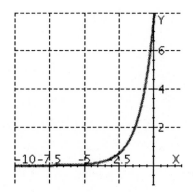

1. The graph of a one-to-one function f is shown. Use the reflection property to sketch the graph of f^{-1}

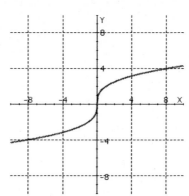

a.

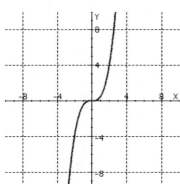

b.

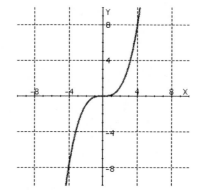

c.

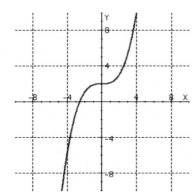

2. The radioactive bismuth isotope ^{210}Bi has a half-life of 5 days. If there is 100 milligrams of present at then the amount remaining after t days is given by:

$$f(t) = 100(2)^{-t/5}$$

How much remains after 25 days?
   a.   2.125 milligrams

   b.   5.125 milligrams

   c.   8.125 milligrams

   d.   12.125 milligrams

   e.   3.125 milligrams

3. If $800 is deposited in a savings account that pays interest at a rate of $10\frac{1}{4}$ % per year compounded continuously, find the balance after 5 years.

   a. $1318.98

   b. $3338.92

   c. $479.20

   d. $1335.57

4. How much money, invested at an interest rate of 9% per year compounded continuously, will amount to $92000 after 17 years?

   a. $4248.72

   b. $39842.56

   c. $19921.28

   d. $100664.03

5. An investment of $900 increased to $6326 in 15 years. If the interest was compounded continuously, find the interest rate.

    a.   10%

    b.   26%

    c.   13%

    d.   15%

6. The 1980 population of the United States was approximately 227 million, and the population has been growing continuously at a rate of 0.7% per year. Predict the population in the year 2030 if this growth trend continues.

    a.   107 million people

    b.   322 million people

    c.   643 million people

    d.   965 million people

7. Express in terms of logarithms of x, y, z, w.

$$\log_2 \frac{x^5 w}{y^2 z^3}$$

    a. $\log_2(x) + \log_2(w) - \log_2(y) + \log_2(z)$

    b. $5\log_2(x) + \log_2(w) - 2\log_2(y) - 3\log_2(z)$

    c. $5\log_2(x) + \log_2(w) - 3\log_2(y) - 2\log_2(z)$

    d. $5\log_2(x) + \log_2(w) + 2\log_2(y) + 3\log_2(z)$

8. Write the expression as one logarithm.

$$7\ln(x) - 9\ln(1/y) - 3\ln(xy)$$

a. $\ln(x^7 - y^9 - (xy)^3)$

b. $\ln(7x - 9y - 3xy)$

c. $\ln(x^6 y^4)$

d. $\ln(x^4 y^6)$

9. Solve the equation.

$$\log_5(x+4) + \log_5(x+8) = 1$$

a. $x = -3$

b. $x = -7$

c. $x = 3$

d. $x = 7$

10. Pareto's law for capitalist countries states that the relationship between annual income y and the number m of individuals whose income exceeds y is where b and k are positive constants. Solve this equation for m.

$$\log m = \log b - k \log y$$

a. $m = \dfrac{b}{y^k}$

b. $m = \dfrac{b}{ky}$

c. $m = by^k$

d. $m = \log \dfrac{b}{y^k}$

11. Find the exact solution using common logarithms, and a two-decimal-place approximation of the solution of the equation.

$$6^{7-x} = 7$$

   a. $\dfrac{\log 7}{\log 6} \approx 1.09$

   b. $7 - \dfrac{\log 6}{\log 7} \approx 6.08$

   c. $\dfrac{\log 6}{\log 7} - 7 \approx -6.77$

   d. $7 - \dfrac{\log 7}{\log 6} \approx 5.91$

12. Find a two-decimal-place approximation of the solution of the equation

$\log (x^2 + 16) - \log (x + 4) = 2 + \log (x - 4)$

   a. $x = -5.60$

   b. $x = 7.16$

   c. $x = 2.48$

   d. $x = 4.04$

13. Find the inverse function of

$$f(x) = \dfrac{8x + 7}{7x - 9}$$

14. Find the inverse function of

$$f(x) = 11x^3 - 3$$

15. The number of bacteria in a certain culture increased from 600 to 1800 between 7:00 A.M. and 9:00 A.M. Assuming the growth is exponential, the number $f(t)$ of bacteria t hours after 7:00 A.M. is given by:

$$f(t) = 600(3)^{t/2}$$

Estimate the number of bacteria in the culture at 10:00 A.M.

16. An economist predicts that the buying power $B(t)$ of a dollar t years from now will be given by:

$$B(t) = (0.95)^t$$

Use the graph of B to approximate when the buying power will be half of what it is today.

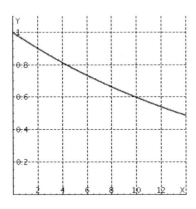

17. Use the graph of $y = e^x$ to help sketch the graph of
$$f(x) = e^{x+4}$$

18. The effective yield (or effective annual interest rate) for an investment is the simple interest rate that would yield at the end of one year the same amount as is yielded by the compounded rate that is actually applied. Approximate, to the nearest 0.01%, the effective yield corresponding to an interest rate of 9% per year compounded quarterly.

19. Solve the equation.

$$\log_6(x+7) + \log_6(x+12) = 1$$

20. Sketch the graph of

$$f(x) = \log_3\left(\frac{1}{x}\right)$$

21. Find the exact solution, using common logarithms, and a two-decimal-place approximation of the solution of the equation

$$9^{x+5} = 6^{1-3x}$$

22. Find a two-decimal-place approximation of the solution of the equation

$$\log(x^2 + 4) - \log(x + 2) = 1 + \log(x - 2)$$

23. Use natural logarithms to solve for x in terms of y

$$y = \frac{e^x - e^{-x}}{14}$$

24. Use the compound interest formula to determine how long it will take for a sum of money to double if it is invested at a rate of 10% per year compounded monthly.

25. If a 100-milligram tablet of an asthma drug is taken orally and if none of the drug is present in the body when the tablet is first taken, the total amount A in the bloodstream after t minutes is predicted to be

$$A = 100[1 - (0.9)^t] \quad \text{for} \quad 0 \leq t \leq 10.$$

Determine the number of minutes needed for 45 milligrams of the drug to have entered the bloodstream.

1. The graph of a one-to-one function *f* is shown. Use the reflection property to sketch the graph of f^{-1}

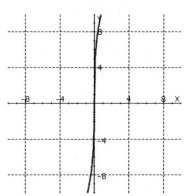

a.

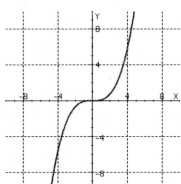

b.

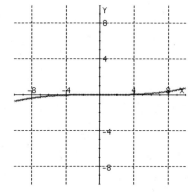

c.

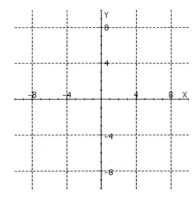

2. The radioactive bismuth isotope ^{210}Bi has a half-life of 5 days. If there is 100 milligrams of present at then the amount remaining after t days is given by:

$$f(t) = 100(2)^{-t/5}$$

How much remains after 10 days?

    a.   24 milligrams

    b.   30 milligrams

    c.   25 milligrams

    d.   34 milligrams

    e.   27 milligrams

3. If \$1000 is deposited in a savings account that pays interest at a rate of $10\frac{1}{4}$ % per year compounded continuously, find the balance after 5 years.

    a.   \$599.00

    b.   \$1669.46

    c.   \$4173.65

    d.   \$1648.72

4. How much money, invested at an interest rate of 10% per year compounded continuously, will amount to \$95000 after 17 years?

    a.   \$104991.24

    b.   \$17354.93

    c.   \$5200.25

    d.   \$34709.87

5. An investment of $1078 increased to $5447 in 18 years. If the interest was compounded continuously, find the interest rate.

    a.   9%

    b.   6%

    c.   11%

    d.   18%

6. The 1980 population of the United States was approximately 227 million, and the population has been growing continuously at a rate of 0.7% per year. Predict the population in the year 2010 if this growth trend continues.

    a.   280 million people

    b.   93 million people

    c.   840 million people

    d.   560 million people

7. Express in terms of logarithms of x, y, z, w.

$$\log_2 \frac{x^4 w}{y^5 z^3}$$

    a. $\log_2 (x) + \log_2 (w) - \log_2 (y) + \log_2 (z)$

    b. $4\log_2 (x) + \log_2 (w) + 5\log_2 (y) + 3\log_2 (z)$

    c. $4\log_2 (x) + \log_2 (w) - 3\log_2 (y) - 5\log_2 (z)$

    d. $4\log_2 (x) + \log_2 (w) - 5\log_2 (y) - 3\log_2 (z)$

8. Write the expression as one logarithm.

$$8\ln(x) - 6\ln(1/y) - 4\ln(xy)$$

a. $\ln(8x - 6y - 4xy)$

b. $\ln(x^2y^4)$

c. $\ln(x^8 - y^6 - (xy)^4)$

d. $\ln(x^4y^2)$

9. Solve the equation.

$$\log_2(x + 4) + \log_2(x + 5) = 1$$

a. $x = 3$

b. $x = 7$

c. $x = -3$

d. $x = -7$

10. Pareto's law for capitalist countries states that the relationship between annual income z and the number m of individuals whose income exceeds z is where a and k are positive constants. Solve this equation for m.

$$\log m = \log a - k \log z$$

a. $m = \dfrac{a}{z^k}$

b. $m = \log \dfrac{a}{z^k}$

c. $m = az^k$

d. $m = \dfrac{a}{kz}$

11. Find the exact solution using common logarithms, and a two-decimal-place approximation of the solution of the equation.

$$4^{2-x} = 11$$

    a. $\dfrac{\log 11}{\log 4} \approx 1.73$

    b. $\dfrac{\log 4}{\log 11} - 2 \approx -1.02$

    c. $2 - \dfrac{\log 4}{\log 11} \approx 1.42$

    d. $2 - \dfrac{\log 11}{\log 4} \approx 0.27$

12. Find a two-decimal-place approximation of the solution of the equation

$\log (x^2 + 9) - \log (x + 3) = 1 + \log (x - 3)$
    a. $x = 3.32$

    b. $x = -4.14$

    c. $x = 2.50$

    d. $x = 4.96$

13. Find the inverse function of

$$f(x) = \dfrac{2x + 7}{7x - 2}$$

14. Find the inverse function of

$$f(x) = 11x^3 - 7$$

15. The number of bacteria in a certain culture increased from 600 to 1800 between 7:00 A.M. and 9:00 A.M. Assuming the growth is exponential, the number $f(t)$ of bacteria t hours after 7:00 A.M. is given by:

$$f(t) = 600(3)^{t/2}$$

Estimate the number of bacteria in the culture at 8:00 A.M.

16. An economist predicts that the buying power $B(t)$ of a dollar t years from now will be given by:

$$B(t) = (0.87)^t$$

Use the graph of B to approximate when the buying power will be half of what it is today.

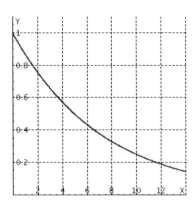

17. Use the graph of $y = e^x$ to help sketch the graph of
$$f(x) = e^{x+4}$$

18. The effective yield (or effective annual interest rate) for an investment is the simple interest rate that would yield at the end of one year the same amount as is yielded by the compounded rate that is actually applied. Approximate, to the nearest 0.01%, the effective yield corresponding to an interest rate of 5% per year compounded quarterly.

19. Solve the equation.

$$\log_4(x+7) + \log_4(x+10) = 1$$

20. Sketch the graph of

$$f(x) = \log_3\left(\frac{1}{x}\right)$$

21. Find the exact solution, using common logarithms, and a two-decimal-place approximation of the solution of the equation

$$9^{x+1} = 2^{1-3x}$$

22. Find a two-decimal-place approximation of the solution of the equation

$$\log(x^2 + 16) - \log(x + 4) = 1 + \log(x - 4)$$

23. Use natural logarithms to solve for x in terms of y

$$y = \frac{e^x - e^{-x}}{8}$$

24. Use the compound interest formula to determine how long it will take for a sum of money to double if it is invested at a rate of 8% per year compounded monthly.

25. If a 100-milligram tablet of an asthma drug is taken orally and if none of the drug is present in the body when the tablet is first taken, the total amount A in the bloodstream after t minutes is predicted to be

$$A = 100[1 - (0.9)^t] \quad \text{for} \quad 0 \le t \le 10.$$

Determine the number of minutes needed for 50 milligrams of the drug to have entered the bloodstream.

Test Form 4-A

1. $f^{-1}(x) = \dfrac{4+9x}{4x-7}$

2. $(-\infty, 0) \cup (0, \infty)$

3. $\sqrt[3]{\dfrac{2+x}{7}}$

4. 5400

5.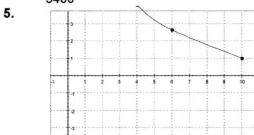

6. 9.5

7. 12.92

8.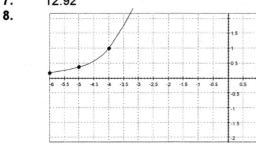

9. 7.19

10. 2019

11. $9\log_a(z) + 3\log_a(x) - 5\log_a(w) - 4\log_a(y)$

12. $3\log\left(\dfrac{y^3}{x}\right) - 3\log(v) + \dfrac{1}{2}\cdot\log\left(x^6\cdot y^2\right) = \log\left(y^7\right)$

13. 7

14. $x = \dfrac{8}{15}$

15. $x = -4$

16.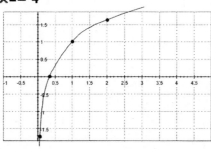

17.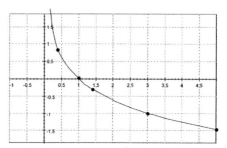

18. $p = \dfrac{c}{y^w}$

19. $5 - \dfrac{\log(9)}{\log(6)}, 3.77$

20. $\dfrac{\log\left(\dfrac{2}{81}\right)}{\log(96)}, -0.81$

21. 5.05

22. $x = \ln\left(y + \sqrt{y^2+1}\right)$

23. 0.7325

24. about 7 years

25. 4.85

Test Form 4-B

1. $f^{-1}(x) = \dfrac{8+7x}{8x-3}$

2. $(-\infty, 0) \cup (0, \infty)$

3. $\sqrt[3]{\dfrac{7+x}{3}}$

4. 1800

5.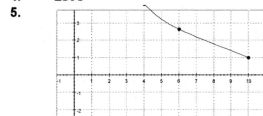

6. 6.5

7. 12.06

8.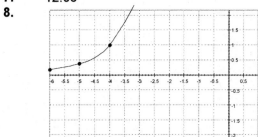

9. 8.24

10. 2002

11. $7\log_a(w) + 5\log_a(z) - 9\log_a(x) - 3\log_a(y)$

12. $2\log\left(\dfrac{x^3}{y}\right) - 3\log(x) + \dfrac{1}{3}\cdot\log\left(y^6 \cdot x^3\right) = \log\left(x^4\right)$

13. 4

14. $x = \dfrac{7}{15}$

15. $x = -5$

16.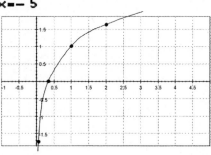

17.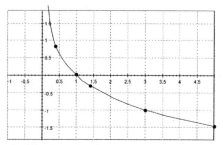

18. $p = \dfrac{c}{x^k}$

19. $6 - \dfrac{\log(3)}{\log(2)}, 4.42$

20. $\dfrac{\log\left(\dfrac{4}{9}\right)}{\log(576)}, -0.13$

21. 5 years

22. $x = \ln\left(8y + \sqrt{64y^2 + 1}\right)$

23. 0.9208

24. about 9 years

25. 3.39

Test Form 4-C

1. c	**2.** d	**3.** d	**4.** b	**5.** d	**6.** a	**7.** c	**8.** d	**9.** b
10. c	**11.** c	**12.** b	**13.** d	**14.** d	**15.** c	**16.** b	**17.** d	**18.** d
19. c	**20.** d	**21.** b	**22.** a	**23.** b	**24.** c	**25.** c		

Test Form 4-D

1. b	**2.** c	**3.** e	**4.** a	**5.** c	**6.** a	**7.** b	**8.** c	**9.** c
10. a	**11.** b	**12.** a	**13.** d	**14.** d	**15.** a	**16.** b	**17.** d	**18.** d
19. a	**20.** d	**21.** c	**22.** c	**23.** b	**24.** c	**25.** c		

Test Form 4-E

1. b
2. e
3. d
4. c
5. c
6. b
7. b
8. d
9. a
10. a
11. d
12. d
13. $f^{-1}(x) = \dfrac{7+9x}{7x-8}$
14. $\sqrt[3]{\dfrac{3+x}{11}}$
15. 3.118
16. 13.5
17.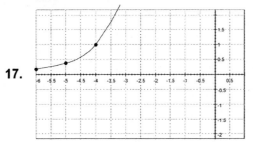
18. 9.31
19. $x = -6$
20.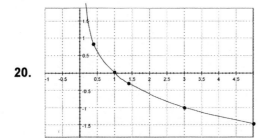
21. $\dfrac{\log\left(\dfrac{6}{59049}\right)}{\log(1944)}, -1.21$
22. 2.21
23. $x = \ln\left(7y + \sqrt{49y^2 + 1}\right)$
24. about 7 years
25. 5.67

Test Form 4-F

1. b
2. c
3. b
4. b
5. a
6. a
7. d
8. d
9. c
10. a
11. d
12. a
13. $f^{-1}(x) = \dfrac{7+2x}{7x-2}$
14. $\sqrt[3]{\dfrac{7+x}{11}}$
15. 1039
16. 5

17.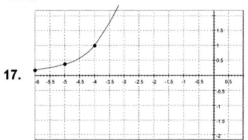

18. 5.09
19. $x = -6$

20.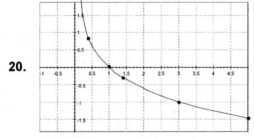

21. $\dfrac{\log\left(\dfrac{2}{9}\right)}{\log(72)}, -0.35$
22. 4.42
23. $x = \ln\left(4y + \sqrt{16y^2 + 1}\right)$
24. about 9 years
25. 6.58

1. As $x \to 0^+$, $f(x) \to L$ for some real number L. Use the graph to predict L

$$f(x) = \frac{4 - 4\cos x}{x}$$

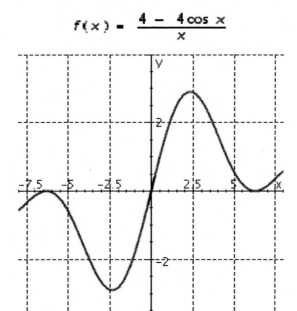

2. A point $P(x,y)$ is shown on the unit circle U corresponding to a real number t. Find the value of the trigonometric function $\cos t$.

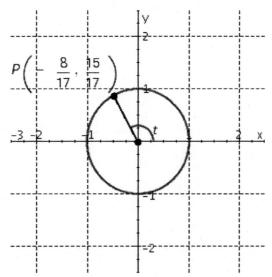

3. The graph of an equation is shown in the figure. Find the amplitude.

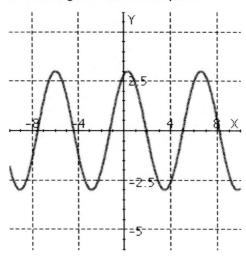

4. The graph of an equation is shown in the figure. Find the period.

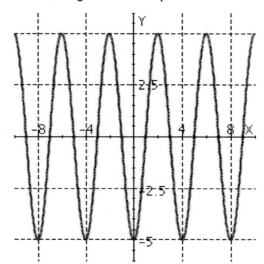

5. Use fundamental identities to find the values of the trigonometric functions for the given conditions.
$\csc \theta = 2$ and $\cot \theta < 0$

6. Find the exact degree measure of the angle: $\dfrac{7\pi}{5} = $ _____ $^\circ$

7. The central angle θ subtended by the arc of length $s = 3$ cm on a circle of radius $r = 3$ cm. Find to the nearest tenth the area of the sector determined by θ.

8. A tire for a compact car is 24 inches in diameter. If the car is travelling at a speed of 55 mi/hr, find to the nearest integer the number of revolutions the tire makes per minute.

9. A forester, 200 feet from the base of a redwood tree, observes that the angle between the ground and the top of the tree is 56°. Estimate the height of the tree. Round your answer to the nearest tenth.

10. Simplify the expression.

$$\frac{\cot^2 \theta - 4}{\cot^2 \theta - \cot \theta - 6}$$

11. Use fundamental identities to find the values of the trigonometric functions for the given conditions.

$\cot \theta = \dfrac{3}{4}$ and $\cos \theta < 0$

$\sin \theta =$ _____

$\cos \theta =$ _____

$\tan \theta =$ _____

$\sec \theta =$ _____

$\csc \theta =$ _____

12. Refer to the graph of $y = \cos x$ to find the exact values of x in the interval $[0, \ 4\pi]$ that satisfy the equation.

$\cos x = -\dfrac{\sqrt{2}}{2}$

13.
Find the reference angle θ_R if $\theta = \dfrac{5\pi}{6}$

14. Find the exact value: $\sin \left(\dfrac{2\pi}{3} \right)$

15. Find the exact value: $\tan(-315°)$

16. Find the phase shift: $y = -7\sin \left(4x - \dfrac{\pi}{4} \right)$

17. Estimate the horizontal asymptote.

$$y = \frac{1 - \cos^2\left(\frac{4}{x}\right)}{\sin\left(\frac{3}{x}\right)}$$

18. Find the period of the equation.

$$y = -\frac{1}{5}\cot\left(\frac{1}{4}x + \frac{\pi}{3}\right)$$

19. Sketch the graph of the equation: $y = \sec 2x$

20. Find an equation using the tangent function that has the same graph as $y = \cot x$. Translate the function as little as possible.

21. Use the graph of a trigonometric function to aid in sketching the graph of the equation without plotting points.

$$y = |\sin x| + 2$$

22. Given the indicated parts of triangle ABC with $\gamma = 90°$, approximate to the nearest tenth the angle β.

$$a = 35, \ b = 10$$

23. An airplane takes off at a **10°** angle and travels at the rate of 340 ft/sec. Approximately how many seconds does it take the airplane to reach an altitude of 11000 feet? Please round the answer to the nearest second.

24. Sketch the graph of the equation: $y = -\sqrt{2}\sin\left(\frac{\pi}{2}x - \frac{\pi}{4}\right)$

25. The graph of an equation is shown in the figure. Write the equation in the form $y = a \sin(bx + c)$ for $a > 0$, $b > 0$, and the least positive real number c.

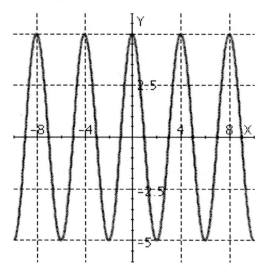

1. As $x \to 0^+$, $f(x) \to L$ for some real number L. Use the graph to predict L

$$f(x) = \frac{9 - 9\cos x}{x}$$

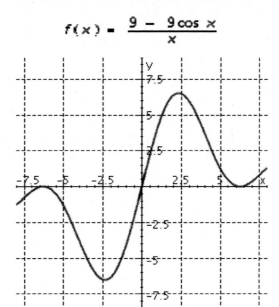

2. A point $P(x,y)$ is shown on the unit circle U corresponding to a real number t. Find the value of the trigonometric function $\sec t$.

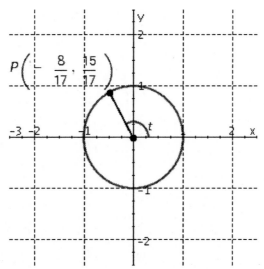

3. The graph of an equation is shown in the figure. Find the amplitude.

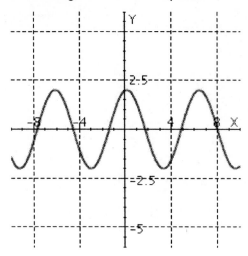

4. The graph of an equation is shown in the figure. Find the period.

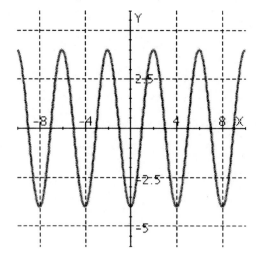

5. Use fundamental identities to find the values of the trigonometric functions for the given conditions.
   csc θ = 4 and cot θ < 0

6. Find the exact degree measure of the angle: $\dfrac{3\pi}{5} = \underline{\hspace{1.5cm}}^{\circ}$

7. The central angle θ subtended by the arc of length s = 15 cm on a circle of radius r = 5 cm. Find to the nearest tenth the area of the sector determined by θ .

8. A tire for a compact car is 25 inches in diameter. If the car is travelling at a speed of 45 mi/hr, find to the nearest integer the number of revolutions the tire makes per minute.

9. A forester, 190 feet from the base of a redwood tree, observes that the angle between the ground and the top of the tree is 55° . Estimate the height of the tree. Round your answer to the nearest tenth.

10. Simplify the expression.

$$\frac{2 - \tan\theta}{2\csc\theta - \sec\theta}$$

11. Use fundamental identities to find the values of the trigonometric functions for the given conditions.

$\cot\theta = \dfrac{5}{12}$ and $\cos\theta < 0$

$\sin\theta = \underline{\hspace{2cm}}$

$\cos\theta = \underline{\hspace{2cm}}$

$\tan\theta = \underline{\hspace{2cm}}$

$\sec\theta = \underline{\hspace{2cm}}$

$\csc\theta = \underline{\hspace{2cm}}$

12. Refer to the graph of $y = \cos x$ to find the exact values of x in the interval $[0,\ 4\pi]$ that satisfy the equation.

$\cos x = -\dfrac{\sqrt{2}}{2}$

13.
Find the reference angle θ_R if $\theta = \dfrac{5\pi}{6}$

14. Find the exact value: $\sin\left(\dfrac{\pi}{6}\right)$

15. Find the exact value: $\tan(-225°)$

16. Find the phase shift: $y = -4\sin\left(3x - \dfrac{\pi}{4}\right)$

17. Estimate the horizontal asymptote.

$$y = \frac{1 - \cos^2\left(\dfrac{9}{x}\right)}{\sin\left(\dfrac{3}{x}\right)}$$

18. Find the period of the equation: $y = -\dfrac{1}{4}\tan\left(\dfrac{1}{3}x + \dfrac{\pi}{3}\right)$

19. Sketch the graph of the equation: $y = \sec 2x$

20. Find an equation using the cotangent function that has the same graph as $y = \tan x$. Translate the function as little as possible.

21. Use the graph of a trigonometric function to aid in sketching the graph of the equation without plotting points.

$$y = |\sin x| + 2$$

22. Given the indicated parts of triangle ABC with $\gamma = 90^\circ$, approximate to the nearest tenth the angle β.
$a = 35, b = 50$

23. An airplane takes off at a 15° angle and travels at the rate of 250 ft/sec. Approximately how long does it take the airplane to reach an altitude of 14000 feet? Please round the answer to the nearest second.

24. Sketch the graph of the equation: $y = -\sqrt{5}\sin\left(\dfrac{\pi}{4}x - \dfrac{\pi}{4}\right)$

25. The graph of an equation is shown in the figure. Write the equation in the form $y = a\sin(bx + c)$ for $a > 0$, $b > 0$, and the least positive real number c.

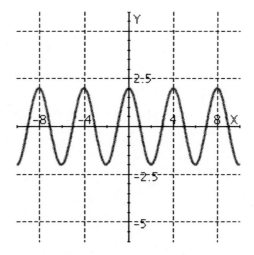

1. Find the exact radian measure of the angle 450 $^{\circ}$.

     a. $\dfrac{5}{2}$

     b. $\dfrac{5\pi}{2}$

     c. π

     d. $\dfrac{5\pi}{4}$

2. Find the period of the equation: $y = -2\sec\left(\dfrac{1}{2}x - \dfrac{\pi}{2}\right)$

     a. 2π

     b. $\dfrac{\pi}{4}$

     c. $\dfrac{\pi}{2}$

     d. 4π

     e. π

3. Find the phase shift: $y = -2\sin\left(4x - \frac{\pi}{2}\right)$

    a. π

    b. $\dfrac{\pi}{2}$

    c. $-\dfrac{\pi}{8}$

    d. -2

    e. $-\dfrac{\pi}{2}$

    f. $\dfrac{\pi}{8}$

4. Find the value of the trigonometric function $\cos(t)$, if possible: $t = \dfrac{5\pi}{4}$

    a. $-\dfrac{1}{2}$

    b. $-\dfrac{\sqrt{2}}{2}$

    c. $\dfrac{\sqrt{2}}{2}$

5. Estimate the horizontal asymptote.

$$y = \frac{1 - \cos^2\left(\dfrac{4}{x}\right)}{\sin\left(\dfrac{3}{x}\right)}$$

    a. $y = -4$

    b. $y = 3$

    c. $y = -3$

    d. $y = 4$

    e. $y = 0$

    f. $y = 16$

6. Given the indicated parts of triangle ABC with $\gamma = 90°$, approximate the value of c

$\alpha = 79°,\ b = 13$

    a.   **12.8**

    b.   **13.2**

    c.   **68.1**

    d.   2.5

7. As $x \to 0^+$, $f(x) \to L$ for some real number L. Use a graph to predict L

$$f(x) = \frac{3x + 6\tan x}{\sin x}$$

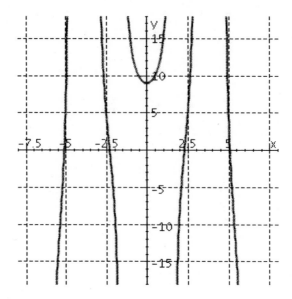

a. $L = 3$

b. $L = 0$

c. $L = 9$

d. $L = 6$

8. If a circular arc of the length $s = 21$ cm subtends the central angle $\theta = 3$ on a circle, find the radius of the circle.

a.   8 cm

b.   7.5 cm

c.   8.5 cm

d.   7 cm

9. A tire for a compact car is 20 inches in diameter. If the car is traveling at a speed of 65 mi/hr, find the number of revolutions the tire makes per minute.

    a.   1071 rev/min

    b.   1104 rev/min

    c.   1092 rev/min

    d.   1106 rev/min

10. Find the reference angle θ_R if $\theta = \dfrac{5\pi}{6}$

    a. $\theta_R = \dfrac{\pi}{2}$

    b. $\theta_R = \dfrac{2\pi}{3}$

    c. $\theta_R = \dfrac{\pi}{6}$

    d. $\theta_R = \dfrac{\pi}{3}$

11. Find the exact value: $\csc(210^\circ)$

    a. $\dfrac{\sqrt{3}}{2}$

    b. -2

    c. $\dfrac{\sqrt{2}}{2}$

    d. $\dfrac{\sqrt{2}}{3}$

12. Approximate the acute angle θ to the nearest **0.01 °**.

tan θ = 4.91

    a. $\theta = 78.49^{0}$

    b. $\theta = 79.92^{0}$

    c. $\theta = 77.29^{0}$

    d. $\theta = 79.59^{0}$

13. Find an equation using the tangent function that has the same graph as $y = \cot x$.

    a. $y = -\tan\left(x + \frac{\pi}{2}\right)$

    b. $y = \tan\left(x + \frac{\pi}{3}\right)$

    c. $y = -\tan x$

    d. $y = -\tan\left(2x + \frac{\pi}{2}\right)$

14. A builder wishes to construct a ramp 22 feet long that rises to a height of 4.5 feet above level ground. Approximate the angle that the ramp should make with the horizontal. Round the answer to the nearest degree.

    a. 15^{0}

    b. 12^{0}

    c. 11^{0}

    d. 14^{0}

15. An airplane flying at an altitude of 8000 feet passes directly over a fixed object on the ground. One minute later, the angle of depression of the object is 42 $^{\circ}$. Approximate the speed of the airplane to the nearest mile per hour.

    a.   99 mi/hr

    b.   98 mi/hr

    c.   100 mi/hr

    d.   101 mi / hr

16. An airplane flying at a speed of 360 mi/hr flies from a point A in the direction 110° for 15 minutes and then flies in the direction 200° for 15 minutes. Approximate, to the nearest mile, the distance from the airplane to A.

    a.   104 mi

    b.   127 mi

    c.   0 mi

    d.   180 mi

17. Simplify the expression: $\dfrac{2 - \tan \theta}{2 \csc \theta - \sec \theta}$

    a. $1 - \sin \theta \cos \theta$

    b. $\dfrac{\cot \theta - 2}{\cot \theta - 3}$

    c. $\sin \theta$

    d. $\cos \theta$

18. Use fundamental identities to find the values of the trigonometric functions for the given conditions.

$\sin \theta = \dfrac{7}{10}$ and $\cos \theta < 0$

a.

$$\sin \theta = \frac{7}{10}, \cos \theta = -\frac{\sqrt{10}}{7}, \tan \theta = \frac{1}{\sqrt{51}}, \cot \theta = \sqrt{10}, \sec \theta = \frac{51}{\sqrt{10}}, \csc \theta = -7$$

b.

$$\sin \theta = \frac{7}{10}, \cos \theta = \frac{\sqrt{51}}{10}, \tan \theta = \frac{7}{\sqrt{51}}, \cot \theta = \frac{\sqrt{51}}{7}, \sec \theta = \frac{10}{\sqrt{51}}, \csc \theta = -\frac{10}{7}$$

c.

$$\sin \theta = \frac{7}{10}, \cos \theta = -\frac{\sqrt{51}}{10}, \tan \theta = -\frac{7}{\sqrt{51}}, \cot \theta = -\frac{\sqrt{51}}{7}, \sec \theta = -\frac{10}{\sqrt{51}}, \csc \theta = \frac{10}{7}$$

d.

$$\sin \theta = \frac{7}{10}, \cos \theta = \frac{\sqrt{10}}{7}, \tan \theta = -\frac{1}{\sqrt{51}}, \cot \theta = -\sqrt{10}, \sec \theta = -\frac{51}{\sqrt{10}}, \csc \theta = 7$$

19. The graph of an equation is shown in the figure. Write the equation in the form $y = a \sin(bx + c)$ for $a > 0$, $b > 0$, and the least positive real number c.

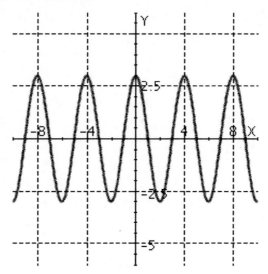

a. $\quad y = 2 \sin\left(\frac{\pi}{2} x + \frac{\pi}{4} \right)$

b. $\quad y = 3 \sin\left(\frac{\pi}{3} x + \frac{\pi}{2} \right)$

c. $\quad y = 3 \sin\left(\frac{\pi}{2} x + \frac{\pi}{2} \right)$

d. $\quad y = 2 \sin\left(\frac{\pi}{3} x + \frac{\pi}{4} \right)$

20. The graph of an equation is shown in the figure. Find the period.

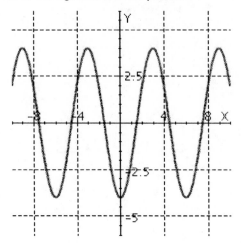

    a.   7

    b.   8

    c.   3

    d.   6

21. Sketch the graph of the equation: $y = \sec 2x$

a.

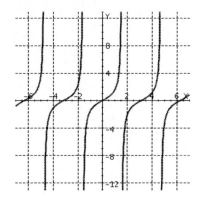

b.

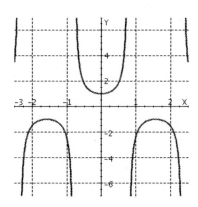

c.

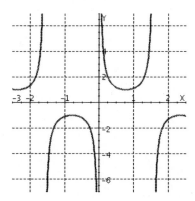

22. Sketch the graph of the equation: $y = 3\sin\left(x - \dfrac{\pi}{3}\right)$

a.

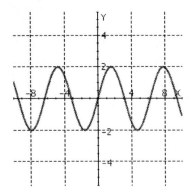

b.

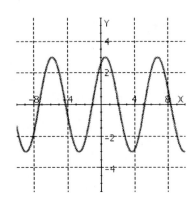

c.

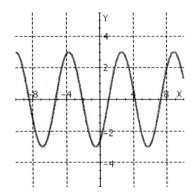

23. Use the graph of a trigonometric function to aid in sketching the graph of the equation without plotting points.

$$y = |\sin x| + 5$$

a.

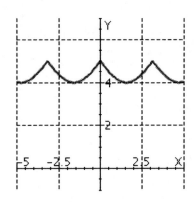

b.

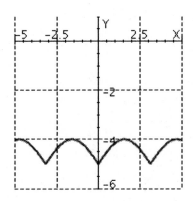

c.

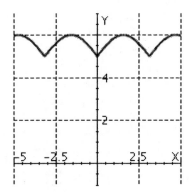

24. Sketch the graph of the equation: $y = -\sqrt{2}\sin\left(\dfrac{\pi}{4}x - \dfrac{\pi}{4}\right)$

a.

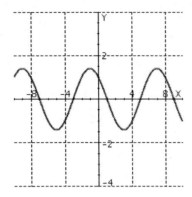

b.

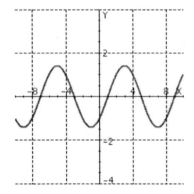

c.

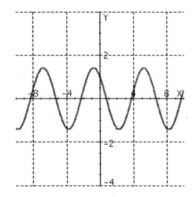

25. A point $P\,(x,y)$ is shown on the unit circle U corresponding to a real number t. Find the value of the trigonometric function cot t.

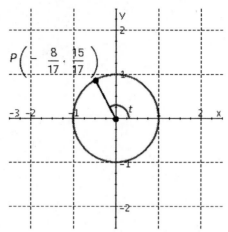

a. $-\dfrac{8}{15}$

b. $-\dfrac{15}{8}$

c. $\dfrac{17}{8}$

1. Find the exact radian measure of the angle 1710°.

    a. $\dfrac{19}{2}$

    b. $\dfrac{19\pi}{2}$

    c. $\dfrac{19\pi}{4}$

    d. π

2. Find the period of the equation.

$$y = -2\sec\left(\frac{1}{2}x - \frac{\pi}{2}\right)$$

    a. π

    b. $\dfrac{\pi}{2}$

    c. 4π

    d. $\dfrac{\pi}{4}$

    e. 2π

3. Find the phase shift.

$$y = -9\sin\left(3x - \frac{\pi}{3}\right)$$

    a. $\dfrac{\pi}{3}$

    b. π

    c. $-\dfrac{\pi}{9}$

    d. $\dfrac{\pi}{9}$

    e. -9

    f. $-\dfrac{\pi}{3}$

4. Find the value of the trigonometric function $\cos(t)$, if possible.

$$t = 5\pi / 4$$

    a. $-\dfrac{1}{2}$

    b. $-\dfrac{\sqrt{2}}{2}$

    c. $\dfrac{\sqrt{2}}{2}$

5. Estimate the horizontal asymptote.

$$y = \frac{1 - \cos^2\left(\frac{6}{x}\right)}{\sin\left(\frac{5}{x}\right)}$$

    a. $y = 6$

    b. $y = -5$

    c. $y = -6$

    d. $y = 36$

    e. $y = 0$

    f. $y = 5$

6. Given the indicated parts of triangle ABC with $\gamma = 90°$, approximate the value of c

$\alpha = 34°$, $b = 26$

    a.   14.5

    b.   21.6

    c.   31.4

    d.   46.5

7. As $x \to 0^{+}$, $f(x) \to L$ for some real number L. Use a graph to predict L

$$f(x) = \frac{6x + 2\tan x}{\sin x}$$

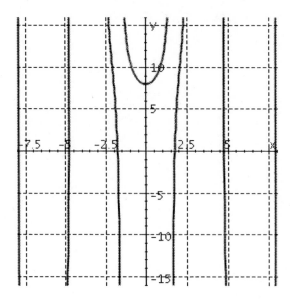

a. $L = 2$

b. $L = 0$

c. $L = 6$

d. $L = 8$

8. If a circular arc of the length $s = 4.5$ cm subtends the central angle $\theta = 1$ on a circle, find the radius of the circle.

a.   6 cm

b.   4.5 cm

c.   5.5 cm

d.   5 cm

9. A tire for a compact car is 25 inches in diameter. If the car is travelling at a speed of 75 mi/hr, find the number of revolutions the tire makes per minute.

    a.   1020 rev/min

    b.   1030 rev/min

    c.   995 rev/min

    d.   1008 rev/min

10. Find the reference angle θ_R if $\theta = \dfrac{5\pi}{6}$

    a. $\theta_R = \dfrac{2\pi}{3}$

    b. $\theta_R = \dfrac{\pi}{3}$

    c. $\theta_R = \dfrac{\pi}{6}$

    d. $\theta_R = \dfrac{\pi}{2}$

11. Find the exact value: $\csc(240°)$

    a. $\sqrt{3}$

    b. $\dfrac{\sqrt{3}}{3}$

    c. $\dfrac{\sqrt{2}}{2}$

    d. $-\dfrac{2}{\sqrt{3}}$

12. Approximate the acute angle θ to the nearest **0.01** °.

    tan θ = 3.45

    a. $\theta = 73.84°$

    b. $\theta = 72.41°$

    c. $\theta = 72.74°$

    d. $\theta = 75.04°$

13. Find an equation using the tangent function that has the same graph as $y = \cot x$.

    a. $y = -\tan x$

    b. $y = \tan\left(x + \frac{\pi}{3}\right)$

    c. $y = -\tan\left(x + \frac{\pi}{2}\right)$

    d. $y = -\tan\left(2x + \frac{\pi}{2}\right)$

14. A builder wishes to construct a ramp 21 feet long that rises to a height of 5.5 feet above level ground. Approximate the angle that the ramp should make with the horizontal. Round the answer to the nearest degree.

    a. $18°$

    b. $15°$

    c. $17°$

    d. $14°$

15. An airplane flying at an altitude of 10000 feet passes directly over a fixed object on the ground. One minute later, the angle of depression of the object is 38 $^{\circ}$. Approximate the speed of the airplane to the nearest mile per hour.

    a.   143 mi/hr

    b.   142 mi/hr

    c.   144 mi/hr

    d.   145 mi / hr

16. An airplane flying at a speed of 360 mi/hr flies from a point A in the direction $159°$ for 30 minutes and then flies in the direction $249°$ for 30 minutes. Approximate, to the nearest mile, the distance from the airplane to A.

    a.   255 mi

    b.   147 mi

    c.   0 mi

    d.   360 mi

17. Simplify the expression.

$$\frac{\sin^3 \theta + \cos^3 \theta}{\sin \theta + \cos \theta}$$

    a. $\cos \theta$

    b. $1 - \sin \theta \cos \theta$

    c. $\sin \theta$

    d. $\dfrac{\cot \theta - 2}{\cot \theta - 3}$

18. Use fundamental identities to find the values of the trigonometric functions for the given conditions.

$\sin\theta = \frac{4}{7}$ and $\cos\theta < 0$

a.

$$\sin\theta = \frac{4}{7}, \cos\theta = -\frac{\sqrt{7}}{4}, \tan\theta = \frac{1}{\sqrt{33}}, \cot\theta = \sqrt{7}, \sec\theta = \frac{33}{\sqrt{7}}, \csc\theta = -4$$

b.

$$\sin\theta = \frac{4}{7}, \cos\theta = \frac{\sqrt{33}}{4}, \tan\theta = \frac{4}{\sqrt{33}}, \cot\theta = \frac{\sqrt{33}}{4}, \sec\theta = \frac{7}{\sqrt{33}}, \csc\theta = -\frac{7}{4}$$

c.

$$\sin\theta = \frac{4}{7}, \cos\theta = \frac{\sqrt{7}}{4}, \tan\theta = -\frac{1}{\sqrt{33}}, \cot\theta = \sqrt{7}, \sec\theta = -\frac{33}{\sqrt{7}}, \csc\theta = 4$$

d.

$$\sin\theta = \frac{4}{7}, \cos\theta = -\frac{\sqrt{33}}{4}, \tan\theta = -\frac{4}{\sqrt{33}}, \cot\theta = -\frac{\sqrt{33}}{4}, \sec\theta = -\frac{7}{\sqrt{33}}, \csc\theta = \frac{7}{4}$$

19. The graph of an equation is shown in the figure. Write the equation in the form $y = a \sin(bx + c)$ for $a > 0$, $b > 0$, and the least positive real number c.

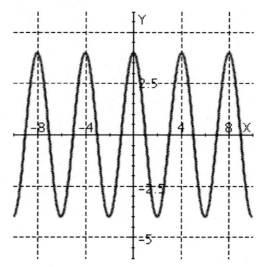

a. $y = 3 \sin\left(\dfrac{\pi}{2}x + \dfrac{\pi}{4}\right)$

b. $y = 3 \sin\left(\dfrac{\pi}{4}x + \dfrac{\pi}{4}\right)$

c. $y = 4 \sin\left(\dfrac{\pi}{4}x + \dfrac{\pi}{2}\right)$

d. $y = 4 \sin\left(\dfrac{\pi}{2}x + \dfrac{\pi}{2}\right)$

20. The graph of an equation is shown in the figure. Find the period.

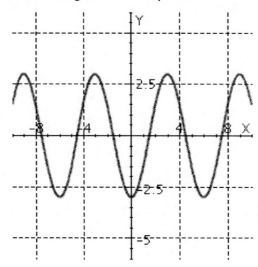

    a.   3

    b.   7

    c.   8

    d.   6

21. Sketch the graph of the equation: $y = \sec 2x$

a.

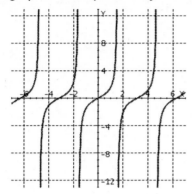

b.

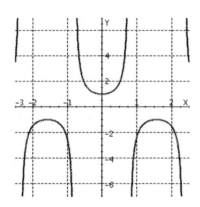

c.

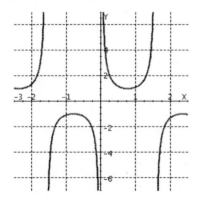

22. Sketch the graph of the equation: $y = 2\sin\left(x + \dfrac{\pi}{3}\right)$

a.

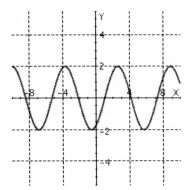

b.

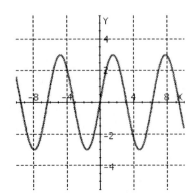

c.

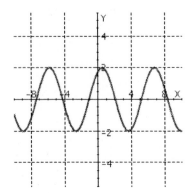

23. Use the graph of a trigonometric function to aid in sketching the graph of the equation without plotting points:

$$y = |\sin x| + 4$$

a.

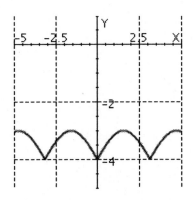

b.

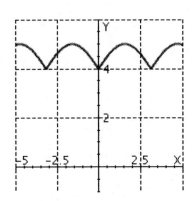

c.

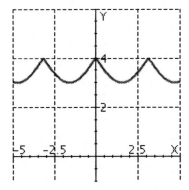

24. Sketch the graph of the equation.

$$y = -\sqrt{5}\sin\left(\frac{\pi}{4}x - \frac{\pi}{4}\right)$$

a.

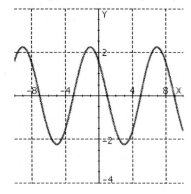

b.

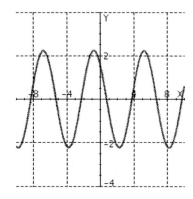

c.

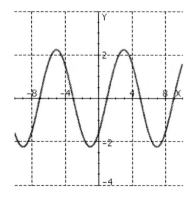

25. A point $P(x,y)$ is shown on the unit circle U corresponding to a real number t. Find the value of the trigonometric function cot t.

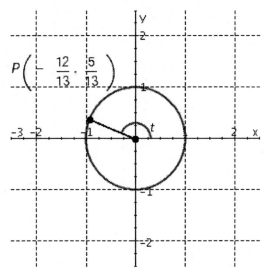

a. $-\dfrac{12}{5}$

b. $\dfrac{13}{12}$

c. $-\dfrac{5}{12}$

1. Find the exact radian measure of the angle $630°$.

    a. $\dfrac{7\pi}{4}$

    b. $\dfrac{7\pi}{2}$

    c. $\dfrac{7}{2}$

    d. π

2. Find the phase shift: $y = -7\sin\left(3x - \dfrac{\pi}{4}\right)$

    a. $\dfrac{\pi}{4}$

    b. $-\dfrac{\pi}{4}$

    c. $-\dfrac{\pi}{12}$

    d. -7

    e. $\dfrac{\pi}{12}$

    f. π

3. Find the value of the trigonometric function $\cos(t)$, if possible: $t = \dfrac{13\pi}{4}$

    a. $-\dfrac{\sqrt{2}}{2}$

    b. $-\dfrac{1}{2}$

    c. $\dfrac{\sqrt{2}}{2}$

4. Sketch the graph of the equation: $y = 4\sin\left(x - \dfrac{\pi}{3}\right)$

a.

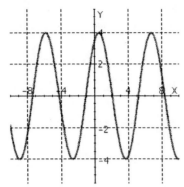

b.

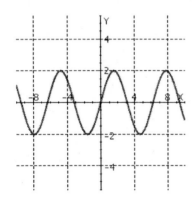

c.

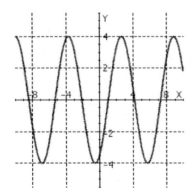

5.

Find the reference angle θ_R if $\theta = \dfrac{5\pi}{6}$

   a. $\theta_R = \dfrac{\pi}{6}$

   b. $\theta_R = \dfrac{\pi}{2}$

   c. $\theta_R = \dfrac{\pi}{3}$

   d. $\theta_R = \dfrac{2\pi}{3}$

6. Find the exact value: $\csc\left(-330^{\circ}\right)$

   a. 2

   b. $\dfrac{\sqrt{3}}{3}$

   c. $\sqrt{2}$

   d. $\dfrac{\sqrt{3}}{2}$

7. Approximate the acute angle θ to the nearest 0.01°.

   $\tan\theta = 3.45$

   a. $\theta = 75.27^{\circ}$

   b. $\theta = 73.84^{\circ}$

   c. $\theta = 72.74^{\circ}$

   d. $\theta = 72.64^{\circ}$

8. Find an equation using the secant function that has the same graph as $y = \csc x$.

  a. $\quad y = -\sec\left(2x + \frac{\pi}{2}\right)$

  b. $\quad y = -\sec\left(x + \frac{\pi}{2}\right)$

  c. $\quad y = \sec\left(x + \frac{\pi}{3}\right)$

  d. $\quad y = -\sec x$

9. An airplane flying at a speed of 240 mi/hr flies from a point A in the direction $168°$ for 45 minutes and then flies in the direction $258°$ for 15 minutes. Approximate, to the nearest mile, the distance from the airplane to A.

  a.   120 mi

  b.   170 mi

  c.   190 mi

  d.   240 mi

10.
Simplify the expression: $\quad \dfrac{\cot^2\theta - 4}{\cot^2\theta - \cot\theta - 6}$

  a. $\quad \dfrac{\cot\theta - 2}{\cot\theta - 3}$

  b. $\quad \sin\theta$

  c. $\quad 1 - \sin\theta\cos\theta$

  d. $\quad \cos\theta$

11. A point $P(x,y)$ is shown on the unit circle U corresponding to a real number t. Find the value of the trigonometric function csc t.

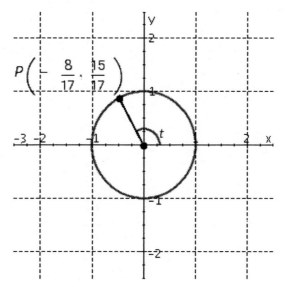

a. $\dfrac{15}{8}$

b. $\dfrac{15}{17}$

c. $\dfrac{17}{15}$

12. Use fundamental identities to find the values of the trigonometric functions for the given conditions.

$\sin \theta = \dfrac{7}{10}$ and $\cos \theta < 0$

a.

$$\sin \theta = \frac{7}{10}, \quad \cos \theta = \frac{\sqrt{51}}{10}, \quad \tan \theta = \frac{7}{\sqrt{51}}$$

$$\cot \theta = \frac{\sqrt{51}}{7}, \quad \sec \theta = \frac{10}{\sqrt{51}}, \quad \csc \theta = -\frac{10}{7}$$

b.

$$\sin \theta = \frac{7}{10}, \quad \cos \theta = -\frac{\sqrt{51}}{10}, \quad \tan \theta = -\frac{7}{\sqrt{51}}$$

$$\cot \theta = -\frac{\sqrt{51}}{7}, \quad \sec \theta = -\frac{10}{\sqrt{51}}, \quad \csc \theta = \frac{10}{7}$$

c.

$$\sin \theta = -\frac{1}{10}, \quad \cos \theta = \frac{\sqrt{10}}{7}, \quad \tan \theta = -\frac{1}{\sqrt{10}}$$

$$\cot \theta = -\sqrt{10}, \quad \sec \theta = -\frac{10}{\sqrt{10}}, \quad \csc \theta = -7$$

d.

$$\sin \theta = \frac{1}{7}, \quad \cos \theta = -\frac{\sqrt{10}}{7}, \quad \tan \theta = \frac{1}{\sqrt{51}}$$

$$\cot \theta = \sqrt{10}, \quad \sec \theta = \frac{51}{\sqrt{10}}, \quad \csc \theta = -7$$

13. Use fundamental identities to find the values of the trigonometric functions for the given conditions.
$\csc \theta = 9$ and $\cot \theta < 0$

14. The central angle θ subtended by the arc of length $s = 4$ cm on a circle of radius $r = 4$ cm. Find to the nearest tenth the area of the sector determined by θ .

15. A tire for a compact car is 24 inches in diameter. If the car is traveling at a speed of 55 mi/hr, find to the nearest integer the number of revolutions the tire makes per minute.

16. Estimate the horizontal asymptote.

$$y = \frac{1 - \cos^2\left(\frac{4}{x}\right)}{\sin\left(\frac{5}{x}\right)}$$

17. Find the period of the equation: $\quad y = -\frac{1}{2}\tan\left(\frac{1}{2}x + \frac{1}{3}\right)$

18. Find an equation using the cosecant function that has the same graph as $y = \sec x$. Translate the function as little as possible.

19. Given the indicated parts of triangle ABC with $\gamma = 90^{\circ}$, approximate to the nearest tenth the angle β.
$a = 15, \ b = 45$

20. An airplane takes off at a **15°** angle and travels at the rate of 290 ft/sec. Approximately how many seconds does it take the airplane to reach an altitude of 13000 feet? Please round the answer to the nearest second.

21. The graph of an equation is shown in the figure. Write the equation in the form $y = a\sin(bx + c)$ for $a > 0$, $b > 0$, and the least positive real number c.

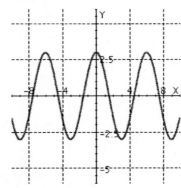

22. As $x \rightarrow 0^+$, $f(x) \rightarrow L$ for some real number L. Use the graph to predict L

$$f(x) = \frac{7 - 7\cos x}{x}$$

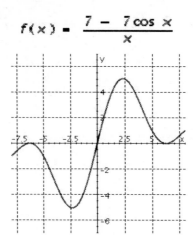

23. Sketch the graph of the equation: $y = \sec 2x$

24. Use the graph of a trigonometric function to aid in sketching the graph of the equation without plotting points.

$$y = |\sin x| + 2$$

25. Sketch the graph of the equation: $y = -\sqrt{2}\sin\left(\frac{\pi}{2}x - \frac{\pi}{4}\right)$

1. Find the exact radian measure of the angle $510\,^{\circ}$.

    a. $\dfrac{17}{6}$

    b. $\dfrac{17\,\pi}{12}$

    c. π

    d. $\dfrac{17\,\pi}{6}$

2. Find the phase shift: $y = -\,2\sin\left(3x - \dfrac{\pi}{4}\right)$

    a. π

    b. $\dfrac{\pi}{4}$

    c. $\dfrac{\pi}{12}$

    d. $-\dfrac{\pi}{4}$

    e. $-\dfrac{\pi}{12}$

    f. $-\,2$

3. Find the value of the trigonometric function $\sin(t)$, if possible: $t = \dfrac{7\pi}{4}$

    a. $\dfrac{\sqrt{2}}{2}$

    b. $-\dfrac{\sqrt{2}}{2}$

    c. $-\dfrac{1}{2}$

4. Sketch the graph of the equation: $y = 2\sin\left(x + \dfrac{\pi}{3}\right)$

a.

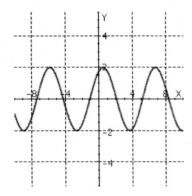

b.

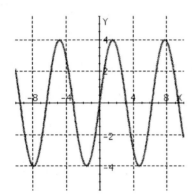

c.

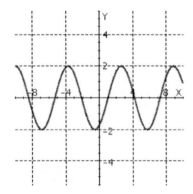

5.

Find the reference angle θ_R if $\theta = \dfrac{11\pi}{18}$

a. $\theta_R = \dfrac{13\pi}{18}$

b. $\theta_R = \dfrac{\pi}{18}$

c. $\theta_R = \dfrac{7\pi}{18}$

d. $\theta_R = \dfrac{5\pi}{18}$

6. Find the exact value: $\csc(-330°)$

a. 2

b. $\dfrac{\sqrt{3}}{3}$

c. $\dfrac{\sqrt{3}}{2}$

d. $\sqrt{2}$

7. Approximate the acute angle θ to the nearest $0.01°$.
   $\tan \theta = 3.45$

a. $\theta = 75.27°$

b. $\theta = 75.04°$

c. $\theta = 74.94°$

d. $\theta = 73.84°$

8. Find an equation using the secant function that has the same graph as $y = \csc x$.

   a. $y = -\sec\left(x + \dfrac{\pi}{2}\right)$

   b. $y = \sec\left(x + \dfrac{\pi}{3}\right)$

   c. $y = -\sec x$

   d. $y = -\sec\left(2x + \dfrac{\pi}{2}\right)$

9. An airplane flying at a speed of 360 mi/hr flies from a point A in the direction $100°$ for 30 minutes and then flies in the direction $190°$ for 45 minutes. Approximate, to the nearest mile, the distance from the airplane to A.

   a. 201 mi

   b. 450 mi

   c. 324 mi

   d. 164 mi

10. Simplify the expression.
$$\frac{\cot^2\theta - 4}{\cot^2\theta - \cot\theta - 6}$$

   a. $\cos\theta$

   b. $\sin\theta$

   c. $1 - \sin\theta\cos\theta$

   d. $\dfrac{\cot\theta - 2}{\cot\theta - 3}$

11. A point $P(x,y)$ is shown on the unit circle U corresponding to a real number t. Find the value of the trigonometric function tan t.

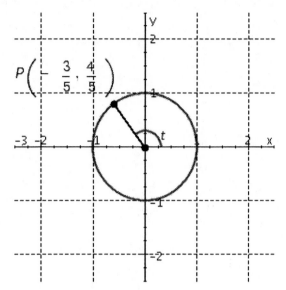

a.　　$-\dfrac{4}{3}$

b.　　$-\dfrac{3}{5}$

c.　　$-\dfrac{3}{4}$

12. Use fundamental identities to find the values of the trigonometric functions for the given conditions.

$\sin\theta = \dfrac{4}{7}$ and $\cos\theta < 0$

   a.

$$\sin\theta = \frac{1}{4}, \quad \cos\theta = -\frac{\sqrt{7}}{4}, \quad \tan\theta = \frac{1}{\sqrt{33}}$$

$$\cot\theta = \sqrt{7}, \quad \sec\theta = \frac{33}{\sqrt{7}}, \quad \csc\theta = -4$$

   b.

$$\sin\theta = \frac{4}{7}, \quad \cos\theta = \frac{\sqrt{33}}{7}, \quad \tan\theta = \frac{4}{\sqrt{33}}$$

$$\cot\theta = \frac{\sqrt{33}}{4}, \quad \sec\theta = \frac{7}{\sqrt{33}}, \quad \csc\theta = -\frac{7}{4}$$

   c.

$$\sin\theta = -\frac{1}{7}, \quad \cos\theta = \frac{\sqrt{7}}{4}, \quad \tan\theta = -\frac{1}{\sqrt{7}}$$

$$\cot\theta = -\sqrt{7}, \quad \sec\theta = -\frac{7}{\sqrt{7}}, \quad \csc\theta = -4$$

   d.

$$\sin\theta = \frac{4}{7}, \quad \cos\theta = -\frac{\sqrt{33}}{7}, \quad \tan\theta = -\frac{4}{\sqrt{33}}$$

$$\cot\theta = -\frac{\sqrt{33}}{4}, \quad \sec\theta = -\frac{7}{\sqrt{33}}, \quad \csc\theta = \frac{7}{4}$$

13. Use fundamental identities to find the values of the trigonometric functions for the given conditions.

$\csc\theta = 6$ and $\cot\theta < 0$

14. The central angle θ subtended by the arc of length $s = 12$ cm on a circle of radius $r = 4$ cm. Find to the nearest tenth the area of the sector determined by θ.

15. A tire for a compact car is 22 inches in diameter. If the car is traveling at a speed of 40 mi/hr, find to the nearest integer the number of revolutions the tire makes per minute.

16. Estimate the horizontal asymptote.

$$y = \frac{1 - \cos^2\left(\frac{2}{x}\right)}{\sin\left(\frac{3}{x}\right)}$$

17. Find the period of the equation: $\quad y = -\frac{1}{4}\cot\left(\frac{1}{2}x + \frac{7}{3}\right)$

18. Find an equation using the tangent function that has the same graph as $y = \cot x$. Translate the function as little as possible.

19. Given the indicated parts of triangle ABC with $\gamma = 90°$, approximate to the nearest tenth the angle β.
$a = 15, b = 35$

20. An airplane takes off at a **15°** angle and travels at the rate of 280 ft/sec. Approximately how long does it take the airplane to reach an altitude of 12000 feet? Please round the answer to the nearest second.

21. The graph of an equation is shown in the figure. Write the equation in the form $y = a \sin(bx + c)$ for $a > 0$, $b > 0$, and the least positive real number c.

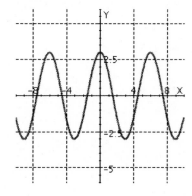

22. As $x \to 0^+$, $f(x) \to L$ for some real number L. Use the graph to predict L

$$f(x) = \frac{9 - 9\cos x}{x}$$

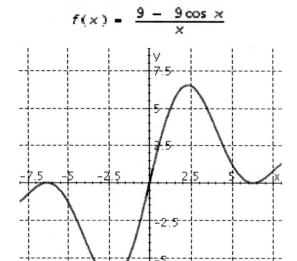

23. Sketch the graph of the equation. Show the asymptotes using dotted lines: $y = \sec 2x$

24. Use the graph of a trigonometric function to aid in sketching the graph of the equation without plotting points.

$$y = |\sin x| + 2$$

25. Sketch the graph of the equation: $y = -\sqrt{2}\sin\left(\frac{\pi}{2}x - \frac{\pi}{4}\right)$

Test Form 5-A

1.   0
2. $-\dfrac{8}{17}$
3.   3
4.   4
5. $\dfrac{1}{2}, -\dfrac{\sqrt{3}}{2}, -\dfrac{1}{\sqrt{3}}, -\sqrt{3}, -\dfrac{2}{\sqrt{3}}, 2$

6.   252
7.   4.5
8.   770
9.   296.5
10. $\dfrac{\cot(\theta) - 2}{\cot(\theta) - 3}$
11. $-\dfrac{4}{5}, \dfrac{3}{5}, \dfrac{4}{3}, -\dfrac{5}{3}, -\dfrac{5}{4}$
12. $\dfrac{3\pi}{4}, \dfrac{5\pi}{4}, \dfrac{11\pi}{4}, \dfrac{13\pi}{4}$
13. $\dfrac{\pi}{6}$
14. $\dfrac{\sqrt{3}}{2}$
15.   1
16. $\dfrac{\pi}{16}$
17. $y = 0$
18. 4π
19.

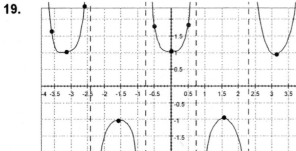

20. $y = -\tan\left(x + \dfrac{\pi}{2}\right)$

21.

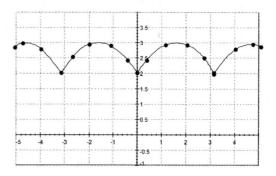

22.   15.9
23.   186
24.

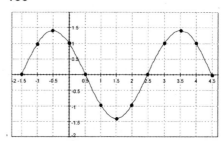

25. $y = 5\sin\left(\dfrac{\pi \cdot x}{2} + \dfrac{\pi}{2}\right)$

Test Form 5-B

1. 0

2. $-\dfrac{17}{8}$

3. 2

4. 4

5. $\dfrac{1}{4}, -\dfrac{\sqrt{15}}{4}, -\dfrac{1}{\sqrt{15}}, -\sqrt{15}, -\dfrac{4}{\sqrt{15}}, 4$

6. 108

7. 37.5

8. 605

9. 271.3

10. $\sin(\theta)$

11. $-\dfrac{12}{13}, -\dfrac{5}{13}, \dfrac{12}{5}, -\dfrac{13}{5}, -\dfrac{13}{12}$

12. $\dfrac{3\pi}{4}, \dfrac{5\pi}{4}, \dfrac{11\pi}{4}, \dfrac{13\pi}{4}$

13. $\dfrac{\pi}{6}$

14. $\dfrac{1}{2}$

15. -1

16. $\dfrac{\pi}{12}$

17. $y = 0$

18. 3π

19.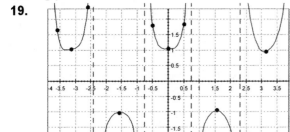

20. $y = -\cot\left(x + \dfrac{\pi}{2}\right)$

21.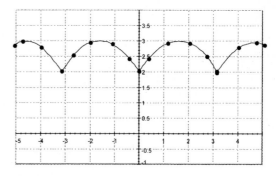

22. 55.0

23. 216

24.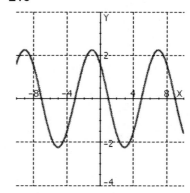

25. $y = 2\sin\left(\dfrac{\pi \cdot x}{2} + \dfrac{\pi}{2}\right)$

Test Form 5-C

1. b	**2.** d	**3.** f	**4.** b	**5.** e	**6.** c	**7.** c	**8.** d	**9.** c
10. c	**11.** b	**12.** a	**13.** a	**14.** b	**15.** d	**16.** b	**17.** c	**18.** c
19. c	**20.** d	**21.** b	**22.** c	**23.** c	**24.** a	**25.** a		

Test Form 5-D

1. b	**2.** c	**3.** d	**4.** b	**5.** e	**6.** c	**7.** d	**8.** b	**9.** d
10. c	**11.** d	**12.** a	**13.** c	**14.** b	**15.** d	**16.** a	**17.** b	**18.** d
19. d	**20.** d	**21.** b	**22.** c	**23.** b	**24.** a	**25.** a		

Test Form 5-E

1. b
2. e
3. a
4. c
5. a
6. a
7. b
8. b
9. c
10. a
11. c
12. b
13. $\dfrac{1}{9}, -\dfrac{\sqrt{80}}{9}, -\dfrac{1}{\sqrt{80}}, -\sqrt{80}, -\dfrac{9}{\sqrt{80}}, 9$

14. 8.0
15. 770
16. $y = 0$
17. 2π
18. $y = \csc\left(x + \dfrac{\pi}{2}\right)$

19. 71.6
20. 173
21. $y = 3\sin\left(\dfrac{\pi \cdot x}{3} + \dfrac{\pi}{2}\right)$

22. 0

23.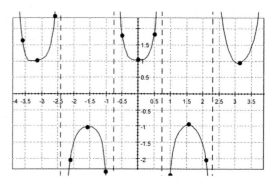

24.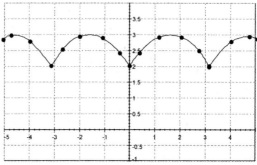

25.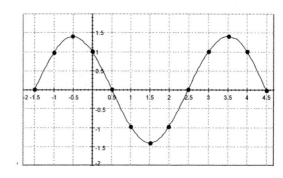

Test Form 5-F

1. d
2. c
3. b
4. a
5. c
6. a
7. d
8. a
9. c
10. d
11. a
12. d
13. $\dfrac{1}{6}, -\dfrac{\sqrt{35}}{6}, -\dfrac{1}{\sqrt{35}}, -\sqrt{35}, -\dfrac{6}{\sqrt{35}}, 6$

14. 24.0
15. 611
16. $y = 0$
17. 2π
18. $y = -\tan\left(x + \dfrac{\pi}{2}\right)$

19. 66.8
20. 166
21. $y = 3\sin\left(\dfrac{\pi \cdot x}{3} + \dfrac{\pi}{2}\right)$

22. 0

23.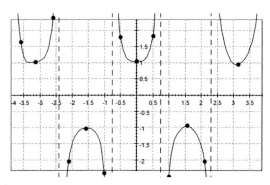

24.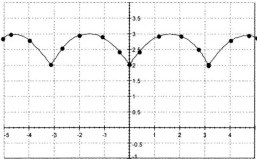

25.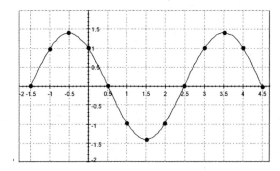

1. Is the following equation an identity?

$$(\sin\theta + \cos\theta)^2 = \sin^2\theta + \cos^2\theta$$

2. Find the solutions of the equation that are in the interval $[0, 2\pi)$.

$$\cos\left(2x - \frac{\pi}{8}\right) = 0$$

3. Find the solutions of the equation that are in the interval $[0, 2\pi)$.

$$\tan^2\theta - \tan\theta = 0$$

4. Find the solutions of the equation that are in the interval $[0, 2\pi)$.

$$2\cos v \sec v - \sec v = 4\cos v - 2$$

5. The average monthly high temperature T (in $^\circ$F) in Augusta, Georgia, can be approximated using the function

$$T(t) = 17\cos\left(\frac{\pi}{6}t - \frac{7\pi}{6}\right) + 75$$

where t is in months and $t = 1$ corresponds to January. Calculate the average high temperature in July.

6. Find the exact values.

$$\cos\frac{\pi}{4} + \cos\frac{\pi}{3}$$

7. If α and β are acute angles such that $\csc \alpha = \dfrac{13}{12}$ and $\cot \beta = \dfrac{4}{3}$, find

$$\tan (\alpha + \beta)$$

8. If $\tan \alpha = -\dfrac{7}{24}$ and $\cot \beta = \dfrac{3}{4}$ for a second-quadrant angle α and a third-quadrant angle β , find

$$\cos (\alpha - \beta)$$

9. Use an addition or subtraction formula to find the solutions of the equation that are in the interval $[0, \pi)$.

$$\sin 8t \cos 5t = \sin 5t \cos 8t$$

10. Use an addition or subtraction formula to find the solutions of the equation that are in the interval $[0, \pi)$.

$$\tan 5t - \tan 8t = 1 + \tan 8t \tan 5t$$

11. If a mass that is attached to a spring is raised y_0 feet and released with an initial vertical velocity of v_0 ft / sec, then the subsequent position y of the mass is given by

$$y = y_0 \cos \omega t + \dfrac{v_0}{\omega} \sin \omega t,$$

where t is time in seconds and ω is a positive constant. If $y_0 = 1$ and $\omega = 4$, find the initial velocities that result in an amplitude of 4 feet.

12. Find the exact values of **sin 2θ, cos 2θ, and tan 2θ** for the given values of θ .

$$\cos \theta = \frac{8}{17} ; 0^\circ < \theta < 90^\circ$$

13. Find the exact values of **sin 2θ, cos 2θ, and tan 2θ** for the given values of θ .

$$\sec \theta = -4; 90^\circ < \theta < 180^\circ$$

14. Use half-angle formulas to find the exact value.

$$\sin 157^\circ 30'$$

15. Use half-angle formulas to find the exact value.

$$\sin \frac{\pi}{12}$$

16. Express in terms of the cosine function with exponent 1.

$$\cos^4 2\theta$$

17. Find the solutions of the equation that are in the interval $[0, \frac{2\pi}{5})$.

$$\sin 10t + \sin 5t = 0$$

18. A graph of $y = 3\sin 4x - 12\sin x$ for $-2\pi \leq x \leq 2\pi$ is shown in the figure. Find the x-intercepts.

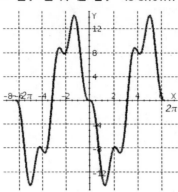

19. If a projectile is fired from ground level with an initial velocity of v ft/sec and at an angle of θ degrees with the horizontal, the range R of the projectile is given by

$$R = \frac{v^2}{16} \sin\theta \cos\theta \, .$$

If $v = 80$ ft/sec, approximate the angles that result in a range of 143 feet.

20. Express as a sum or difference.
$$3\cos 6x \sin 8x$$

21. Express as a product.
$$\cos 6x - \cos 2x$$

22. Use sum-to-product formulas to find the solutions of the equation.
$$\sin 5t + \sin 3t = 0$$

23. Use sum-to-product formulas to find the solutions of the equation.

$$\sin 8x - \sin 4x = 2\cos 6x$$

24. Find the exact value of the expression.

$$\arctan\left(\tan\frac{5\pi}{3}\right)$$

25. Find the exact value of the expression.

$$\sin\left(\arcsin\frac{1}{2} + \arccos 0\right)$$

1. Is the following equation an identity?

$$\cot(\tan\theta) = 1$$

2. Find the solutions of the equation that are in the interval $[0, 2\pi)$.

$$\cos\left(2x - \frac{\pi}{8}\right) = 0$$

3. Find the solutions of the equation that are in the interval $[0, 2\pi)$.

$$\cot^2\theta - \cot\theta = 0$$

4. Find the solutions of the equation that are in the interval $[0, 2\pi)$.

$$2\cos v \csc v - \csc v = 4\cos v - 2$$

5. Find the exact values.

$$\cos\frac{\pi}{3} + \cos\frac{\pi}{4}$$

6. If α and β are acute angles such that $\csc\alpha = \frac{13}{12}$ and $\cot\beta = \frac{4}{3}$, find

$$\sin(\alpha + \beta)$$

7. If $\tan \alpha = -\dfrac{7}{24}$ and $\cot \beta = \dfrac{3}{4}$ for a second-quadrant angle α and a third-quadrant angle β, find

$$\cos(\alpha + \beta)$$

8. Use an addition or subtraction formula to find the solutions of the equation that are in the interval $[0, \tau)$

$$\sin 5t \cos 2t = \sin 2t \cos 5t$$

9. Use an addition or subtraction formula to find the solutions of the equation that are in the interval $[0, \tau)$

$$\tan 3t - \tan 6t = 1 + \tan 6t \tan 3t$$

10. Use the formula

$$a\cos Bx + b\sin Bx = A\cos(Bx - C),$$

where $A = \sqrt{a^2 + b^2}$ and $\tan C = \dfrac{b}{a}$ with $-\dfrac{\tau}{2} < C < \dfrac{\tau}{2}$

to determine the period of $f(x)$.

$$f(x) = 2\cos 4x - 2\sin 4x$$

11. Find the exact values of $\sin 2\theta$, $\cos 2\theta$, and $\tan 2\theta$ for the given values of θ.

$$\cos \theta = \dfrac{8}{17}; \; 0° < \theta < 90°$$

12. Use half-angle formulas to find the exact value.

$$\sin 157°30'$$

13. Use half-angle formulas to find the exact value.

$$\tan \frac{3\pi}{8}$$

14. Express in terms of the cosine function with exponent 1.

$$\cos^4 2\theta$$

15. Find the solutions of the equation that are in the interval $\left[\, 0, \, \frac{2\pi}{11} \,\right)$.

$$\sin 22t + \sin 11t = 0$$

16. A graph of $y = 3\sin 4x - 12\sin x$ for $-2\pi \le x \le 2\pi$ is shown in the figure. Find the x-intercepts.

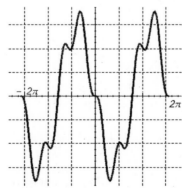

17. If a projectile is fired from ground level with an initial velocity of v ft/sec and at an angle of θ degrees with the horizontal, the range R of the projectile is given by

$$R = \frac{v^2}{16} \sin \theta \cos \theta .$$

If $v = 87$ ft/sec, approximate the angles that result in a range of 145 feet.

18. Express as a sum or difference.

$$3\cos 4x \sin 9x$$

19. Express as a product.

$$\cos 15x - \cos 3x$$

20. Use sum-to-product formulas to find the solutions of the equation.

$$\sin 7t + \sin 5t = 0$$

21. Use sum-to-product formulas to find the solutions of the equation.

$$\sin 6x - \sin 2x = 2\cos 4x$$

22. Find the exact value of the expression.

$$\arctan\left(\tan \frac{11\pi}{6} \right)$$

23. Find the exact value of the expression.

$$\sin\left(\arcsin \frac{\sqrt{3}}{2} + \arccos 1 \right)$$

24. If a mass that is attached to a spring is raised y_0 feet and released with an initial vertical velocity of v_0 ft / sec, then the subsequent position y of the mass is given by

$$y = y_0 \cos \omega t + \frac{v_0}{\omega} \sin \omega t,$$

where t is time in seconds and ω is a positive constant. If $y_0 = 1$ and $\omega = 5$, find the initial velocities that result in an amplitude of 3 feet.

25. Find the exact values of $\sin 2\theta$, $\cos 2\theta$, and $\tan 2\theta$ for the given values of θ

$$\sec \theta = -3; \quad 90° < \theta < 180°$$

1. If an earthquake has a total horizontal displacement of *S* meters along its fault line, then the horizontal movement *M* of a point on the surface of Earth *d* kilometers from the fault line can be estimated using the formula

$$M = \frac{S}{2}\left(1 - \frac{2}{\pi}\tan^{-1}\frac{d}{D}\right)$$

where *D* is the depth (in kilometers) below the surface of the focal point of the earthquake.
For the San Francisco earthquake of 1906, *S* was 3 meters and *D* was 3.63 kilometers. Approximate *M* for *d* = 3 kilometers. Round the answer to the nearest hundred.

    a.   *M* = 0.84 m

    b.   *M* = 0.79 m

    c.   *M* = 0.94 m

    d.   *M* = 0.99 m

2. Find the exact value: $\cos\frac{\pi}{3} + \cos\frac{\pi}{4}$

    a. $\frac{\sqrt{5}}{3}$

    b. 2

    c. $\frac{1 + \sqrt{2}}{2}$

    d. $\sqrt{5} - \sqrt{2}$

3. Find the exact value of the expression: $\arctan\left(\tan\dfrac{\pi}{4}\right)$

    a. $\dfrac{5\pi}{6}$

    b. $\dfrac{\pi}{3}$

    c. $\dfrac{\pi}{4}$

4. A graph of $y = 3\cos x - 3\sin 2x$ for $-2\pi \le x \le 2\pi$ is shown in the figure. Find the x-intercepts.

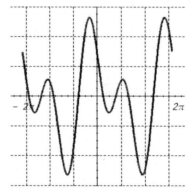

    a. $-\dfrac{3\pi}{2},\ -\dfrac{\pi}{2},\ -\dfrac{11\pi}{6},\ -\dfrac{7\pi}{6},\ \dfrac{\pi}{6},\ \dfrac{5\pi}{6}$

    b. $\pm\dfrac{3\pi}{2},\ \pm\dfrac{\pi}{2},\ -\dfrac{11\pi}{6},\ -\dfrac{7\pi}{6},\ \dfrac{\pi}{6},\ \dfrac{5\pi}{6}$

    c. $\dfrac{3\pi}{2},\ \dfrac{\pi}{2},\ -\dfrac{11\pi}{6},\ -\dfrac{7\pi}{6},\ \dfrac{\pi}{6},\ \dfrac{5\pi}{6}$

    d. $\pm\dfrac{3\pi}{2},\ \pm\dfrac{\pi}{2},\ -\dfrac{11\pi}{6},\ -\dfrac{7\pi}{6},\ \pm\dfrac{\pi}{6},\ \dfrac{7\pi}{6}$

5. Find the exact values of $\sin(\theta/2)$, $\cos(\theta/2)$, and $\tan(\theta/2)$ for the given conditions.

$\sec\theta = \dfrac{61}{60}$; $0° < \theta < 90°$

    a. $\sin(\theta/2) = \dfrac{\sqrt{122}}{122}$, $\cos(\theta/2) = -\dfrac{\sqrt{122}}{122}$, $\tan(\theta/2) = \dfrac{1}{11}$

    b. $\sin(\theta/2) = -\dfrac{\sqrt{122}}{122}$, $\cos(\theta/2) = \dfrac{11\sqrt{122}}{122}$, $\tan(\theta/2) = -\dfrac{1}{11}$

    c. $\sin(\theta/2) = \dfrac{1}{122}$, $\cos(\theta/2) = -\dfrac{11\sqrt{122}}{122}$, $\tan(\theta/2) = -\dfrac{1}{11}$

    d. $\sin(\theta/2) = \dfrac{\sqrt{122}}{122}$, $\cos(\theta/2) = \dfrac{11\sqrt{122}}{122}$, $\tan(\theta/2) = \dfrac{1}{11}$

6. Use inverse trigonometric functions to find the solutions of the equation that are in the given interval, and approximate the solutions to four decimal places.

$2\tan^2 t + 9\tan t + 3 = 0$; $\left(-\dfrac{\tau}{2}, \dfrac{\tau}{2}\right)$

    a. $t = -0.1478$, $t = -1.5337$

    b. $t = -0.3478$, $t = -1.3337$

    c. $t = -0.0478$, $t = -1.0337$

    d. $t = -0.2478$, $t = -1.2337$

7. If a projectile is fired from ground level with an initial velocity of v ft/sec and at an angle of θ degrees with the horizontal, the range R of the projectile is given by

$$R = \frac{v^2}{16} \sin \theta \cos \theta$$

If $v = 86$ ft/sec, approximate the angles that result in a range of 155 feet.

    a. $24.47°$ and $65.53°$

    b. $21.06°$ and $68.94°$

    c. $28.01°$ and $61.99°$

    d. $10.84°$ and $79.16°$

8. Find the solutions of the equation that are in the interval $[0, 2\pi)$.

$$\cos^2 x + \cos x - 4 = 0$$

    a. $\dfrac{\pi}{4}, \dfrac{7\pi}{8}, \pi, \dfrac{7\pi}{4}$

    b. $0, \pi, \dfrac{\pi}{4}, \dfrac{3\pi}{4}, \dfrac{7\pi}{4}$

    c. $0, \dfrac{\pi}{2}, \dfrac{\pi}{8}, \dfrac{7\pi}{8}, \dfrac{15\pi}{8}$

    d.   no solution

9. Find the solutions of the equation that are in the interval $[0,\ 2\pi)$.

$$2\tan t - \sec^2 t = 0$$

    a. $\dfrac{\pi}{4},\ \dfrac{7\pi}{4}$

    b. $\dfrac{2\pi}{3},\ \dfrac{5\pi}{3}$

    c. $\dfrac{\pi}{2},\ \dfrac{3\pi}{2}$

    d.   no solution

    e. $\dfrac{\pi}{4},\ \dfrac{5\pi}{4}$

10. Tell whether the reduction formula is correct or incorrect.

$$\tan\left(\theta - \dfrac{\pi}{2}\right) = \dfrac{1}{\sin\theta}$$

    a.   incorrect

    b.   correct

11. Find the solutions of the equation that are in the interval $[0,\ \dfrac{2\pi}{7})$.

$$\cos 7u + \cos 14u = 0$$

    a. $0,\ \dfrac{\pi}{7},\ \dfrac{4\pi}{21},\ \dfrac{8\pi}{21}$

    b. $\dfrac{\pi}{7},\ \dfrac{2\pi}{21},\ \dfrac{4\pi}{21}$

    c. $0,\ \dfrac{2\pi}{21},\ \dfrac{4\pi}{21}$

    d. $\dfrac{\pi}{7},\ \dfrac{\pi}{21},\ \dfrac{5\pi}{21}$

12. Find the solutions of the equation that are in the interval $[\, 0, \dfrac{2\pi}{5} \,)$.

$$\tan 10\, x = \tan 5\, x$$

a. $0, \dfrac{\pi}{20}$

b. $\dfrac{\pi}{5}, 0$

c. $0, \dfrac{2\pi}{5}$

d. $\dfrac{\pi}{5}$

13. Express as a sum or difference.

$$3\cos 3\, x \sin 9\, x$$

a. $\dfrac{1}{2} \cos(\, 7x \,) - \dfrac{1}{2} \cos(\, 13x \,)$

b. $\dfrac{3}{2} \sin(\, 12x \,) + \dfrac{3}{2}\sin(6x)$

c. $\cos(\, 6x \,) + \cos(\, 12x \,)$

d. $\dfrac{3}{2} \sin(\, 6x \,) - \dfrac{3}{2} \sin(\, 12x \,)$

14. Express as a product.

$$\cos 13\, x - \cos 3\, x$$

a. $2\cos(\, 8x \,) \cos(\, 5x \,)$

b. $-\,2\sin(\, 7x \,) \cos(\, 6x \,)$

c. $2\cos(\, 7x \,) \sin(\, 6x \,)$

d. $-\,2\sin(\, 8x \,) \sin(\, 5x \,)$

15. Use sum-to-product formulas to find the solutions of the equation.

$$\sin 11\,t + \sin 9\,t = 0$$

a. $t = \dfrac{\pi}{2} + \dfrac{\pi}{10}\,n$

b. $t = \dfrac{\pi}{8}\,n$

c. $t = \dfrac{\pi}{10}\,n$

d. $t = \dfrac{\pi}{2} + \dfrac{\pi}{8}\,n$

16. Use the graph of f to find the simplest expression $g(x)$ such that the equation $f(x) = g(x)$ is an identity.

$$f(x) = \frac{\sin 2x + \sin x}{\cos 2x + \cos x + 1}$$

a. $g(x) = \sin x$

b. $g(x) = \sec x$

c. $g(x) = \tan x$

d. $g(x) = \cos x$

17. If the following expression is equated to one of the expressions below, the resulting equation is an identity.

$$\frac{\sec^2 4\theta}{2 - \sec^2 4\theta}$$

a. $\sec 8\theta$

b. $2\csc 8\theta$

c. $\cot 8\theta$

d. $2\cos 8\theta$

18. If α and β are acute angles such that $\csc \alpha = \dfrac{13}{12}$ and $\cot \beta = \dfrac{4}{3}$, find

$\sin (\alpha + \beta)$

a. $\dfrac{6}{65}$

b. $-\dfrac{5}{65}$

c. $\dfrac{63}{65}$

d. $-\dfrac{3}{5}$

19. If a mass that is attached to a spring is raised y_0 feet and released with an initial vertical velocity of v_0 ft / sec, then the subsequent position y of the mass is given by

$$y = y_0 \cos \omega t + \frac{v_0}{\omega} \sin \omega t,$$

where t is time in seconds and ω is a positive constant. If $y_0 = 2$ and $\omega = 4$, find the initial velocities that result in an amplitude of 4 feet.

a. $v_0 = \pm\, 4\sqrt{26}$ ft/sec

b. $v_0 = \pm\, 7\sqrt{12}$ ft/sec

c. $v_0 = \pm\, 4\sqrt{12}$ ft/sec

20. Make the trigonometric substitution $x = a \tan \theta$ for $-\tau/2 < \theta < \tau/2$ and $a > 0$. Use fundamental identities to simplify the resulting expression.

$$\frac{1}{x^2 + a^2}$$

     a. $a^2 \sec^2 \theta \csc \theta$

     b. $\dfrac{1}{a^2} \cos^2 \theta$

     c. $\dfrac{1}{a} \cos \theta$

     d. $a \sec \theta$

21. Find the exact values of $\sin 2\theta$, $\cos 2\theta$, and $\tan 2\theta$ for the given values of θ.

$\cos \theta = \dfrac{5}{13}$; $0° < \theta < 90°$

     a. $-\dfrac{120}{169}, -\dfrac{119}{169}, -\dfrac{120}{119}$

     b. $\dfrac{120}{169}, -\dfrac{119}{169}, -\dfrac{120}{119}$

     c. $-\dfrac{120}{169}, \dfrac{119}{169}, \dfrac{120}{119}$

     d. $\dfrac{5}{13}, \dfrac{12}{13}, \dfrac{5}{12}$

22. Use the formula
$$a\cos Bx + b\sin Bx = A\cos(Bx - C),$$

where $A = \sqrt{a^2 + b^2}$ and $\tan C = \dfrac{b}{a}$ with $-\dfrac{\pi}{2} < C < \dfrac{\pi}{2}$

to express $f(x)$ in terms of the cosine function.

$f(x) = \cos 4x + \sqrt{3}\sin 4x$

  a. $\quad f(x) = 2\cos\left(5x - \dfrac{\pi}{3}\right)$

  b. $\quad f(x) = 2\cos\{4x - \pi\}$

  c. $\quad f(x) = 2\cos\left(4x - \dfrac{\pi}{3}\right)$

  d. $\quad f(x) = \cos\left(4x - \dfrac{\pi}{5}\right)$

23. Verify the identity.
$$\frac{\sin 6\theta + \sin 8\theta}{\cos 6\theta - \cos 8\theta} = \cot 3\theta$$

  a. Not identical

  b. Identical

24. Verify the identity.

$$\frac{\sin \theta + \sin 11\theta}{\cos \theta + \cos 11\theta} = \tan 4\theta$$

    a.   Not identical

    b.   Identical

25.

    Verify the identity: $\dfrac{\tan^2 x}{\sec x + 1} = \dfrac{1 - \cos x}{\cos x}$

    a.   valid

    b.   invalid

1. If an earthquake has a total horizontal displacement of S meters along its fault line, then the horizontal movement M of a point on the surface of Earth d kilometers from the fault line can be estimated using the formula

$$M = \frac{S}{2}\left(1 - \frac{2}{\pi}\tan^{-1}\frac{d}{D}\right)$$

where D is the depth (in kilometers) below the surface of the focal point of the earthquake.
For the San Francisco earthquake of 1906, S was 4 meters and D was 3.24 kilometers. Approximate M for $d = 6$ kilometers. Round the answer to the nearest hundred.

   a. $M = 0.68$ m

   b. $M = 0.48$ m

   c. $M = 0.63$ m

   d. $M = 0.53$ m

2. Find the exact value.
$$\cos\frac{\pi}{6} + \cos\frac{\pi}{3}$$

   a. 4

   b. $\frac{\sqrt{2}}{3}$

   c. $\frac{\sqrt{3}+1}{2}$

   d. $\sqrt{2} - 1$

3. Find the exact value of the expression.
$$\arccos(\cos 0)$$

   a. $-\frac{\pi}{2}$

   b. 0

   c. $\frac{\pi}{3}$

4. A graph of $y = 5\cos x - 5\sin 2x$ for $-2\pi \leq x \leq 2\pi$ is shown in the figure. Find the *x*-intercepts.

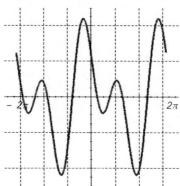

a. $\dfrac{3\pi}{2}, \dfrac{\pi}{2}, -\dfrac{11\pi}{6}, -\dfrac{7\pi}{6}, \dfrac{\pi}{6}, \dfrac{5\pi}{6}$

b. $\pm\dfrac{3\pi}{2}, \pm\dfrac{\pi}{2}, -\dfrac{11\pi}{6}, -\dfrac{7\pi}{6}, \dfrac{\pi}{6}, \dfrac{5\pi}{6}$

c. $-\dfrac{3\pi}{2}, -\dfrac{\pi}{2}, -\dfrac{11\pi}{6}, -\dfrac{7\pi}{6}, \dfrac{\pi}{6}, \dfrac{5\pi}{6}$

d. $\pm\dfrac{3\pi}{2}, \pm\dfrac{\pi}{2}, -\dfrac{11\pi}{6}, -\dfrac{7\pi}{6}, \pm\dfrac{\pi}{6}, \dfrac{7\pi}{6}$

5. Find the exact values of $\sin(\theta/2)$, $\cos(\theta/2)$, and $\tan(\theta/2)$ for the given conditions.

$\sec \theta = \dfrac{5}{4}; \quad 0° < \theta < 90°$

a. $\sin(\theta/2) = \dfrac{1}{10}, \ \cos(\theta/2) = -\dfrac{3\sqrt{10}}{10}, \ \tan(\theta/2) = -\dfrac{1}{3}$

b. $\sin(\theta/2) = -\dfrac{\sqrt{10}}{10}, \ \cos(\theta/2) = \dfrac{3\sqrt{10}}{10}, \ \tan(\theta/2) = -\dfrac{1}{3}$

c. $\sin(\theta/2) = \dfrac{\sqrt{10}}{10}, \ \cos(\theta/2) = -\dfrac{\sqrt{10}}{10}, \ \tan(\theta/2) = \dfrac{1}{3}$

d. $\sin(\theta/2) = \dfrac{\sqrt{10}}{10}, \ \cos(\theta/2) = $ _____ $\dfrac{1}{3}$

6. Use inverse trigonometric functions to find the solutions of the equation that are in the given interval, and approximate the solutions to four decimal places.

$$2\tan^2 t + 9\tan t + 3 = 0; \qquad \left(-\frac{\pi}{2}, \frac{\pi}{2}\right)$$

    a. $t = -0.3478, \ t = -1.3337$

    b. $t = -0.6478, \ t = -1.6337$

    c. $t = -0.2478, \ t = -1.2337$

    d. $t = -0.1478, \ t = -1.5337$

7. If a projectile is fired from ground level with an initial velocity of v ft/sec and at an angle of θ degrees with the horizontal, the range R of the projectile is given by

$$R = \frac{v^2}{16} \sin\theta \cos\theta$$

If $v = 82$ ft/sec, approximate the angles that result in a range of 150 feet.

    a. $32.70°$ and $57.30°$

    b. $18.78°$ and $71.22°$

    c. $22.77°$ and $67.23°$

    d. $17.01°$ and $72.99°$

8. Find the solutions of the equation that are in the interval $[0, 2\pi)$.

$$\sin^2 x + \sin x - 4 = 0$$

    a.   no solution

    b. $0, \ \dfrac{\pi}{2}, \ \dfrac{\pi}{6}, \ \dfrac{5\pi}{6}, \ \dfrac{11\pi}{6}$

    c. $\dfrac{\pi}{4}, \ \dfrac{5\pi}{6}, \ \pi, \ \dfrac{7\pi}{4}$

    d. $0, \ \pi, \ \dfrac{\pi}{4}, \ \dfrac{3\pi}{4}, \ \dfrac{7\pi}{4}$

9. Find the solutions of the equation that are in the interval $[0, 2\pi)$.

$$2\cot t - \csc^2 t = 0$$

a. $\dfrac{\pi}{4}, \dfrac{3\pi}{4}$

b. $\dfrac{\pi}{2}, \dfrac{3\pi}{2}$

c. $\dfrac{\pi}{4}, \dfrac{5\pi}{4}$

d. $\dfrac{6\pi}{7}, \dfrac{13\pi}{7}$

e.   no solution

10. Tell whether the reduction formula is correct or incorrect.

$$\tan\left(\theta - \dfrac{\pi}{2}\right) = \dfrac{1}{\sin\theta}$$

a.   incorrect

b.   correct

11. Find the solutions of the equation that are in the interval $[0, \dfrac{2\pi}{5})$.

$$\cos 5u + \cos 10u = 0$$

a. $0, \dfrac{2\pi}{15}, \dfrac{4\pi}{15}$

b. $\dfrac{\pi}{5}, \dfrac{2\pi}{15}, \dfrac{4\pi}{15}$

c. $\dfrac{\pi}{5}, \dfrac{\pi}{15}, \dfrac{\pi}{3}$

d. $0, \dfrac{\pi}{5}, \dfrac{4\pi}{15}, \dfrac{8\pi}{15}$

12. Find the solutions of the equation that are in the interval $\left[\, 0, \, \dfrac{2\pi}{9} \, \right)$.

$$\tan 18x = \tan 9x$$

a. $\dfrac{\pi}{9},\ 0$

b. $0,\ \dfrac{\pi}{36}$

c. $0,\ \dfrac{2\pi}{9}$

d. $\dfrac{\pi}{9}$

13. Express as a sum or difference.

$$3\cos 3x \sin 7x$$

a. $\dfrac{1}{2}\cos(5x) - \dfrac{1}{2}\cos(9x)$

b. $\dfrac{3}{2}\sin(4x) - \dfrac{3}{2}\sin(10x)$

c. $\cos(4x) + \cos(10x)$

d. $\dfrac{3}{2}\sin(10x) + \dfrac{3}{2}\sin(4x)$

14. Express as a product.

$$\cos 12x - \cos 4x$$

a. $2\cos(9x)\sin(3x)$

b. $-\,2\sin(8x)\sin(4x)$

c. $-\,2\sin(9x)\cos(3x)$

d. $2\cos(8x)\cos(4x)$

15. Use sum-to-product formulas to find the solutions of the equation.

$$\sin 9\,t + \sin 7\,t = 0$$

a. $t = \dfrac{\pi}{8}\,n$

b. $t = \dfrac{\pi}{10}\,n$

c. $t = \dfrac{\pi}{2} + \dfrac{\pi}{8}\,n$

d. $t = \dfrac{\pi}{2} + \dfrac{\pi}{10}\,n$

16. Use the graph of f to find the simplest expression $g(x)$ such that the equation $f(x) = g(x)$ is an identity.

$$f(x) = \frac{\sin 2x + \sin x}{\cos 2x + \cos x + 1}$$

a. $g(x) = \sin x$

b. $g(x) = \cos x$

c. $g(x) = \tan x$

d. $g(x) = \sec x$

17. If the following expression is equated to one of the expressions below, the resulting equation is an identity.

$$\frac{\sec^2 2\theta}{2 - \sec^2 2\theta}$$

a. $\cot 4\theta$

b. $\sec 4\theta$

c. $2\csc 4\theta$

d. $2\cos 4\theta$

18. If α and β are acute angles such that $\cos \alpha = \dfrac{4}{5}$ and $\tan \beta = \dfrac{8}{15}$, find

$\cos (\alpha + \beta)$

  a. $\dfrac{36}{85}$

  b. $-\dfrac{6}{11}$

  c. $-\dfrac{11}{85}$

  d. $\dfrac{3}{5}$

19. If a mass that is attached to a spring is raised y_0 feet and released with an initial vertical velocity of v_0 ft / sec, then the subsequent position y of the mass is given by

$$y = y_0 \cos \omega t + \frac{v_0}{\omega} \sin \omega t,$$

where t is time in seconds and ω is a positive constant. If $y_0 = 2$ and $\omega = 6$, find the initial velocities that result in an amplitude of 4 feet.

  a. $v_0 = \pm\, 6\sqrt{12}$ ft/sec

  b. $v_0 = \pm\, 6\sqrt{26}$ ft/sec

  c. $v_0 = \pm\, 7\sqrt{12}$ ft/sec

20. Make the trigonometric substitution $x = a \tan \theta$ for $-\pi/2 < \theta < \pi/2$ and $a > 0$. Use fundamental identities to simplify the resulting expression.

$$\frac{1}{x^2 + a^2}$$

a. $a \sec \theta$

b. $\dfrac{1}{a} \cos \theta$

c. $\dfrac{1}{a^2} \cos^2 \theta$

d. $a^2 \sec^2 \theta \csc \theta$

21. Find the exact values of $\sin 2\theta$, $\cos 2\theta$, and $\tan 2\theta$ for the given values of θ.

$$\cos \theta = \frac{8}{17} \; ; \; 0^\circ < \theta < 90^\circ$$

a. $\dfrac{8}{17}, \; \dfrac{15}{17}, \; \dfrac{8}{15}$

b. $-\dfrac{240}{289}, \; -\dfrac{161}{289}, \; -\dfrac{240}{161}$

c. $\dfrac{240}{289}, \; -\dfrac{161}{289}, \; -\dfrac{240}{161}$

d. $-\dfrac{240}{289}, \; \dfrac{161}{289}, \; \dfrac{240}{161}$

22. Use the formula $a\cos Bx + b\sin Bx = A\cos(Bx - C)$,

where $A = \sqrt{a^2 + b^2}$ and $\tan C = \dfrac{b}{a}$ with $-\dfrac{\pi}{2} < C < \dfrac{\pi}{2}$

to express $f(x)$ in terms of the cosine function.

$f(x) = \sqrt{3}\cos 8x + \sin 8x$

   a. $f(x) = 2\cos(8x - \pi)$

   b. $f(x) = \cos\left(8x - \dfrac{\pi}{2}\right)$

   c. $f(x) = 2\cos\left(8x - \dfrac{\pi}{6}\right)$

   d. $f(x) = 2\cos\left(3x - \dfrac{\pi}{6}\right)$

23. Verify the identity.

$$\frac{\sin 8\theta + \sin 10\theta}{\cos 8\theta - \cos 10\theta} = \cot 3\theta$$

   a.   Not identical

   b.   Identical

24. Verify the identity.

$$\frac{\sin \theta + \sin 5\theta}{\cos \theta + \cos 5\theta} = \tan 8\theta$$

    a.   Identical

    b.   Not identical

25. Verify the identity: $(\sin \theta + \cos \theta)^2 = \sin^2 \theta + \cos^2 \theta$

    a.   valid

    b.   invalid

1. A graph of $y = 3\cos x - 3\sin 2x$ for $-2\pi \le x \le 2\pi$ is shown in the figure. Find the x-intercepts.

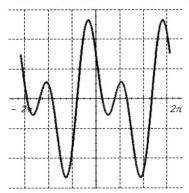

a. $\dfrac{3\pi}{2}, \dfrac{\pi}{2}, -\dfrac{11\pi}{6}, -\dfrac{7\pi}{6}, \dfrac{\pi}{6}, \dfrac{5\pi}{6}$

b. $\pm\dfrac{3\pi}{2}, \pm\dfrac{\pi}{2}, -\dfrac{11\pi}{6}, -\dfrac{7\pi}{6}, \pm\dfrac{\pi}{6}, \dfrac{7\pi}{6}$

c. $\pm\dfrac{3\pi}{2}, \pm\dfrac{\pi}{2}, -\dfrac{11\pi}{6}, -\dfrac{7\pi}{6}, \dfrac{\pi}{6}, \dfrac{5\pi}{6}$

d. $-\dfrac{3\pi}{2}, -\dfrac{\pi}{2}, -\dfrac{11\pi}{6}, -$

2. Find the solutions of the equation that are in the interval $[0, 2\pi)$.

$$\sin^2 x + \sin x - 4 = 0$$

a. $0, \dfrac{\pi}{2}, \dfrac{\pi}{7}, \dfrac{6\pi}{7}, \dfrac{13\pi}{7}$

b. $0, \pi, \dfrac{\pi}{4}, \dfrac{3\pi}{4}, \dfrac{7\pi}{4}$

c. no solution

d. $\dfrac{\pi}{4}, \dfrac{6\pi}{7}, \pi, \dfrac{7\pi}{4}$

3. Tell whether the reduction formula is correct or incorrect.

$$\tan\left(\theta - \frac{\pi}{2}\right) = -\cot\theta$$

    a.   correct

    b.   incorrect

4. Find the solutions of the equation that are in the interval $[0, \frac{2\pi}{7})$.

$$\tan 14x = \tan 7x$$

    a. $\frac{\pi}{7}, 0$

    b. $0, \frac{2\pi}{7}$

    c. $\frac{\pi}{7}$

    d. $0, \frac{\pi}{28}$

5. Express as a sum or difference.

$$3\cos 6x \sin 9x$$

    a. $\frac{3}{2}\sin(3x) - \frac{3}{2}\sin(15x)$

    b. $\cos(3x) + \cos(15x)$

    c. $\frac{1}{2}\cos(4x) - \frac{1}{2}\cos(16x)$

    d. $\frac{3}{2}\sin(15x) + \frac{3}{2}\sin(4x)$

6. Express as a product.

$$\cos 14x - \cos 4x$$

    a. $-2\sin(8x)\cos(4x)$

    b. $2\cos(8x)\sin(4x)$

    c. $2\cos(9x)\cos(5x)$

    d. $-2\sin(9x)\sin(5x)$

7. Use the graph of f to find the simplest expression $g(x)$ such that the equation $f(x) = g(x)$ is an identity.

$$f(x) = \frac{\sin 2x + \cos x}{-\cos 2x + \sin x + 1}$$

    a. $g(x) = \sec x$

    b. $g(x) = \sin x$

    c. $g(x) = \cos x$

    d. $g(x) = \cot x$

8. If α and β are acute angles such that $\csc \alpha = \frac{13}{12}$ and $\cot \beta = \frac{4}{3}$, find $\tan(\alpha + \beta)$

    a. $\frac{7}{16}$

    b. $-\frac{63}{16}$

    c. $-\frac{63}{2}$

    d. $\frac{6}{7}$

9. Use the formula $a\cos 8x + b\sin 8x = A\cos(8x - C)$,

where $A = \sqrt{a^2 + b^2}$ and $\tan C = \dfrac{b}{a}$ with $-\dfrac{\pi}{2} < C < \dfrac{\pi}{2}$

to express $f(x)$ in terms of the cosine function.

$f(x) = \cos 8x + \sin 8x$

a. $f(x) = \cos\left(8x - \dfrac{\pi}{7}\right)$

b. $f(x) = \sqrt{2}\cos\left(8x - \dfrac{\pi}{4}\right)$

c. $f(x) = \sqrt{2}\cos(8x - \pi)$

d. $f(x) = \sqrt{2}\cos\left(7x - \dfrac{\pi}{4}\right)$

10. Verify the identity.

$$\frac{\sin 6\theta + \sin 8\theta}{\cos 6\theta - \cos 8\theta} = \cot \theta$$

a.   Not identical

b.   Identical

11. Verify the identity.

$$\frac{\sin \theta + \sin 9\theta}{\cos \theta + \cos 9\theta} = \tan 5\theta$$

a.   Not identical

b.   Identical

12. Verify the identity: $\dfrac{\cot x}{\csc x + 1} = \dfrac{\csc x - 1}{\cot x}$

   a.   valid

   b.   invalid

13. Find the solutions of the equation that are in the interval $[0, 2\pi)$.

$$\cos\left(2x - \frac{\pi}{8}\right) = 0$$

14. Find the solutions of the equation that are in the interval $[0, 2\pi)$.

$$\tan^2 \theta - \tan \theta = 0$$

15. On a cloudy day with D hours of daylight, the intensity of sunlight I (in calories/cm^2) may be approximated by

$$I = I_m \sin^2 \frac{\pi t}{D} \quad \text{for } 0 \le t \le D$$

where $t = 0$ corresponds to sunrise and I_m is the maximum intensity. If $D = 12$, approximately how many hours after sunrise is $I = \frac{1}{2} I_m$

16. Find the exact values.

$$\cos \frac{\pi}{3} + \cos \frac{\pi}{4}$$

17. If $\tan \alpha = -\dfrac{7}{24}$ and $\cot \beta = \dfrac{3}{4}$ for a second-quadrant angle α and a third-quadrant angle β, find

$$\tan (\alpha + \beta)$$

18. Use an addition or subtraction formula to find the solutions of the equation that are in the interval $[0, \pi)$

$$\sin 7t \cos 4t = \sin 4t \cos 7t$$

19. Use an addition or subtraction formula to find the solutions of the equation that are in the interval $[0, \pi)$

$$\cos 4t \cos t = -\sin 4t \sin t$$

20. Find the exact values of $\sin 2\theta$, $\cos 2\theta$, and $\tan 2\theta$ for the given values of θ.

$$\cos \theta = \dfrac{5}{13} \; ; \; 0° < \theta < 90°$$

21. Use half-angle formulas to find the exact value.

$$\tan \dfrac{\pi}{8}$$

22. If a projectile is fired from ground level with an initial velocity of v ft/sec and at an angle of θ degrees with the horizontal, the range R of the projectile is given by

$$R = \dfrac{v^2}{16} \sin \theta \cos \theta \; .$$

If $v = 75$ ft/sec, approximate the angles that result in a range of 150 feet.

23. Use sum-to-product formulas to find the solutions of the equation.

$$\sin 7t + \sin 5t = 0$$

24. Use sum-to-product formulas to find the solutions of the equation.

$$\sin 7x - \sin 3x = 2\cos 5x$$

25. If a mass that is attached to a spring is raised y_0 feet and released with an initial vertical velocity of v_0 ft / sec, then the subsequent position y of the mass is given by

$$y = y_0 \cos \omega t + \frac{v_0}{\omega} \sin \omega t,$$

where t is time in seconds and ω is a positive constant. If $y_0 = 1$ and $\omega = 6$, find the initial velocities that result in an amplitude of 3 feet.

1. A graph of $y = 2\cos x - 2\sin 2x$ for $-2\pi \le x \le 2\pi$ is shown in the figure. Find the x-intercepts.

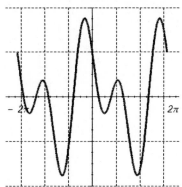

a. $\quad \dfrac{3\pi}{2},\ \dfrac{\pi}{2},\ -\dfrac{11\pi}{6},\ -\dfrac{7\pi}{6},\ \dfrac{\pi}{6},\ \dfrac{5\pi}{6}$

b. $\quad \pm\dfrac{3\pi}{2},\ \pm\dfrac{\pi}{2},\ -\dfrac{11\pi}{6},\ -\dfrac{7\pi}{6},\ \dfrac{\pi}{6},\ \dfrac{5\pi}{6}$

c. $\quad -\dfrac{3\pi}{2},\ -\dfrac{\pi}{2},\ -\dfrac{11\pi}{6},\ -$

d. $\quad \pm\dfrac{3\pi}{2},\ \pm\dfrac{\pi}{2},\ -\dfrac{11\pi}{6},\ -\dfrac{7\pi}{6},\ \pm\dfrac{\pi}{6},\ \dfrac{7\pi}{6}$

2. Find the solutions of the equation that are in the interval $[0,\ 2\pi)$.

$$\sin^2 x + \sin x - 3 = 0$$

a. $\quad 0,\ \pi,\ \dfrac{\pi}{3},\ \dfrac{2\pi}{3},\ \dfrac{5\pi}{3}$

b. $\quad \dfrac{\pi}{3},\ \dfrac{3\pi}{4},\ \pi,\ \dfrac{5\pi}{3}$

c. $\quad 0,\ \dfrac{\pi}{2},\ \dfrac{\pi}{4},\ \dfrac{3\pi}{4},\ \dfrac{7\pi}{4}$

d. $\quad$ no solution

3. Tell whether the reduction formula is correct or incorrect. $\tan\left(\theta + \tau\right) = \csc\theta$

    a.   incorrect

    b.   correct

4. Find the solutions of the equation that are in the interval $\left[0, \dfrac{2\tau}{11}\right)$.

$$\tan 22\,x = \tan 11\,x$$

    a. $\dfrac{\tau}{11}, \; 0$

    b. $0, \; \dfrac{\tau}{44}$

    c. $0, \; \dfrac{2\tau}{11}$

    d. $\dfrac{\tau}{11}$

5. Express as a sum or difference.

$$3\cos 2\,x \sin 5\,x$$

    a. $\dfrac{3}{2}\sin\left(7x\right) + \dfrac{3}{2}\sin(3x)$

    b. $\dfrac{3}{2}\sin\left(3x\right) - \dfrac{3}{2}\sin\left(7x\right)$

    c. $\cos\left(3x\right) + \cos\left(7x\right)$

    d. $\dfrac{1}{2}\cos\left(4x\right) - \dfrac{1}{2}\cos\left(8x\right)$

6. Express as a product.

$$\cos 11\,x - \cos 7\,x$$

    a. $2\cos(9x)\cos(2x)$

    b. $2\cos(8x)\sin(1x)$

    c. $-\,2\sin(8x)\cos(1x)$

    d. $-\,2\sin(9x)\sin(2x)$

7. Use the graph of f to find the simplest expression $g(x)$ such that the equation $f(x) = g(x)$ is an identity.

$$f(x) = \frac{\sin 2x + \cos x}{-\cos 2x + \sin x + 1}$$

    a. $g(x) = \sin x$

    b. $g(x) = \cot x$

    c. $g(x) = \sec x$

    d. $g(x) = \cos x$

8. If α and β are acute angles such that $\csc \alpha = \dfrac{13}{12}$ and $\cot \beta = \dfrac{4}{3}$, find

$$\sin(\alpha + \beta)$$

    a. $-\dfrac{3}{5}$

    b. $-\dfrac{5}{65}$

    c. $\dfrac{63}{65}$

    d. $\dfrac{6}{65}$

9. Use the formula $a\cos Bx + b\sin Bx = A\cos(Bx - C)$,

where $A = \sqrt{a^2 + b^2}$ and $\tan C = \dfrac{b}{a}$ with $-\dfrac{\pi}{2} < C < \dfrac{\pi}{2}$

to express $f(x)$ in terms of the cosine function.

$f(x) = \cos 2x + \sin 2x$

  a. $f(x) = \sqrt{2}\cos\left(2x - \dfrac{\pi}{4}\right)$

  b. $f(x) = \cos\left(2x - \dfrac{\pi}{7}\right)$

  c. $f(x) = \sqrt{2}\cos\left(3x - \dfrac{\pi}{4}\right)$

  d. $f(x) = \sqrt{2}\cos(2x - \pi)$

10. Verify the identity.

$$\frac{\sin 5\theta + \sin 7\theta}{\cos 5\theta - \cos 7\theta} = \cot 4\theta$$

  a.   Not identical

  b.   Identical

11. Verify the identity.

$$\frac{\sin \theta + \sin 13\theta}{\cos \theta + \cos 13\theta} = \tan 7\theta$$

  a.   Not identical

  b.   Identical

12. Verify the identity: $\dfrac{1}{\csc y - \cot y} = \csc y + \cot y$

    a.   valid

    b.   invalid

13. Find the solutions of the equation that are in the interval $[0, 2\pi)$.

$$\cos\left(2x - \frac{\pi}{4}\right) = 0$$

14. Find the solutions of the equation that are in the interval $[0, 2\pi)$.

$$\cot^2 \theta - \cot \theta = 0$$

15. On a cloudy day with D hours of daylight, the intensity of sunlight I (in calories/cm^2) may be approximated by

$$I = I_m \sin^2 \frac{\pi t}{D} \quad \text{for } 0 \le t \le D$$

where $t = 0$ corresponds to sunrise and I_m is the maximum intensity. If $D = 12$, approximately how many hours after sunrise is $I = \dfrac{1}{4} I_m$

16. Find the exact values. $\cos \dfrac{\pi}{3} + \cos \dfrac{\pi}{6}$

17. If $\tan \alpha = -\dfrac{7}{24}$ and $\cot \beta = \dfrac{3}{4}$ for a second-quadrant angle α and a third-quadrant angle β, find

$$\cos(\alpha + \beta)$$

18. Use an addition or subtraction formula to find the solutions of the equation that are in the interval $[0, \pi)$

$$\sin 4t \cos t = \sin t \cos 4t$$

19. Use an addition or subtraction formula to find the solutions of the equation that are in the interval $[0, \pi)$

$$\cos 4t \cos t = -\sin 4t \sin t$$

20. Find the exact values of $\sin 2\theta,\ \cos 2\theta,\ \text{and}\ \tan 2\theta$ for the given values of θ.

$$\cos \theta = \frac{3}{5}\ ;\ 0^\circ < \theta < 90^\circ$$

21. Use half-angle formulas to find the exact value. $\sin \dfrac{\pi}{12}$

22. If a projectile is fired from ground level with an initial velocity of v ft/sec and at an angle of θ degrees with the horizontal, the range R of the projectile is given by

$$R = \frac{v^2}{16} \sin \theta \cos \theta .$$

If $v = 85$ ft/sec, approximate the angles that result in a range of 146 feet.

23. Use sum-to-product formulas to find the solutions of the equation.

$$\sin 7t + \sin 5t = 0$$

24. Use sum-to-product formulas to find the solutions of the equation.

$$\sin 5x - \sin x = 2\cos 3x$$

25. If a mass that is attached to a spring is raised y_0 feet and released with an initial vertical velocity of v_0 ft / sec, then the subsequent position y of the mass is given by

$$y = y_0 \cos \omega t + \frac{v_0}{\omega} \sin \omega t,$$

where t is time in seconds and ω is a positive constant. If $y_0 = 1$ and $\omega = 5$, find the initial velocities that result in an amplitude of 6 feet.

Test Form 6-A

1. no

2. $\dfrac{5}{16} \cdot \pi, \dfrac{13}{16} \cdot \pi, \dfrac{21}{16} \cdot \pi, \dfrac{29}{16} \cdot \pi$

3. $0, \dfrac{\pi}{4}, \pi, \dfrac{5\pi}{4}$

4. $\dfrac{\pi}{3}, \dfrac{5\pi}{3}$

5. 92

6. $\dfrac{(\sqrt{2}+1)}{2}$

7. $-\dfrac{63}{16}$

8. $\dfrac{44}{125}$

9. $0, \dfrac{\pi}{3}, \dfrac{2\pi}{3}$

10. $\dfrac{\pi}{4}, \dfrac{7\pi}{12}, \dfrac{11\pi}{12}$

11. $4\sqrt{15}, -4\sqrt{15}$

12. $\dfrac{240}{289}; -\dfrac{161}{289}; -\dfrac{240}{161}$

13. $-\dfrac{\sqrt{15}}{8}; -\dfrac{7}{8}; \dfrac{\sqrt{15}}{7}$

14. $\dfrac{1}{2} \cdot \sqrt{2-\sqrt{2}}$

15. $\dfrac{1}{2} \cdot \sqrt{2-\sqrt{3}}$

16. $\dfrac{3}{8} + \dfrac{1}{2} \cdot \cos(4\theta) + \dfrac{1}{8} \cdot \cos(8\theta)$

17. $0, \dfrac{\pi}{5}, \dfrac{2\pi}{15}, \dfrac{4\pi}{15}$

18. $0, \pi, -\pi, 2\pi, -2\pi$

19. $22.82, 67.18$

20. $\dfrac{3}{2} \cdot \sin(14x) + \dfrac{3}{2} \cdot \sin(2x)$

21. $-2\sin(4x) \cdot \sin(2x)$

22. $\dfrac{\pi}{4} \cdot n$

23. $\dfrac{\pi}{12} + \dfrac{\pi}{6} \cdot n, \dfrac{\pi}{4} + \pi \cdot n$

24. $-\dfrac{\pi}{3}$

25. $\dfrac{\sqrt{3}}{2}$

Test Form 6-B

1. no

2. $\frac{5}{16}\cdot\pi, \frac{13}{16}\cdot\pi, \frac{21}{16}\cdot\pi, \frac{29}{16}\cdot\pi$

3. $\frac{\pi}{4}, \frac{\pi}{2}, \frac{5\pi}{4}, \frac{3\pi}{2}$

4. $\frac{\pi}{6}, \frac{\pi}{3}, \frac{5\pi}{6}, \frac{5\pi}{3}$

5. $\frac{(1+\sqrt{2})}{2}$

6. $\frac{63}{65}$

7. $\frac{4}{5}$

8. $0, \frac{\pi}{3}, \frac{2\pi}{3}$

9. $\frac{\pi}{4}, \frac{7\pi}{12}, \frac{11\pi}{12}$

10. $\frac{\pi}{2}$

11. $\frac{240}{289}; -\frac{161}{289}; -\frac{240}{161}$

12. $\frac{1}{2}\cdot\sqrt{2-\sqrt{2}}$

13. $\sqrt{2}+1$

14. $\frac{3}{8} + \frac{1}{2}\cdot\cos(4\theta) + \frac{1}{8}\cdot\cos(8\theta)$

15. $0, \frac{\pi}{11}, \frac{2\pi}{33}, \frac{4\pi}{33}$

16. $0, \pi, -\pi, 2\pi, -2\pi$

17. $18.90, 71.10$

18. $\frac{3}{2}\cdot\sin(13x) + \frac{3}{2}\cdot\sin(5x)$

19. $-2\sin(9x)\cdot\sin(6x)$

20. $\frac{\pi}{6}\cdot n$

21. $\frac{\pi}{8} + \frac{\pi}{4}\cdot n, \frac{\pi}{4} + \pi\cdot n$

22. $-\frac{\pi}{6}$

23. $\frac{\sqrt{3}}{2}$

24. $5\sqrt{8}, -5\sqrt{8}$

25. $-\frac{4\sqrt{2}}{9}; -\frac{7}{9}; \frac{4\sqrt{2}}{7}$

Test Form 6-C

1. a	**2.** c	**3.** c	**4.** b	**5.** d	**6.** b	**7.** b	**8.** d	**9.** e
10. a	**11.** d	**12.** b	**13.** b	**14.** d	**15.** c	**16.** c	**17.** a	**18.** c
19. c	**20.** b	**21.** b	**22.** c	**23.** a	**24.** a	**25.** a		

Test Form 6-D

1. c	**2.** c	**3.** b	**4.** b	**5.** d	**6.** a	**7.** c	**8.** a	**9.** c
10. a	**11.** c	**12.** a	**13.** d	**14.** b	**15.** a	**16.** c	**17.** b	**18.** a
19. a	**20.** c	**21.** c	**22.** c	**23.** a	**24.** b	**25.** b		

Test Form 6-E

1. c
2. c
3. a
4. a
5. d
6. d
7. d
8. b
9. b
10. b
11. b
12. a
13. $\frac{5}{16} \cdot \pi, \frac{13}{16} \cdot \pi, \frac{21}{16} \cdot \pi, \frac{29}{16} \cdot \pi$
14. $0, \frac{\pi}{4}, \pi, \frac{5\pi}{4}$
15. 3.00,9
16. $\frac{(1+\sqrt{2})}{2}$

17. $\frac{3}{4}$
18. $0, \frac{\pi}{3}, \frac{2\pi}{3}$
19. $\frac{\pi}{6}, \frac{\pi}{2}, \frac{5\pi}{6}$
20. $\frac{120}{169}; -\frac{119}{169}; -\frac{120}{119}$
21. $\sqrt{2} - 1$
22. 29.29,60.71
23. $\frac{\pi}{6} \cdot n$
24. $\frac{\pi}{10} + \frac{\pi}{5} \cdot n, \frac{\pi}{4} + \pi \cdot n$
25. $6\sqrt{8}, -6\sqrt{8}$

Test Form 6-F

1. b
2. d
3. a
4. a
5. a
6. d
7. b
8. c
9. a
10. a
11. b
12. a
13. $\frac{3}{8} \cdot \pi, \frac{7}{8} \cdot \pi, \frac{11}{8} \cdot \pi, \frac{15}{8} \cdot \pi$
14. $\frac{\pi}{4}, \frac{\pi}{2}, \frac{5\pi}{4}, \frac{3\pi}{2}$
15. 2.00,10
16. $\frac{(1+\sqrt{3})}{2}$

17. $\frac{4}{5}$
18. $0, \frac{\pi}{3}, \frac{2\pi}{3}$
19. $\frac{\pi}{6}, \frac{\pi}{2}, \frac{5\pi}{6}$
20. $\frac{24}{25}; -\frac{7}{25}; -\frac{24}{7}$
21. $\frac{1}{2} \cdot \sqrt{2-\sqrt{3}}$
22. 20.14,69.86
23. $\frac{\pi}{6} \cdot n$
24. $\frac{\pi}{6} + \frac{\pi}{3} \cdot n, \frac{\pi}{4} + \pi \cdot n$
25. $5\sqrt{35}, -5\sqrt{35}$

1. Given that $a = \langle 2, -4 \rangle$, $b = \langle 5, 4 \rangle$, and $c = \langle -5, 3 \rangle$, find the number

   $(a - b) \cdot (b + c)$.

2. Solve $\triangle ABC$ $a = 2.0$, $b = 3.0$, $c = 4.5$

   angle α: _____ $^\circ$
   angle β: _____ $^\circ$
   angle γ: _____ $^\circ$

3. Two automobiles leave a city at the same time and travel along straight highways that differ in direction by 84°. If their speeds are 60 mi/hr and 45 mi/hr, respectively, approximately how far apart are the cars at the end of 10 minutes? Round the answer to the nearest integer.

4. An airplane flies 165 miles from point A in the direction 130° and then travels in the direction 245° for 90 miles. Approximately how far is the airplane from A? Round the answer to the nearest integer.

5. A jogger runs at a constant speed of one mile every 8 minutes in the direction S40°E for 32 minutes and then in the direction N20°E for the next 16 minutes. Approximate, to the nearest tenth of a mile, the straight line distance from the endpoint to the starting point of the jogger's course.

6. Approximate the area of triangle ABC $\alpha = 60^\circ$, $b = 20$, $c = 27$

   Round the answer to the nearest integer.

7. A triangular field has sides of lengths a, b, and c (in yards). Approximate the number of acres in the field (1 acre = 4840 yd^2).

$$a = 280 , b = 350 , c = 500$$

Round the answer to the nearest hundredth.

8. Find $\| \mathbf{a} \|$. $\mathbf{a} = - \langle 9, - 5 \rangle$

9. Find $5\,\mathbf{a} - 2\,\mathbf{b}$. $\mathbf{a} = \mathbf{i} + 5\,\mathbf{j}, \quad \mathbf{b} = 4\,\mathbf{i} - 6\,\mathbf{j}$

10. Find the smallest positive angle θ from the positive x-axis to the vector OP that corresponds to $\mathbf{a}$.

$\mathbf{a} = \langle - 5, - 5 \rangle$

11. Find the magnitude of the vector $\mathbf{a}$. $\mathbf{a} = - 5\,\mathbf{i} + 6\,\mathbf{j}$

12. A quarterback releases a football with a speed of 55 ft/sec at an angle of 20° with the horizontal. Approximate the horizontal component of the vector that is described. Round the answer to the nearest hundredth.

13. Find a unit vector that has the same direction as the vector $\mathbf{a}$. $\mathbf{a} = \langle 0, 4 \rangle$

14. Find a vector that has the opposite direction of $9\,\mathbf{i} - 9\,\mathbf{j}$ and three times the magnitude.

15. If forces F_1, F_2,..., F_n act at a point P, the net (or resultant) force F is the sum $F_1 + F_2 + \cdots + F_n$. If $F = 0$ the forces are said to be in equilibrium. The given forces act at the origin O of an xy-plane. Find an additional force G such that equilibrium occurs.

$$F_1 = \langle 7, 6 \rangle, \quad F_2 = \langle -6, -2 \rangle, \quad F_3 = \langle 6, 4 \rangle$$

16. Find the dot product of the two vectors $\langle -5, 8 \rangle$ and $\langle 2, 2 \rangle$.

17. Find the angle between the two vectors $3i - j$ and $-5i + 3j$.

18. Find the angle between the two vectors $\langle -9, 7 \rangle$ and $\langle -8, 3 \rangle$.

19. Determine m such that the two vectors are orthogonal. $7i - 8j$ and $3i + 2mj$

20. If c represents a constant force, find the work done if the point of application of c moves along the line segment from P to Q.

$$c = 2i + 6j \text{ and } P(0, 0), Q(3, -3)$$

21. Express the complex number in trigonometric form with $0 \le \theta \le 2\pi$.

$$8 + 7i$$

22. Use trigonometric forms to find $z_1 z_2$ and z_1/z_2.

$$z_1 = -2 + i, \ z_2 = 2 + i$$

23. Use De Moivre's theorem to change the given complex number to the form $a + bi$, where a and b are real numbers.

$$\left(\sqrt{3} + i\right)^{13}$$

24. Find the solutions of the equation. $x^6 + 64 = 0$

25. Express in the form $a + bi$, where a and b are real numbers. $18\left(\cos \dfrac{\pi}{4} + i \sin \dfrac{\pi}{4}\right)$

1. Given that $a = \langle 4, -4 \rangle$, $b = \langle 1, 2 \rangle$, and $c = \langle -2, 2 \rangle$, find the number

   $(a - b) \cdot (b + c)$.

2. Solve $\triangle ABC$ $a = 2.0$, $b = 3.0$, $c = 3.5$

   angle α: _____ $^\circ$
   angle β: _____ $^\circ$
   angle γ: _____ $^\circ$

3. Two automobiles leave a city at the same time and travel along straight highways that differ in direction by 84°. If their speeds are 60 mi/hr and 45 mi/hr, respectively, approximately how far apart are the cars at the end of 20 minutes? Round the answer to the nearest integer.

4. An airplane flies 165 miles from point A in the direction 130° and then travels in the direction 245° for 70 miles. Approximately how far is the airplane from A? Round the answer to the nearest integer.

5. A jogger runs at a constant speed of one mile every 8 minutes in the direction S40°E for 32 minutes and then in the direction N20°E for the next 16 minutes. Approximate, to the nearest tenth of a mile, the straight line distance from the endpoint to the starting point of the jogger's course.

6. Approximate the area of triangle ABC $\alpha = 60^\circ$, $b = 20$, $c = 28$

   Round the answer to the nearest integer.

7. A triangular field has sides of lengths a, b, and c (in yards). Approximate the number of acres in the field
    (1 acre = 4840 yd^2).

$$a = 315 \text{ , } b = 350 \text{ , } c = 500$$

Round the answer to the nearest hundredth.

8. Find $\| \mathbf{a} \|$. $\mathbf{a} = - \langle 7, -6 \rangle$

9. Find $6\,\mathbf{a} - 4\,\mathbf{b}$. $\mathbf{a} = \mathbf{i} + 6\,\mathbf{j}, \mathbf{b} = 6\,\mathbf{i} - 6\,\mathbf{j}$

10. Find the smallest positive angle θ from the positive x-axis to the vector OP that corresponds to $\mathbf{a}$.
    $\mathbf{a} = \langle 6, 6 \rangle$

11. Find the magnitude of the vector $\mathbf{a}$. $\mathbf{a} = -5\,\mathbf{i} + 6\,\mathbf{j}$

12. A quarterback releases a football with a speed of 40 ft/sec at an angle of $25°$ with the horizontal.
    Approximate the horizontal component of the vector that is described. Round the answer to the nearest
    hundredth.

13. Find a unit vector that has the same direction as the vector $\mathbf{a}$. $\mathbf{a} = \langle 0, 4 \rangle$

14. Find a vector that has the opposite direction of $2\,\mathbf{i} - 4\,\mathbf{j}$ and two times the magnitude.

15. If forces $F_1, F_2, ..., F_n$ act at a point P, the net (or resultant) force F is the sum $F_1 + F_2 + \cdots + F_n$. If $F = 0$ the forces are said to be in equilibrium. The given forces act at the origin O of an xy-plane. Find an additional force G such that equilibrium occurs.

$$F_1 = \langle 5, 7 \rangle, \; F_2 = \langle -4, -5 \rangle, \; F_3 = \langle 5, 4 \rangle$$

16. Find the dot product of the two vectors $\langle -6, 8 \rangle$ and $\langle 5, 4 \rangle$

17. Find the angle between the two vectors $10i - j$ and $-10i + 8j$.

18. Find the angle between the two vectors $\langle -6, 5 \rangle$ and $\langle -9, 6 \rangle$.

19. Determine m such that the two vectors are orthogonal. $3i - 2j$ and $5i + 8mj$

20. If c represents a constant force, find the work done if the point of application of c moves along the line segment from P to Q.

$$c = 5i + 2j \text{ and } P(0, 0), Q(5, -5)$$

21. Express the complex number in trigonometric form with $0 \le \theta \le 2\pi$.

$$9 + 8i$$

22. Use trigonometric forms to find $z_1 z_2$ and z_1/z_2.

$$z_1 = -4 + i, \; z_2 = 4 + i$$

23. Use De Moivre's theorem to change the given complex number to the form $a + bi$, where a and b are real numbers.

$$\left(\sqrt{3} + i\right)^5$$

24. Find the solutions of the equation.

$$x^6 + 64 = 0$$

25. Express in the form $a + bi$, where a and b are real numbers.

$$6\left(\cos \frac{7}{4} + i \sin \frac{7}{4}\right)$$

1. Solve $\triangle ABC$ $a = 10.0$, $b = 15.0$, $c = 12.0$

    a. 42° , 88° , 51°

    b. 48° , 88° , 51°

    c. 48° , 85° , 53°

    d. 42° , 85° , 53°

2. Two automobiles leave a city at the same time and travel along straight highways that differ in direction by 84° . If their speeds are 60 mi/hr and 45 mi/hr, respectively, approximately how far apart are the cars at the end of 30 minutes?

    a.   38 mi

    b.   42 mi

    c.   36 mi

    d.   39 mi

3. An airplane flies 165 miles from point A in the direction 130° and then travels in the direction 245° for 80 miles. Approximately how far is the airplane from A?

    a.   156 mi

    b.   153 mi

    c.   150 mi

    d.   148 mi

4. A jogger runs at a constant speed of one mile every 8 minutes in the direction S40°E for 32 minutes and then in the direction N20°E for the next 16 minutes. Approximate, to the nearest tenth of a mile, the straight line distance from the endpoint to the starting point of the jogger's course.

     a.   3.5 mi

     b.   4.8 mi

     c.   2.5 mi

     d.   3.3 mi

5. Approximate the area of triangle ABC

$$\alpha = 60^\circ, \ b = 20, \ c = 35$$

     a.   247

     b.   303

     c.   175

     d.   606

6. A triangular field has sides of lengths a, b, and c (in yards). Approximate the number of acres in the field (1 acre = 4840 yd^2).

$$a = 320, \ b = 350, \ c = 500$$

     a.   10.89 acres

     b.   11.17 acres

     c.   11.50 acres

     d.   10.30 acres

7. Find $\| \mathbf{a} \|$.

$$\mathbf{a} = -<4, -9>$$

  a. $\| \mathbf{a} \| = \sqrt{99}$

  b. $\| \mathbf{a} \| = \sqrt{97}$

  c. $\| \mathbf{a} \| = \sqrt{94}$

  d. $\| \mathbf{a} \| = \sqrt{96}$

8. Find $4\,\mathbf{a} - 5\,\mathbf{b}$.

$$\mathbf{a} = \mathbf{i} + 3\,\mathbf{j}, \ \mathbf{b} = 3\,\mathbf{i} - 4\,\mathbf{j}$$

  a. $- 11\mathbf{i} + 32\mathbf{j}$

  b. $- 14\mathbf{i} + 35\mathbf{j}$

  c. $- 12\mathbf{i} + 33\mathbf{j}$

  d. $- 9\mathbf{i} + 30\mathbf{j}$

9. Find the smallest positive angle θ from the positive x-axis to the vector OP that corresponds to $\mathbf{a}$.

$$\mathbf{a} = <4, -4>$$

  a. $\theta = \dfrac{7\pi}{4}$

  b. $\theta = \dfrac{3\pi}{4}$

  c. $\theta = \dfrac{5\pi}{4}$

10. Find the magnitude of the vector **a**.

$$\mathbf{a} = -8\,\mathbf{i} + 9\,\mathbf{j}$$

a. $\sqrt{148}$

b. $\sqrt{145}$

c. $\sqrt{147}$

d. $\sqrt{146}$

11. A quarterback releases a football with a speed of 60 ft/sec at an angle of 30° with the horizontal. Approximate the horizontal component of the vector that is described.

a.   53.76 ft/sec

b.   48.36 ft/sec

c.   50.76 ft/sec

d.   51.96 ft/sec

12. Find a unit vector that has the same direction as the vector **a**. $\mathbf{a} = \langle 0, 2 \rangle$

a. $\langle 1, 0 \rangle$

b. $\langle 1, -2 \rangle$

c. $\langle 0, 1 \rangle$

d. $\langle 1, 1 \rangle$

13. Find a vector that has the opposite direction of $5\,\mathbf{i} - 9\,\mathbf{j}$ and two times the magnitude.

     a. $-\ 11\mathbf{i}\ +\ 19\mathbf{j}$

     b. $-\ 12\mathbf{i}\ +\ 20\mathbf{j}$

     c. $-\ 10\mathbf{i}\ +\ 18\mathbf{j}$

     d. $-\ 7\mathbf{i}\ +\ 15\mathbf{j}$

14. If forces $\mathbf{F}_1$, $\mathbf{F}_2$,..., $\mathbf{F}_n$ act at a point P, the net (or resultant) force $\mathbf{F}$ is the sum $\mathbf{F}_1 + \mathbf{F}_2 + \cdot\cdot\cdot + \mathbf{F}_n$. If $\mathbf{F} = 0$ the forces are said to be in equilibrium. The given forces act at the origin O of an xy-plane. Find an additional force $\mathbf{G}$ such that equilibrium occurs.

$$\mathbf{F}_1 = \langle 4, 2 \rangle,\ \mathbf{F}_2 = \langle -7, -3 \rangle,\ \mathbf{F}_3 = \langle 5, 2 \rangle$$

     a. $\langle -4, -3 \rangle$

     b. $\langle -1, -2 \rangle$

     c. $\langle -2, -1 \rangle$

     d. $\langle -5, -4 \rangle$

15. Find the dot product of the two vectors $\langle -8,\ 7 \rangle$ and $\langle 3,\ 10 \rangle$.

     a.   94

     b.   -26

     c.   86

     d.   46

16. Find the angle between the two vectors 2 **i** - **j** and -10 **i** + 9 **j**.

    a. $164° \ 35'$

    b. $74° \ 35'$

    c. $74° \ 58'$

    d. $254° \ 58'$

17. Find the angle between the two vectors $\langle - 9, \ 10 \rangle$ and $\langle - 5, \ 2 \rangle$.

    a. $116° \ 13'$

    b. $206° \ 21'$

    c. $116° \ 21'$

    d. $26° \ 13'$

18. Determine *m* such that the two vectors are orthogonal.

$$5 \ i - 4 \ j \ \text{and} \ 7 \ i + 2 \ m\textbf{j}$$

    a. $\dfrac{20}{14}$

    b. $-\dfrac{20}{14}$

    c. $-\dfrac{35}{8}$

    d. $\dfrac{35}{8}$

19. Given that $a = \langle 1, -5 \rangle$, $b = \langle 3, 4 \rangle$, and $c = \langle -5, 4 \rangle$, find the number $(a - b) \cdot (b + c)$.

    a.   76

    b.   -68

    c.   56

    d.   -80

20. If c represents a constant force, find the work done if the point of application of c moves along the line segment from P to Q.

$$c = 5\,i + 3\,j \text{ and } P(0, 0), Q(5, -1)$$

    a.   28

    b.   22

    c.   10

    d.   -10

21. Express the complex number in trigonometric form with $0 \le \theta \le 2\pi$.

$$3 + 2i$$

    a. $\sqrt{13} \text{ cis } \dfrac{\pi}{2}$

    b. $\sqrt{13} \text{ cis } (\tan^{-1} \dfrac{2}{3})$

    c. $\sqrt{13} \text{ cis } \dfrac{2}{3}$

    d. $\sqrt{13} \text{ cis } (\tan \dfrac{2}{3})$

22. Express in the form $a + bi$, where a and b are real numbers.

$$18\left(\cos \frac{\pi}{4} + i \sin \frac{\pi}{4}\right)$$

a. $18\sqrt{2} + 18\sqrt{2}\, i$

b. $9\sqrt{2} - 9\sqrt{2}\, i$

c. $9\sqrt{2} + 9\sqrt{2}\, i$

d. $9\sqrt{3} + 9\, i$

23. Use trigonometric forms to find $z_1 z_2$ and z_1/z_2.

$$z_1 = -4 + i,\ z_2 = 4 + i$$

a.
$$z_1 z_2 = -17,\ \frac{z_1}{z_2} = -\frac{15}{17} + \frac{8}{17}\, i$$

b.
$$z_1 z_2 = -17,\ \frac{z_1}{z_2} = \frac{15}{17} - \frac{8}{17}\, i$$

c.
$$z_1 z_2 = 17,\ \frac{z_1}{z_2} = \frac{15}{17} + \frac{8}{17}\, i$$

d.
$$z_1 z_2 = 17,\ \frac{z_1}{z_2} = 15 + 8\, i$$

24. Use De Moivre's theorem to change the given complex number to the form $a + bi$, where a and b are real numbers.

$$\left(\sqrt{3} + i\right)^{11}$$

a. $1024\sqrt{3} - 1024\,i$

b. $1024\sqrt{3} + 1024\,i$

c. $- 1024\sqrt{3} - 1024\,i$

d. $- 1024\sqrt{3} + 1024\,i$

25. Find the solutions of the equation.

$$x^6 + 729 = 0$$

a. $3i, \; -3i, \; \dfrac{3}{2} + \dfrac{3\sqrt{3}\,i}{2}, \; \dfrac{3}{2} - \dfrac{3\sqrt{3}\,i}{2}, \; -\dfrac{3}{2} + \dfrac{3\sqrt{3}\,i}{2}, \; -\dfrac{3}{2} - \dfrac{3\sqrt{3}\,i}{2}$

b. $3i, \; -3i, \; \dfrac{3\sqrt{3}}{2} + \dfrac{3i}{2}, \; \dfrac{3\sqrt{3}}{2} - \dfrac{3i}{2}, \; -\dfrac{3\sqrt{3}}{2} + \dfrac{3i}{2}, \; -\dfrac{3\sqrt{3}}{2} - \dfrac{3i}{2}$

c. $6i, \; -6i, \; 3 + 3\sqrt{3}\,i, \; 3 - 3\sqrt{3}\,i, \; -3 + 3\sqrt{3}\,i, \; -3 - 3\sqrt{3}\,i$

d. $6i, \; -6i, \; 3\sqrt{3} + 3i, \; 3\sqrt{3} - 3i, \; -3\sqrt{3} + 3i, \; -3\sqrt{3} - 3i$

1. Solve $\triangle ABC$ $a = 10.0$, $b = 15.0$, $c = 12.0$

   a. $48^{\,0}$, $85^{\,0}$, $53^{\,0}$

   b. $48^{\,0}$, $82^{\,0}$, $51^{\,0}$

   c. $42^{\,0}$, $85^{\,0}$, $53^{\,0}$

   d. $42^{\,0}$, $82^{\,0}$, $51^{\,0}$

2. Two automobiles leave a city at the same time and travel along straight highways that differ in direction by $84^{\,0}$. If their speeds are 60 mi/hr and 45 mi/hr, respectively, approximately how far apart are the cars at the end of 30 minutes?

   a.   33 mi

   b.   42 mi

   c.   38 mi

   d.   36 mi

3. An airplane flies 165 miles from point A in the direction $130^{\,0}$ and then travels in the direction $245^{\,0}$ for 70 miles. Approximately how far is the airplane from A?

   a.   147 mi

   b.   156 mi

   c.   152 mi

   d.   150 mi

4. A jogger runs at a constant speed of one mile every 8 minutes in the direction S40°E for 36 minutes and then in the direction N20°E for the next 16 minutes. Approximate, to the nearest tenth of a mile, the straight line distance from the endpoint to the starting point of the jogger's course.

    a.   2.9 mi

    b.   4.1 mi

    c.   5.2 mi

    d.   3.9 mi

5. Approximate the area of triangle ABC: $\alpha = 60^{\circ}$, $b = 20$, $c = 30$

    a.   260

    b.   520

    c.   150

    d.   212

6. A triangular field has sides of lengths a, b, and c (in yards). Approximate the number of acres in the field (1 acre = 4840 yd^2).

$$a = 300, \; b = 350, \; c = 500$$

    a.   10.67 acres

    b.   11.00 acres

    c.   11.87 acres

    d.   10.06 acres

7. Find $\| \mathbf{a} \|$.

$$\mathbf{a} = -\langle 9, -7 \rangle$$

    a. $\| \mathbf{a} \| = \sqrt{133}$

    b. $\| \mathbf{a} \| = \sqrt{130}$

    c. $\| \mathbf{a} \| = \sqrt{128}$

    d. $\| \mathbf{a} \| = \sqrt{129}$

8. Find $5\,\mathbf{a} - 5\,\mathbf{b}$.

$$\mathbf{a} = \mathbf{i} + 3\,\mathbf{j},\ \mathbf{b} = 5\,\mathbf{i} - 2\,\mathbf{j}$$

a. $-\ 18\mathbf{i}\ +\ 23\mathbf{j}$

b. $-\ 17\mathbf{i}\ +\ 22\mathbf{j}$

c. $-\ 20\mathbf{i}\ +\ 25\mathbf{j}$

d. $-\ 21\mathbf{i}\ +\ 26\mathbf{j}$

9. Find the smallest positive angle θ from the positive x-axis to the vector OP that corresponds to **a**.

$$\mathbf{a} = <-5, -5>$$

a. $\theta = \dfrac{3\pi}{4}$

b. $\theta = \dfrac{5\pi}{4}$

c. $\theta = \dfrac{\pi}{4}$

10. Find the magnitude of the vector **a**.

$$\mathbf{a} = -7\,\mathbf{i} + 6\,\mathbf{j}$$

a. $\sqrt{85}$

b. $\sqrt{88}$

c. $\sqrt{84}$

d. $\sqrt{83}$

11. A quarterback releases a football with a speed of 55 ft/sec at an angle of 35° with the horizontal. Approximate the horizontal component of the vector that is described.

    a.   41.45 ft/sec

    b.   43.85 ft/sec

    c.   43.25 ft/sec

    d.   45.05 ft/sec

12. Find a unit vector that has the same direction as the vector **a**.

$$a = \langle 0, 6 \rangle$$

    a. $\langle 1, -6 \rangle$

    b. $\langle 1, 1 \rangle$

    c. $\langle 0, 1 \rangle$

    d. $\langle 1, 0 \rangle$

13. Find a vector that has the opposite direction of 2 **i** - 7 **j** and four times the magnitude.

    a. $-$ **8i** + **28j**

    b. $-$ **11i** + **31j**

    c. $-$ **7i** + **27j**

    d. $-$ **10i** + **30j**

14. If forces F_1, F_2,..., F_n act at a point P, the net (or resultant) force F is the sum $F_1 + F_2 + \cdots + F_n$. If $F = 0$ the forces are said to be in equilibrium. The given forces act at the origin O of an xy-plane. Find an additional force G such that equilibrium occurs.

$$F_1 = \langle 5, 7 \rangle, \ F_2 = \langle -9, -9 \rangle, \ F_3 = \langle 5, 9 \rangle$$

   a. $\langle -1, -7 \rangle$

   b. $\langle -2, -6 \rangle$

   c. $\langle -4, -10 \rangle$

   d. $\langle -3, -9 \rangle$

15. Find the dot product of the two vectors $\langle -5, \ 7 \rangle$ and $\langle 9, \ 9 \rangle$.

   a.   108

   b.   18

   c.   116

   d.   46

16. Find the angle between the two vectors $8\,\mathbf{i} - \mathbf{j}$ and $-10\,\mathbf{i} + 4\,\mathbf{j}$.

   a. $255°\ 32'$

   b. $75°\ 19'$

   c. $165°\ 19'$

   d. $75°\ 32'$

17. Find the angle between the two vectors $\langle -3, \ 8 \rangle$ and $\langle -9, \ 10 \rangle$.

    a. $111° \ 26'$

    b. $21° \ 26'$

    c. $111° \ 43'$

    d. $201° \ 43'$

18. Determine m such that the two vectors are orthogonal.

$$5\,\mathbf{i} - 8\,\mathbf{j} \text{ and } 7\,\mathbf{i} + 4\,m\mathbf{j}$$

    a. $\dfrac{35}{32}$

    b. $\dfrac{40}{28}$

    c. $-\dfrac{40}{28}$

    d. $-\dfrac{35}{32}$

19. Given that $\mathbf{a} = \langle 1, \ -4 \rangle$, $\mathbf{b} = \langle 5, \ 3 \rangle$, and $\mathbf{c} = \langle -3, \ 2 \rangle$, find the number $(\mathbf{a} - \mathbf{b}) \cdot (\mathbf{b} + \mathbf{c})$.

    a.   -23

    b.   -43

    c.   27

    d.   3

20. If **c** represents a constant force, find the work done if the point of application of **c** moves along the line segment from P to Q.

$$\mathbf{c} = 4\,\mathbf{i} + 4\,\mathbf{j} \text{ and } P(0, 0),\ Q(5, -3)$$

   a.   32

   b.   1

   c.   8

   d.   -8

21. Express the complex number in trigonometric form with $0 \leq \theta \leq 2\pi$.

$$9 + 8i$$

   a. $\sqrt{145}\ \text{cis}\left(\tan^{-1}\dfrac{8}{9}\right)$

   b. $\sqrt{145}\ \text{cis}\ \dfrac{8}{9}$

   c. $\sqrt{145}\ \text{cis}\left(\tan\dfrac{8}{9}\right)$

   d. $\sqrt{145}\ \text{cis}\ \dfrac{\pi}{2}$

22. Express in the form $a + bi$, where a and b are real numbers. $\quad 8\left(\cos\dfrac{\pi}{4} + i\sin\dfrac{\pi}{4}\right)$

   a. $8\sqrt{2} + 8\sqrt{2}\,i$

   b. $4\sqrt{2} + 4\sqrt{2}\,i$

   c. $4\sqrt{2} - 4\sqrt{2}\,i$

   d. $4\sqrt{3} + 4i$

23. Use trigonometric forms to find $z_1 z_2$ and z_1/z_2.

$$z_1 = -6 + i, \, z_2 = 6 + i$$

a.
$$z_1 z_2 = -37, \quad \frac{z_1}{z_2} = \frac{35}{37} - \frac{12}{37} i$$

b.
$$z_1 z_2 = 37, \quad \frac{z_1}{z_2} = 35 + 12 i$$

c.
$$z_1 z_2 = -37, \quad \frac{z_1}{z_2} = -\frac{35}{37} + \frac{12}{37} i$$

d.
$$z_1 z_2 = 37, \quad \frac{z_1}{z_2} = \frac{35}{37} + \frac{12}{37} i$$

24. Use De Moivre's theorem to change the given complex number to the form $a + bi$, where a and b are real numbers.

$$\left(\sqrt{3} + i \right)^{13}$$

a. $-4096 \sqrt{3} + 4096 i$

b. $4096 \sqrt{3} + 4096 i$

c. $4096 \sqrt{3} - 4096 i$

d. $-4096 \sqrt{3} - 4096 i$

25. Find the solutions of the equation.

$$x^6 + 64 = 0$$

a. $2i, \, -2i, \, \dfrac{2}{2} + \dfrac{2\sqrt{3}\,i}{2}, \, \dfrac{2}{2} - \dfrac{2\sqrt{3}\,i}{2}, \, -\dfrac{2}{2} + \dfrac{2\sqrt{3}\,i}{2}, \, -\dfrac{2}{2} - \dfrac{2\sqrt{3}\,i}{2}$

b. $4i, \, -4i, \, 2\sqrt{3} + 2i, \, 2\sqrt{3} - 2i, \, -2\sqrt{3} + 2i, \, -2\sqrt{3} - 2i$

c. $4i, \, -4i, \, 2 + 2\sqrt{3}\,i, \, 2 - 2\sqrt{3}\,i, \, -2 + 2\sqrt{3}\,i, \, -2 - 2\sqrt{3}\,i$

d. $2i, \, -2i, \, \dfrac{2\sqrt{3}}{2} + \dfrac{2i}{2}, \, \dfrac{2\sqrt{3}}{2} - \dfrac{2i}{2}, \, -\dfrac{2\sqrt{3}}{2} + \dfrac{2i}{2}, \, -\dfrac{2\sqrt{3}}{2} - \dfrac{2i}{2}$

1. Two automobiles leave a city at the same time and travel along straight highways that differ in direction by 84^0. If their speeds are 60 mi/hr and 45 mi/hr, respectively, approximately how far apart are the cars at the end of 30 minutes?

   a.   34 mi

   b.   42 mi

   c.   36 mi

   d.   33 mi

2. A jogger runs at a constant speed of one mile every 8 minutes in the direction S40^{0}E for 28 minutes and then in the direction N20^{0}E for the next 16 minutes. Approximate, to the nearest tenth of a mile, the straight line distance from the endpoint to the starting point of the jogger's course.

   a.   4.3 mi

   b.   3.0 mi

   c.   4.0 mi

   d.   2.8 mi

3. A triangular field has sides of lengths a, b, and c (in yards). Approximate the number of acres in the field (1 acre = 4840 yd^2).

$$a = 320 , b = 350 , c = 500$$

   a.   11.17 acres

   b.   10.89 acres

   c.   11.50 acres

   d.   10.30 acres

4. Find 4 **a** - 6 **b**.

$$\mathbf{a} = \mathbf{i} + 5\,\mathbf{j}, \mathbf{b} = 3\,\mathbf{i} - 4\,\mathbf{j}$$

    a.   – **11i** + **41j**

    b.   – **15i** + **45j**

    c.   – **12i** + **42j**

    d.   – **14i** + **44j**

5. Find the magnitude of the vector **a**.

$$\mathbf{a} = -6\,\mathbf{i} + 7\,\mathbf{j}$$

    a. $\sqrt{82}$

    b. $\sqrt{87}$

    c. $\sqrt{85}$

    d. $\sqrt{84}$

6. Find a unit vector that has the same direction as the vector **a**. $\mathbf{a} = \langle 0, 4 \rangle$

    a. $\langle 1, -4 \rangle$

    b. $\langle 1, 0 \rangle$

    c. $\langle 0, 1 \rangle$

    d. $\langle 1, 1 \rangle$

7. If forces F_1, F_2,..., F_n act at a point P, the net (or resultant) force F is the sum $F_1 + F_2 + \cdots + F_n$. If $F = 0$ the forces are said to be in equilibrium. The given forces act at the origin O of an xy-plane. Find an additional force G such that equilibrium occurs.

$$F_1 = \langle 7, 3 \rangle, F_2 = \langle -2, -4 \rangle, F_3 = \langle 8, 4 \rangle$$

   a. $\langle -11, -1 \rangle$

   b. $\langle -14, -4 \rangle$

   c. $\langle -13, -3 \rangle$

   d. $\langle -10, -6 \rangle$

8. Find the angle between the two vectors $5\,i - j$ and $-6\,i + 10\,j$.

   a. $222° \, 27'$

   b. $42° \, 27'$

   c. $42° \, 16'$

   d. $132° \, 16'$

9. Determine m such that the two vectors are orthogonal. $3\,i - 4\,j$ and $5\,i + 2\,m j$

   a. $-\dfrac{15}{8}$

   b. $-\dfrac{12}{10}$

   c. $\dfrac{12}{10}$

   d. $\dfrac{15}{8}$

10. If **c** represents a constant force, find the work done if the point of application of **c** moves along the line segment from P to Q.

$$\mathbf{c} = 7\mathbf{i} + 4\mathbf{j} \text{ and } P(0, 0), Q(3, -2)$$

    a.   22

    b.   29

    c.   13

    d.   2

11. Express in the form $a + bi$, where a and b are real numbers.

$$18\left(\cos \frac{\top}{4} + i \sin \frac{\top}{4}\right)$$

    a. $9\sqrt{2} - 9\sqrt{2}\,i$

    b. $9\sqrt{3} + 9\,i$

    c. $9\sqrt{2} + 9\sqrt{2}\,i$

    d. $18\sqrt{2} + 18\sqrt{2}\,i$

12. Use De Moivre's theorem to change the given complex number to the form $a + bi$, where a and b are real numbers.

$$\left(\sqrt{3} + i\right)^5$$

    a. $16\sqrt{3} + 16\,i$

    b. $-16\sqrt{3} + 16\,i$

    c. $-16\sqrt{3} - 16\,i$

    d. $16\sqrt{3} - 16\,i$

13. Solve $\triangle ABC$

$$a = 2.0 , b = 3.0 , c = 3.5$$

angle α: _____ $^\circ$

angle β: _____ $^\circ$

angle γ: _____ $^\circ$

14. An airplane flies 165 miles from point A in the direction 130° and then travels in the direction 245° for 85 miles. Approximately how far is the airplane from A? Round the answer to the nearest integer.

15. Given that $a = \langle 4, -5 \rangle$, $b = \langle 3, 2 \rangle$, and $c = \langle -3, 4 \rangle$, find the number $(a - b) \cdot (b + c)$.

16. A triangular field has sides of lengths a, b, and c (in yards). Approximate the number of acres in the field (1 acre = 4840 yd^2).

$$a = 320 , b = 350 , c = 500$$

17. Find $6\,a - 2\,b$.

$$a = i + 6\,j, \ b = 4\,i - 3\,j$$

18. Find the magnitude of the vector a.

$$a = -8\,i + 7\,j$$

19. Find a unit vector that has the same direction as the vector **a**. $\mathbf{a} = \langle 0, 4 \rangle$

20. If forces $\mathbf{F}_1$, $\mathbf{F}_2$,..., $\mathbf{F}_n$ act at a point P, the net (or resultant) force $\mathbf{F}$ is the sum $\mathbf{F}_1 + \mathbf{F}_2 + \cdots + \mathbf{F}_n$. If $\mathbf{F} = 0$ the forces are said to be in equilibrium. The given forces act at the origin O of an xy-plane. Find an additional force **G** such that equilibrium occurs.

$$\mathbf{F}_1 = \langle 5, 7 \rangle, \ \mathbf{F}_2 = \langle -3, -9 \rangle, \ \mathbf{F}_3 = \langle 5, 3 \rangle$$

21. Find the angle between the two vectors 10**i** - **j** and -2**i** + 2**j**.

22. Determine m such that the two vectors are orthogonal.   5**i** - 2**j** and 3**i** + 4m**j**

23. Express the complex number in trigonometric form with $0 \leq \theta \leq 2\pi$.

$$5 + 4i$$

24. Use trigonometric forms to find $z_1 z_2$ and z_1/z_2: $z_1 = -2 + i$, $z_2 = 2 + i$

25. Find the solutions of the equation: $x^6 + 1 = 0$

1. Two automobiles leave a city at the same time and travel along straight highways that differ in direction by 84 ^{0}. If their speeds are 60 mi/hr and 45 mi/hr, respectively, approximately how far apart are the cars at the end of 30 minutes?

      a.   30 mi

      b.   36 mi

      c.   38 mi

      d.   39 mi

2. A jogger runs at a constant speed of one mile every 8 minutes in the direction S40 ^{0} E for 24 minutes and then in the direction N20 ^{0} E for the next 16 minutes. Approximate, to the nearest tenth of a mile, the straight line distance from the endpoint to the starting point of the jogger's course.

      a.   1.3 mi

      b.   3.6 mi

      c.   2.6 mi

      d.   2.4 mi

3. A triangular field has sides of lengths a, b, and c (in yards). Approximate the number of acres in the field (1 acre = 4840 yd^2).

$$a = 320 , b = 350 , c = 500$$

Select the correct answer. The choices have been rounded to the nearest hundredth.

      a.   12.70 acres

      b.   11.50 acres

      c.   11.83 acres

      d.   12.11 acres

4. Find 2 **a** - 6 **b**.

$$\mathbf{a} = \mathbf{i} + 6\,\mathbf{j},\ \mathbf{b} = 3\,\mathbf{i} - 5\,\mathbf{j}$$

    a.   − 14i + 40j

    b.   − 19i + 45j

    c.   − 15i + 41j

    d.   − 16i + 42j

5. Find the magnitude of the vector **a**.

$$\mathbf{a} = -8\,\mathbf{i} + 7\,\mathbf{j}$$

    a. $\sqrt{116}$

    b. $\sqrt{111}$

    c. $\sqrt{113}$

    d. $\sqrt{114}$

6. Find a unit vector that has the same direction as the vector **a**.

$\mathbf{a} = \langle 0, 4 \rangle$

    a. $\langle 0, 1 \rangle$

    b. $\langle 1, 0 \rangle$

    c. $\langle 1, -4 \rangle$

    d. $\langle 1, 1 \rangle$

7. If forces F_1, F_2,..., F_n act at a point P, the net (or resultant) force F is the sum $F_1 + F_2 + \cdots + F_n$. If $F = 0$ the forces are said to be in equilibrium. The given forces act at the origin O of an xy-plane. Find an additional force G such that equilibrium occurs.
$F_1 = \langle 8, 9 \rangle$, $F_2 = \langle -3, -9 \rangle$, $F_3 = \langle 7, 5 \rangle$

  a. $\langle -11, -4 \rangle$

  b. $\langle -12, -5 \rangle$

  c. $\langle -10, -3 \rangle$

  d. $\langle -15, -8 \rangle$

8. Find the angle between the two vectors $4\,i - j$ and $-9\,i + 6\,j$.

  a. $160°\ 21'$

  b. $250°\ 35'$

  c. $70°\ 21'$

  d. $70°\ 35'$

9. Determine m such that the two vectors are orthogonal.
$$9\,i - 8\,j \text{ and } 3\,i + 2\,mj$$

  a. $\dfrac{72}{6}$

  b. $-\dfrac{72}{6}$

  c. $-\dfrac{27}{16}$

  d. $\dfrac{27}{16}$

10. If **c** represents a constant force, find the work done if the point of application of **c** moves along the line segment from P to Q.

$$\mathbf{c} = 4\,\mathbf{i} + 2\,\mathbf{j} \text{ and } P(0, 0),\ Q(1, -4)$$

    a.   4

    b.   12

    c.   -4

    d.   14

11. Express in the form $a + bi$, where a and b are real numbers.

$$18\left(\cos \frac{\pi}{4} + i \sin \frac{\pi}{4}\right)$$

    a. $9\sqrt{3} + 9i$

    b. $9\sqrt{2} + 9\sqrt{2}\,i$

    c. $18\sqrt{2} + 18\sqrt{2}\,i$

    d. $9\sqrt{2} - 9\sqrt{2}\,i$

12. Use De Moivre's theorem to change the given complex number to the form $a + bi$, where a and b are real numbers.

$$\left(\sqrt{3} + i\right)^{11}$$

    a. $-1024\sqrt{3} - 1024\,i$

    b. $1024\sqrt{3} + 1024\,i$

    c. $1024\sqrt{3} - 1024\,i$

    d. $-1024\sqrt{3} + 1024\,i$

13. Solve $\triangle ABC$

$$a = 2.0 \ , \ b = 3.0 \ , \ c = 3.5$$

angle α: _____ $^{\circ}$
angle β: _____ $^{\circ}$
angle γ: _____ $^{\circ}$

14. An airplane flies 165 miles from point A in the direction 130° and then travels in the direction 245° for 70 miles. Approximately how far is the airplane from A? Round the answer to the nearest integer.

15. Given that $\mathbf{a} = \langle 3, \ -5 \rangle$, $\mathbf{b} = \langle 1, \ 1 \rangle$, and $\mathbf{c} = \langle -1, \ 1 \rangle$, find the number $(\mathbf{a} - \mathbf{b}) \cdot (\mathbf{b} + \mathbf{c})$.

16. A triangular field has sides of lengths a, b, and c (in yards). Approximate the number of acres in the field (1 acre = 4840 yd^2).

$$a = 300 \ , \ b = 350 \ , \ c = 500$$

17. Find $5\,\mathbf{a} - 5\,\mathbf{b}$:　　$\mathbf{a} = \mathbf{i} + 6\,\mathbf{j}, \mathbf{b} = 4\,\mathbf{i} - 4\,\mathbf{j}$

18. Find the magnitude of the vector $\mathbf{a}$:　　$\mathbf{a} = -4\,\mathbf{i} + 5\,\mathbf{j}$

19. Find a unit vector that has the same direction as the vector $\mathbf{a}$.
$\mathbf{a} = \langle 0, 6 \rangle$

20. If forces F_1, F_2,..., F_n act at a point P, the net (or resultant) force F is the sum $F_1 + F_2 + \cdots + F_n$. If $F = 0$ the forces are said to be in equilibrium. The given forces act at the origin O of an xy-plane. Find an additional force G such that equilibrium occurs.

$$F_1 = \langle 8, 6 \rangle, \; F_2 = \langle -6, -5 \rangle, \; F_3 = \langle 8, 7 \rangle$$

21. Find the angle between the two vectors $8\mathbf{i} - \mathbf{j}$ and $-7\mathbf{i} + 2\mathbf{j}$.

22. Determine m such that the two vectors are orthogonal: $9\mathbf{i} - 4\mathbf{j}$ and $3\mathbf{i} + 2m\mathbf{j}$

23. Express the complex number in trigonometric form with $0 \le \theta \le 2\pi$.

$$5 + 4i$$

24. Use trigonometric forms to find $z_1 z_2$ and z_1/z_2: $z_1 = -6 + i$, $z_2 = 6 + i$

25. Find the solutions of the equation: $x^6 + 729 = 0$

Test Form 7-A

1. -56
   $21°$
2. $32°$
   $127°$
3. 12 mi
4. 151
5. 3.5
6. 234
7. 9.80
8. $\sqrt{106}$
9. $-3i+37j$
10. $\dfrac{5\pi}{4}$
11. $\sqrt{61}$
12. 51.68
13. $\langle 0, 1\rangle$
14. $\langle -27, 27\rangle$
15. $\langle -7, -8\rangle$
16. 6
17. $167, 28$
18. $17, 19$
19. $\dfrac{21}{16}$
20. -12
21. $\sqrt{113}\cdot\text{cis}\left(\arctan\left(\dfrac{7}{8}\right)\right)$
22. $-5, -\dfrac{3}{5}+\dfrac{4i}{5}$
23. $4096\sqrt{3}+4096i$
24. $2i, -1-2i, \dfrac{2\sqrt{3}}{2}+\dfrac{2i}{2}, \dfrac{2\sqrt{3}}{2}-\dfrac{2i}{2}, \dfrac{-1\cdot2\sqrt{3}}{2}+\dfrac{2i}{2}, \dfrac{-1\cdot2\sqrt{3}}{2}-\dfrac{2i}{2}$
25. $9\sqrt{2}+9\sqrt{2}\cdot i$

Test Form 7-B

1. -27
   35°
2. 59°
   86°
3. 24 mi
4. 150
5. 3.5
6. 242
7. 11.30
8. $\sqrt{85}$
9. -18i+60j
10. $\dfrac{7}{4}$
11. $\sqrt{61}$
12. 36.25
13. $\langle 0, 1 \rangle$
14. $\langle -4, 8 \rangle$
15. $\langle -6, -6 \rangle$
16. 2
17. 147,3
18. 6,7
19. $\dfrac{15}{16}$
20. 15
21. $\sqrt{145} \cdot \text{cis}\left(\arctan\left(\dfrac{8}{9} \right) \right)$
22. $-17, -\dfrac{15}{17} + \dfrac{8i}{17}$
23. $-16\sqrt{3} + 16i$
24. $2i, -1 \cdot 2i, \dfrac{2\sqrt{3}}{2} + \dfrac{2i}{2}, \dfrac{2\sqrt{3}}{2} - \dfrac{2i}{2}, \dfrac{-1 \cdot 2\sqrt{3}}{2} + \dfrac{2i}{2}, \dfrac{-1 \cdot 2\sqrt{3}}{2} - \dfrac{2i}{2}$
25. $3\sqrt{2} + 3\sqrt{2} \cdot i$

Test Form 7-C

1. d	**2.** c	**3.** c	**4.** a	**5.** b	**6.** c	**7.** b	**8.** a	**9.** a
10. b	**11.** d	**12.** c	**13.** c	**14.** c	**15.** d	**16.** a	**17.** d	**18.** d
19. b	**20.** b	**21.** b	**22.** c	**23.** a	**24.** a	**25.** b		

Test Form 7-D

1. c	**2.** d	**3.** d	**4.** d	**5.** a	**6.** a	**7.** b	**8.** c	**9.** b
10. a	**11.** d	**12.** c	**13.** a	**14.** a	**15.** b	**16.** c	**17.** b	**18.** a
19. b	**20.** c	**21.** a	**22.** b	**23.** c	**24.** b	**25.** d		

Test Form 7-E

1. c
2. b
3. c
4. d
5. c
6. c
7. c
8. d
9. d
10. c
11. c
12. b
13. 35°
    59°
    86°
14. 150
15. -42
16. 11.50
17. $\langle -2, 42 \rangle$
18. $\sqrt{113}$
19. $\langle 0, 1 \rangle$
20. $\langle -7, -1 \rangle$
21. 140,43
22. $\dfrac{15}{8}$
23. $\sqrt{41} \cdot \text{cis}\left(\arctan\left(\dfrac{4}{5} \right) \right)$
24. $-5, -\dfrac{3}{5} + \dfrac{4i}{5}$

25. $i, -1 \cdot 1i, \dfrac{\sqrt{3}}{2} + \dfrac{i}{2}, \dfrac{\sqrt{3}}{2} - \dfrac{i}{2}, \dfrac{-1 \cdot 1\sqrt{3}}{2} + \dfrac{i}{2}, \dfrac{-1 \cdot 1\sqrt{3}}{2} - \dfrac{i}{2}$

Test Form 7-F

1. b
2. c
3. b
4. d
5. c
6. a
7. b
8. a
9. d
10. c
11. b
12. c
13. 35°
    59°
    86°
14. 150
15. -12
16. 10.67
17. $\langle -15, 50 \rangle$
18. $\sqrt{41}$
19. $\langle 0, 1 \rangle$
20. $\langle -10, -8 \rangle$
21. 171,11
22. $\dfrac{27}{8}$
23. $\sqrt{41} \cdot \text{cis}\left(\arctan\left(\dfrac{4}{5} \right) \right)$
24. $-37, -\dfrac{35}{37} + \dfrac{12i}{37}$
25. $3i, -1\cdot 3i, \dfrac{3\sqrt{3}}{2} + \dfrac{3i}{2}, \dfrac{3\sqrt{3}}{2} - \dfrac{3i}{2}, \dfrac{-1\cdot 3\sqrt{3}}{2} + \dfrac{3i}{2}, \dfrac{-1\cdot 3\sqrt{3}}{2} - \dfrac{3i}{2}$

1. Use Cramer's rule to solve the system.

$$\begin{cases} x - 6y - 3z = -1 \\ 6x + y + z = 8 \\ x + 3y - 6z = 71 \end{cases}$$

If the equations of the system are dependent, or if a system is inconsistent, so indicate.

2. Find the inverse of the matrix if it exists.

$$\begin{bmatrix} 1 & 5 & 6 \\ -5 & 1 & 0 \\ 6 & -1 & 1 \end{bmatrix}$$

3. Find the maximum and minimum values of the objective function

$$C = 4x + 2y + 4$$

on the region bordered by the polygon in the figure.

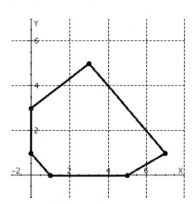

4. Use the method of substitution to solve the system

$$\begin{cases} x + 3y = 35 \\ x^2 + y^2 = 1225 \end{cases}$$

5. Solve the system.

$$\begin{cases} 2x + 9y = 7 \\ 3x + 2y = 5 \end{cases}$$

6. Solve the system.

$$\begin{cases} 2x - 7y = 10 \\ -4x + 14y = 12 \end{cases}$$

If the system is dependent or inconsistent, indicate as such.

7. The price of admission to a high school play was $2 for students and $5 for nonstudents. If 400 tickets were sold for a total of $1550, how many of each kind were purchased?

number of students: _____

number of nonstudents: _____

8. A silversmith has two alloys, one containing 35% silver and the other 85% silver. How much of each should be melted and combined to obtain 900 grams of an alloy containing 50% silver?

First alloy (35%): _____ g

Second alloy (85%): _____ g

9. A small furniture company manufactures sofas and recliners. Each sofa requires 11 hours of labor and $65 in materials, while a recliner can be built for $30 in 5 hours. The company has 370 hours of labor available each week and can afford to buy $2200 worth of materials. How many sofas and recliners can be produced if all labor hours and all materials must be used?

_____ sofas

_____ recliners

10. Sketch the graph of the inequality

$$y + 2 < x^2$$

11. R is determined by the constraints:

$$x - 6y \geq -24,$$

$$9x - 26y \leq 36,$$
$$x + y \geq 4$$

Find the maximum value of

$$C = 4x - 2y$$

on R.

12. Region R is determined by the constraints:

$$y \geq 0,$$

$$3x + y \geq 3,$$
$$x + 5y \leq 15,$$
$$2x + y \leq 12$$

Find the minimum value of

$$C = 9x + y$$

on R.

13. Use matrices to solve the system.
$$\begin{cases} 2x - 3y - z = 2 \\ 3x + 2y + z = -5 \\ 5x - 2y - z = 0 \end{cases}$$
If the equations of the system are dependent, or if the system is inconsistent, so indicate.

14. Use matrices to solve the system.

$$\begin{cases} 5x + 4y = 39 \\ x - 4y = 3 \\ x + y = -4 \end{cases}$$

If the equations of the system are dependent, or if a system is inconsistent, so indicate.

15. Find -3*B* if:

$$B = \begin{bmatrix} -3 & 7 \\ -7 & 6 \\ 8 & 9 \end{bmatrix}$$

16. Find *A - B* if:

$$A = \begin{bmatrix} 0 & -2 & 2 \\ 5 & 4 & -2 \end{bmatrix}, B = \begin{bmatrix} 8 & -3 & 0 \\ 0 & 7 & 2 \end{bmatrix}$$

17. Let

$$A = \begin{bmatrix} 4 & -5 & 9 \\ -5 & 5 & 4 \end{bmatrix} \text{ and } B = \begin{bmatrix} 2 & 1 \\ 0 & 1 \\ -4 & 7 \end{bmatrix}$$

Find *AB*.

18. Find the inverse of the matrix if it exists.

$$\begin{bmatrix} 5 & 8 \\ 10 & 16 \end{bmatrix}$$

19. Solve the system

$$\begin{cases} 9x + 2y = 4 \\ 4x + 3y = 9 \end{cases}$$

using the inverse method.

20. Find the determinant of the matrix.

$$\begin{bmatrix} 5 & 9 & -8 \\ 9 & 1 & 5 \\ -4 & 8 & 0 \end{bmatrix}$$

21. Find the determinant of the matrix.

$$\begin{bmatrix} 32 & -22 & 82 \\ -30 & 90 & -40 \\ 48 & 4 & 12 \end{bmatrix}$$

22. Find the determinant of the matrix after introducing zeros.

$$\begin{bmatrix} 7 & 1 & -2 & 2 \\ 2 & 0 & 1 & 3 \\ 0 & 1 & 7 & 8 \\ -1 & 2 & 0 & -7 \end{bmatrix}$$

23. Find the partial fraction decomposition.

$$\frac{x + 73}{x^2 - 6x - 7}$$

24. Sketch the graph of the system of inequalities

$$\begin{cases} x + y < 3 \\ 4 - y < 2x \end{cases}$$

25. Find a system of inequalities whose graph is shown.

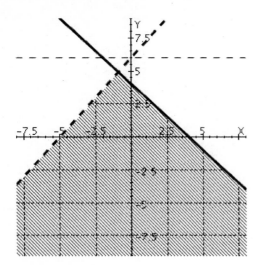

1. Use Cramer's rule to solve the system.

$$\begin{cases} x - 8y - 5z = -6 \\ 8x + y + z = 7 \\ x + 5y - 8z = 61 \end{cases}$$

If the equations of the system are dependent, or if a system is inconsistent, so indicate.

2. Find the inverse of the matrix if it exists.

$$\begin{bmatrix} 1 & 3 & 4 \\ -3 & 1 & 0 \\ 4 & -1 & 1 \end{bmatrix}$$

3. Find the maximum and minimum values of the objective function

$$C = 5x + 4y + 7$$

on the region bordered by the polygon in the figure.

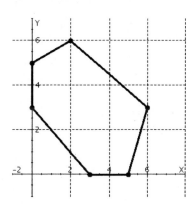

4. Use the method of substitution to solve the system

$$\begin{cases} x + 2y = 25 \\ x^2 + y^2 = 625 \end{cases}$$

5. Solve the system.

$$\begin{cases} 5x - 6y = 4 \\ 3x + 7y = 8 \end{cases}$$

6. Solve the system.

$$\begin{cases} 3x - 5y = 10 \\ -6x + 10y = 14 \end{cases}$$

If the system is dependent or inconsistent, indicate as such.

7. The price of admission to a high school play was $5 for students and $7 for nonstudents. If 450 tickets were sold for a total of $2774, how many of each kind were purchased?

number of students: _____

number of nonstudents: _____

8. A silversmith has two alloys, one containing 40% silver and the other 60% silver. How much of each should be melted and combined to obtain 900 grams of an alloy containing 50% silver?

First alloy (40%): _____ g

Second alloy (60%): _____ g

9. A small furniture company manufactures sofas and recliners. Each sofa requires 12 hours of labor and $65 in materials, while a recliner can be built for $40 in 5 hours. The company has 475 hours of labor available each week and can afford to buy $3025 worth of materials. How many sofas and recliners can be produced if all labor hours and all materials must be used?

_____ sofas

_____ recliners

10. Sketch the graph of the inequality

$$y + 2 < x^2$$

11. *R* is determined by the constraints:

$$x - 7y \geq -28,$$

$$5x - 3y \leq 20,$$
$$x + y \geq 4$$

Find the maximum value of

$$C = 4x - 2y$$

on *R*.

12. Region *R* is determined by the constraints:

$$y \geq 0,$$

$$3x + y \geq 3,$$
$$x + 5y \leq 15,$$
$$2x + y \leq 12$$

Find the minimum value of

$$C = 8x + y$$

on *R*.

13. Use matrices to solve the system.
$$\begin{cases} 2x - 3y + z = 3 \\ 3x + 2y - z = -7 \\ 5x - 2y + z = 0 \end{cases}$$
If the equations of the system are dependent, or if the system is inconsistent, so indicate.

14. Use matrices to solve the system.

$$\begin{cases} 3x + 5y = 36 \\ x - 2y = 1 \\ x + y = -2 \end{cases}$$

If the equations of the system are dependent, or if a system is inconsistent, so indicate.

15. Find -3*B* if:

$$B = \begin{bmatrix} 6 & 8 \\ -2 & 8 \\ 9 & 6 \end{bmatrix}$$

16. Find *A* - *B* if:

$$A = \begin{bmatrix} 0 & -8 & 3 \\ 5 & 9 & -6 \end{bmatrix}, \ B = \begin{bmatrix} 5 & -5 & 0 \\ 0 & 2 & 1 \end{bmatrix}$$

17. Let

$$A = \begin{bmatrix} 3 & -1 & 6 \\ -2 & 8 & 2 \end{bmatrix} \text{ and } B = \begin{bmatrix} 2 & 1 \\ 0 & 1 \\ -4 & 7 \end{bmatrix}$$

Find *AB*.

18. Find the inverse of the matrix if it exists.

$$\begin{bmatrix} 3 & 6 \\ 6 & 12 \end{bmatrix}$$

19. Solve the system

$$\begin{cases} 7x + 2y = 4 \\ 4x + 5y = 7 \end{cases}$$

using the inverse method.

20. Find the determinant of the matrix.

$$\begin{bmatrix} 9 & 6 & -8 \\ 0 & 4 & 5 \\ -3 & 2 & 9 \end{bmatrix}$$

21. Find the determinant of the matrix.

$$\begin{bmatrix} 34 & -21 & 92 \\ -32 & 85 & -32 \\ 47 & 3 & 10 \end{bmatrix}$$

22. Find the determinant of the matrix after introducing zeros.

$$\begin{bmatrix} 6 & 1 & -4 & 4 \\ 4 & 0 & 1 & 9 \\ 0 & 1 & 6 & 2 \\ -1 & 4 & 0 & -6 \end{bmatrix}$$

23. Find the partial fraction decomposition.

$$\frac{x + 34}{x^2 - 4x - 12}$$

24. Sketch the graph of the system of inequalities

$$\begin{cases} x + y < 3 \\ 4 - y < 2x \end{cases}$$

25. Find a system of inequalities whose graph is shown.

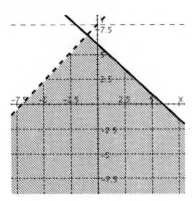

1. Find the maximum and minimum values of the objective function

$$C = 4x + 3y + 3$$

on the region bordered by the polygon in the figure.

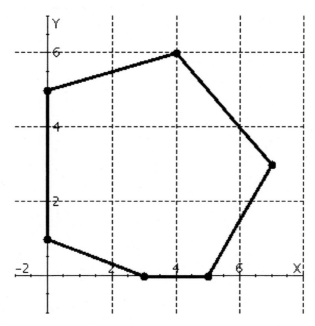

a.   The maximum is 45, the minimum is 6.

b.   The maximum is 40, the minimum is 12.

c.   The maximum is 40, the minimum is 6.

d.   The maximum is 39, the minimum is 9.

2. Sketch the graph of the inequality $y + 6 < x^2$

a.

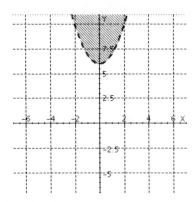

b.

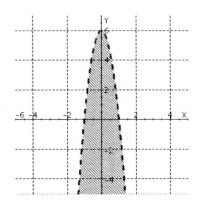

c.

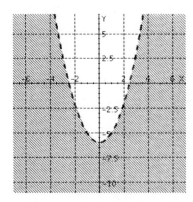

3. Find the partial fraction decomposition. $\dfrac{x + 42}{x^2 - 6x - 16}$

    a. $\dfrac{5}{x - 2} - \dfrac{4}{x + 8}$

    b. $\dfrac{4}{x - 8} - \dfrac{5}{x + 2}$

    c. $\dfrac{5}{x - 8} - \dfrac{4}{x + 2}$

4. Use the method of substitution to solve the system

$$\begin{cases} x + 3y = 10 \\ x^2 + y^2 = 100 \end{cases}$$

    a. $(-8, 6)$

    b.   no solution

    c. $(10, 0)$

    d. $(10, 0), (-8, 6)$

5. Solve the system.

$$\begin{cases} 2x + 8y = 7 \\ 3x - 5y = 4 \end{cases}$$

a. $\left(\dfrac{13}{34}, \dfrac{67}{34} \right)$

b. $\left(\dfrac{67}{34}, \dfrac{13}{34} \right)$

c. $\left(\dfrac{34}{13}, \dfrac{67}{13} \right)$

d. $\left(\dfrac{34}{67}, \dfrac{13}{67} \right)$

e.   no solution

6. Solve the system.
$$\begin{cases} 4x - 13y = 9 \\ -8x + 26y = 12 \end{cases}$$

a.   The system is dependent.

b. $(0, 0)$

c. $(0, \infty)$

d.   The system is inconsistent.

7. The price of admission to a high school play was $2 for students and $5 for nonstudents. If 450 tickets were sold for a total of $1680, how many of each kind were purchased?

   Select the two correct answers.
   a.   205 students

   b.   195 students

   c.   260 nonstudents

   d.   190 students

   e.   245 nonstudents

8. A silversmith has two alloys, one containing 35% silver and the other 55% silver. How much of each should be melted and combined to obtain 1000 grams of an alloy containing 50% silver?

   Select the correct answer(s).
   a.   500 grams

   b.   625 grams

   c.   280 grams

   d.   750 grams

   e.   250 grams

9. A small furniture company manufactures sofas and recliners. Each sofa requires 8 hours of labor and $70 in materials, while a recliner can be built for $25 in 7 hours. The company has 430 hours of labor available each week and can afford to buy $1950 worth of materials. How many recliners and sofas can be produced if all labor hours and all materials must be used?

Select the correct answer(s).
   a.   10 sofas

   b.   50 recliners

   c.   40 recliners

   d.   45 recliners

   e.   15 sofas

10. R is determined by the constraints:

$$x - 3y \geq -12,$$

$$6x - 2y \leq 24,$$
$$x + y \geq 4$$

Find the maximum value of

$$C = 4x - 2y$$

on R.
   a.   maximum of 12

   b.   maximum of 0

   c.   maximum of 5

   d.   maximum of 14

11. Region R is determined by the constraints:

$$y \geq 0,$$
$$3x + y \geq 3,$$
$$x + 5y \leq 15,$$
$$2x + y \leq 12$$

Find the minimum value of

$$C = 9x + y$$

on R.

    a.   minimum of 3 at $(0, 3)$

    b.   minimum of 1 at $(1, 0)$

    c.   minimum of - 9 at $(1, 0)$

    d.   minimum of 9 at $(0, 3)$

12. Use matrices to solve the system.

$$\begin{cases} x - 3y - 3z = -7 \\ 2x + y + z = 7 \\ x + 2y - 3z = 3 \end{cases}$$

    a. $x = -2, y = -6, z = 1$

    b. $x = 2, y = 2, z = 1$

    c.   The system is inconsistent

    d. $x = -2, y = 2, z = 3$

    e. $x = 3, y = 1, z = -1$

    f.   The equations are dependent

13. Use matrices to solve the system.

$$\begin{cases} 3x + 3y = 24 \\ x - 3y = 4 \\ x + y = -7 \end{cases}$$

a. $x = -1$, $y = 6$

b. $x = 5$, $y = -7$

c. $x = 7$, $y = 1$

d.   The system is inconsistent

e.   The equations are dependent

14. Find $-3B$ if:

$$B = \begin{bmatrix} 5 & 6 \\ -4 & 2 \\ 8 & 4 \end{bmatrix}$$

a.
$$-3B = \begin{bmatrix} -15 & -18 \\ 12 & -6 \\ -24 & -12 \end{bmatrix}$$

b.
$$-3B = \begin{bmatrix} 15 & 18 \\ -12 & 6 \\ 24 & 12 \end{bmatrix}$$

c.
$$-3B = \begin{bmatrix} -15 & 24 \\ -12 & -6 \\ -24 & -12 \end{bmatrix}$$

d.
$$-3B = \begin{bmatrix} -15 & 24 \\ 12 & -6 \\ 27 & -12 \end{bmatrix}$$

e.
$$-3B = \begin{bmatrix} -18 & -24 \\ 12 & -6 \\ -27 & -12 \end{bmatrix}$$

15. Find $A - B$ if:

$$A = \begin{bmatrix} 0 & -2 & 2 \\ 7 & 3 & -7 \end{bmatrix}, \quad B = \begin{bmatrix} 6 & -9 & 0 \\ 0 & 1 & 1 \end{bmatrix}$$

a. $A - B = \begin{bmatrix} -6 & 7 & 8 \\ 7 & 2 & 2 \end{bmatrix}$

b. $A - B = \begin{bmatrix} -6 & 2 & 7 \\ 2 & 7 & 8 \end{bmatrix}$

c. $A - B = \begin{bmatrix} -3 & 6 & 7 \\ 7 & 8 & 2 \end{bmatrix}$

d. $A - B = \begin{bmatrix} -6 & 7 & 2 \\ 7 & 2 & 8 \end{bmatrix}$

16. Let

$$A = \begin{bmatrix} 7 & -3 & 1 \\ -3 & 4 & 7 \end{bmatrix} \quad \text{and} \quad B = \begin{bmatrix} 2 & 1 \\ 0 & 1 \\ -4 & 7 \end{bmatrix}$$

Find AB.

a. $AB = \begin{bmatrix} 50 & 34 \\ -10 & 11 \end{bmatrix}$

b. $AB = \begin{bmatrix} 50 & 7 \\ -3 & 4 \end{bmatrix}$

c. $AB = \begin{bmatrix} 11 & 10 \\ -1 & 7 \end{bmatrix}$

d. $AB = \begin{bmatrix} 10 & 11 \\ -34 & 50 \end{bmatrix}$

17. Find the inverse of the matrix if it exists.

$$\begin{bmatrix} 9 & 2 \\ 4 & 5 \end{bmatrix}$$

a. $\dfrac{1}{9}\begin{bmatrix} 5 & 4 \\ -2 & 37 \end{bmatrix}$

b. Does not exist

c. $\dfrac{1}{37}\begin{bmatrix} 5 & -2 \\ -4 & 9 \end{bmatrix}$

d. $5\begin{bmatrix} 9 & 4 \\ 2 & 1 \end{bmatrix}$

18. Find the inverse of the matrix if it exists.

$$\begin{bmatrix} 1 & 3 & 4 \\ -3 & 1 & 0 \\ 4 & -1 & 1 \end{bmatrix}$$

a. $\dfrac{1}{15}\begin{bmatrix} 1 & -6 & 4 \\ 3 & -15 & 3 \\ -1 & 4 & 10 \end{bmatrix}$

b. $\dfrac{1}{4}\begin{bmatrix} 1 & -15 & 1 \\ -7 & -6 & -12 \\ 0 & 13 & 3 \end{bmatrix}$

c. $\dfrac{1}{6}\begin{bmatrix} 1 & -7 & -4 \\ 3 & -15 & -12 \\ -1 & 13 & 10 \end{bmatrix}$

d. Does not exist

19. Solve the system

$$\begin{cases} 5x + 4y = 20 \\ 8x + 9y = 19 \end{cases}$$

using the inverse method.

    a. $x = -2, y = 2$

    b. $x = 8, y = -5$

    c.   The equations are dependent

    d.   The system is inconsistent

    e. $x = -8, y = 2$

20. Find the determinant of the matrix.

$$\begin{bmatrix} 3 & 5 & -1 \\ 3 & 8 & 2 \\ -2 & 4 & 7 \end{bmatrix}$$

    a.   - 18

    b.   - 5

    c.   - 9

21. Find the determinant of the matrix.

$$\begin{bmatrix} 23 & -22 & 91 \\ -33 & 94 & -35 \\ 48 & 2 & 7 \end{bmatrix}$$

    a.   - 367976

    b.   - 1103928

    c.   - 122659

22.

Find the determinant of the matrix after introducing zeros.

$$\begin{bmatrix} 4 & 1 & -5 & 5 \\ 5 & 0 & 1 & 8 \\ 0 & 1 & 4 & 3 \\ -1 & 5 & 0 & -4 \end{bmatrix}$$

    a.   418

    b.   419

    c.   416

    d.   417

23. Use Cramer's rule to solve the system.

$$\begin{cases} x - 7y - 3z = -37 \\ 7x + y + z = 59 \\ x + 3y - 7z = 77 \end{cases}$$

a.   The system is inconsistent.

b. $(7, 11, -8)$

c. $(10, 8, -9)$

d. $(8, 9, -6)$

e. $(9, 10, -7)$

f.   The equations are dependent.

24. Sketch the graph of the system of inequalities
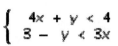
$$\begin{cases} 4x + y < 4 \\ 3 - y < 3x \end{cases}$$

a.

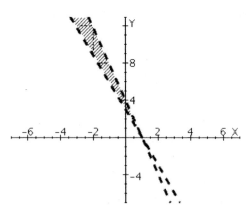

b.

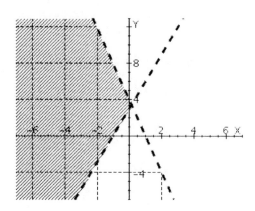

c.

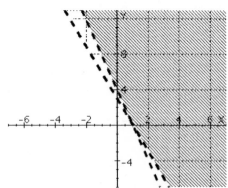

25. Find a system of inequalities whose graph is shown.

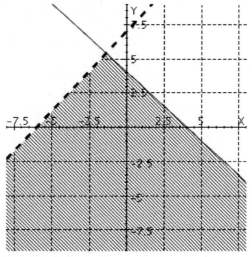

a.
$$\begin{cases} y \le -x - 4 \\ y < \dfrac{6}{7}x - 6 \end{cases}$$

b.
$$\begin{cases} y \le -x + 4 \\ y < \dfrac{7}{6}x + 7 \end{cases}$$

c.
$$\begin{cases} y > x + 7 \\ y < -\dfrac{7}{6}x + 4 \end{cases}$$

1. Find the maximum and minimum values of the objective function

$$C = 8x + 7y + 2$$

on the region bordered by the polygon in the figure.

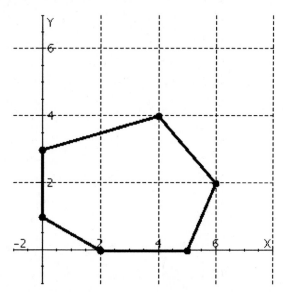

a.   The maximum is 64, the minimum is 15.

b.   The maximum is 64, the minimum is 9.

c.   The maximum is 63, the minimum is 12.

d.   The maximum is 69, the minimum is 9.

2. Sketch the graph of the inequality

$$y + 6 < x^2$$

a.

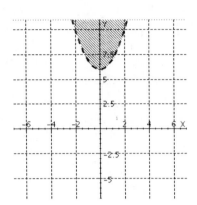

b.

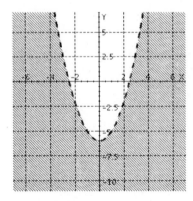

c.

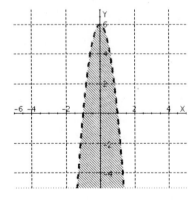

3. Find the partial fraction decomposition.

$$\frac{x + 23}{x^2 - 2x - 63}$$

a. $\dfrac{1}{x - 9} - \dfrac{2}{x + 7}$

b. $\dfrac{2}{x - 7} - \dfrac{1}{x + 9}$

c. $\dfrac{2}{x - 9} - \dfrac{1}{x + 7}$

4. Use the method of substitution to solve the system

$$\begin{cases} x + 3y = 25 \\ x^2 + y^2 = 625 \end{cases}$$

a. (25, 0)

b. no solution

c. (25, 0), (-20, 15)

d. (-20, 15)

5. Solve the system.

$$\begin{cases} 5x - 6y = 4 \\ 3x + 7y = 8 \end{cases}$$

a. $\left(\dfrac{53}{28}, \dfrac{76}{28} \right)$

b. $\left(\dfrac{28}{53}, \dfrac{76}{53} \right)$

c. $\left(\dfrac{76}{53}, \dfrac{28}{53} \right)$

d. $\left(\dfrac{53}{76}, \dfrac{28}{76} \right)$

e.   no solution

6. Solve the system.

$$\begin{cases} 3x - 7y = 6 \\ -6x + 14y = 16 \end{cases}$$

a.   The system is inconsistent.

b. $(0, \infty)$

c.   The system is dependent.

d. $(0, 0)$

7. The price of admission to a high school play was $5 for students and $7 for nonstudents. If 250 tickets were sold for a total of $1434, how many of each kind were purchased?

Select the two correct answers.
   a.   158 students

   b.   163 students

   c.   173 students

   d.   92 nonstudents

   e.   77 nonstudents

8. A silversmith has two alloys, one containing 25% silver and the other 65% silver. How much of each should be melted and combined to obtain 500 grams of an alloy containing 50% silver?

Select the correct answer(s).
   a.   343.75 grams

   b.   187.5 grams

   c.   300 grams

   d.   237.5 grams

   e.   312.5 grams

9. A small furniture company manufactures sofas and recliners. Each sofa requires 9 hours of labor and $45 in materials, while a recliner can be built for $40 in 5 hours. The company has 335 hours of labor available each week and can afford to buy $2275 worth of materials. How many recliners and sofas can be produced if all labor hours and all materials must be used?

Select the correct answer(s).

    a.   40 recliners

    b.   15 sofas

    c.   35 recliners

    d.   20 sofas

    e.   20 recliners

10. R is determined by the constraints:

$$x - 6y \geq -24,$$

$$9x - 26y \leq 36,$$
$$x + y \geq 4$$

Find the maximum value of

$$C = 4x - 2y$$

on R.

    a.   maximum of 104

    b.   maximum of 95

    c.   maximum of 0

    d.   maximum of 102

11. Region R is determined by the constraints:

$$y \geq 0,$$

$$3x + y \geq 3,$$
$$x + 5y \leq 15,$$
$$2x + y \leq 12$$

Find the minimum value of

$$C = 7x + y$$

on R.

    a.   minimum of 1 at (1, 0)

    b.   minimum of - 7 at (1, 0)

    c.   minimum of 3 at (0, 3)

    d.   minimum of 7 at (0, 3)

12. Use matrices to solve the system.

$$\begin{cases} x - 3y - 3z = -15 \\ 2x + y + z = 12 \\ x + 3y - 2z = 1 \end{cases}$$

    a.   The system is inconsistent

    b. $x = -2$, $y = -7$, $z = 4$

    c. $x = -2$, $y = 3$, $z = 4$

    d. $x = 4$, $y = 1$, $z = -4$

    e.   The equations are dependent

    f. $x = 3$, $y = 2$, $z = 4$

13. Use matrices to solve the system.

$$\begin{cases} 4x + 2y = 38 \\ x - 4y = 5 \\ x + y = -7 \end{cases}$$

a. $x = 9$, $y = 1$

b. $x = -9$, $y = 1$

c.   The equations are dependent

d.   The system is inconsistent

e. $x = 5$, $y = -5$

14. Find $-3B$ if:

$$B = \begin{bmatrix} 2 & 8 \\ -9 & 5 \\ 1 & 9 \end{bmatrix}$$

a.
$$-3B = \begin{bmatrix} -6 & 30 \\ 27 & -15 \\ 6 & -27 \end{bmatrix}$$

b.
$$-3B = \begin{bmatrix} -9 & -30 \\ 27 & -15 \\ -6 & -27 \end{bmatrix}$$

c.
$$-3B = \begin{bmatrix} 6 & 24 \\ -27 & 15 \\ 3 & 27 \end{bmatrix}$$

d.
$$-3B = \begin{bmatrix} -6 & 30 \\ -27 & -15 \\ -3 & -27 \end{bmatrix}$$

e.
$$-3B = \begin{bmatrix} -6 & -24 \\ 27 & -15 \\ -3 & -27 \end{bmatrix}$$

15. Find *A - B* if:

$$A = \begin{bmatrix} 0 & -4 & 6 \\ 2 & 6 & -7 \end{bmatrix}, B = \begin{bmatrix} 8 & -8 & 0 \\ 0 & 5 & 7 \end{bmatrix}$$

a.
$$A - B = \begin{bmatrix} -8 & 2 & 14 \\ 4 & 1 & 6 \end{bmatrix}$$

b.
$$A - B = \begin{bmatrix} -6 & 8 & 4 \\ 2 & 14 & 1 \end{bmatrix}$$

c.
$$A - B = \begin{bmatrix} -8 & 4 & 6 \\ 2 & 1 & 14 \end{bmatrix}$$

d.
$$A - B = \begin{bmatrix} -8 & 1 & 2 \\ 6 & 4 & 14 \end{bmatrix}$$

16. Let

$$A = \begin{bmatrix} 3 & -8 & 8 \\ -8 & 8 & 3 \end{bmatrix} \text{ and } B = \begin{bmatrix} 2 & 1 \\ 0 & 1 \\ -4 & 7 \end{bmatrix}$$

Find *AB*.

a. $AB = \begin{bmatrix} -51 & 26 \\ -8 & 3 \end{bmatrix}$

b. $AB = \begin{bmatrix} -21 & 28 \\ -26 & 51 \end{bmatrix}$

c. $AB = \begin{bmatrix} -21 & 3 \\ -8 & 8 \end{bmatrix}$

d. $AB = \begin{bmatrix} -26 & 51 \\ -28 & 21 \end{bmatrix}$

17. Find the inverse of the matrix if it exists.

$$\begin{bmatrix} 7 & 2 \\ 4 & 3 \end{bmatrix}$$

a. $\dfrac{1}{13} \begin{bmatrix} 3 & -2 \\ -4 & 7 \end{bmatrix}$

b. $3 \begin{bmatrix} 7 & 4 \\ 2 & 1 \end{bmatrix}$

c. Does not exist

d. $\dfrac{1}{7} \begin{bmatrix} 3 & 4 \\ -2 & 13 \end{bmatrix}$

18. Find the inverse of the matrix if it exists.

$$\begin{bmatrix} 1 & 4 & 5 \\ -4 & 1 & 0 \\ 5 & -1 & 1 \end{bmatrix}$$

a. $\dfrac{1}{24} \begin{bmatrix} 1 & -12 & 5 \\ 4 & -24 & 4 \\ -1 & 5 & 17 \end{bmatrix}$

b. Does not exist

c. $\dfrac{1}{12} \begin{bmatrix} 1 & -9 & -5 \\ 4 & -24 & -20 \\ -1 & 21 & 17 \end{bmatrix}$

d. $\dfrac{1}{5} \begin{bmatrix} 1 & -24 & 1 \\ -9 & -12 & -20 \\ 0 & 21 & 4 \end{bmatrix}$

19. Solve the system

$$\begin{cases} 3x + 2y = -22 \\ 4x + 9y = -23 \end{cases}$$

using the inverse method.

a. $x = -8, y = 1$

b. The equations are dependent

c. $x = -6, y = 8$

d. The system is inconsistent

e. $x = 8, y = 8$

20. Find the determinant of the matrix.

$$\begin{bmatrix} 4 & 9 & -6 \\ 3 & 5 & 2 \\ -5 & 2 & 5 \end{bmatrix}$$

a.   - 654

b.   - 327

c.   - 164

21. Find the determinant of the matrix.

$$\begin{bmatrix} 28 & -12 & 81 \\ -30 & 87 & -37 \\ 47 & 8 & 7 \end{bmatrix}$$

a.   - 920883

b.   - 102320

c.   - 306961

22. Find the determinant of the matrix after introducing zeros.

$$\begin{bmatrix} 2 & 1 & -4 & 4 \\ 4 & 0 & 1 & 7 \\ 0 & 1 & 2 & 5 \\ -1 & 4 & 0 & -2 \end{bmatrix}$$

a.   389

b.   388

c.   386

d.   387

23. Use Cramer's rule to solve the system.

$$\begin{cases} x - 7y - 4z = -5 \\ 7x + y + z = 57 \\ x + 4y - 7z = 34 \end{cases}$$

a. $(7 , 5 , - 4)$

b. The system is inconsistent.

c. $(10 , 2 , - 5)$

d. The equations are dependent.

e. $(9 , 4 , - 3)$

f. $(8 , 3 , - 2)$

24. Sketch the graph of the system of inequalities

$$\begin{cases} 5x + y < 5 \\ 1 - y < 2x \end{cases}$$

a.

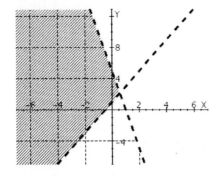

b.

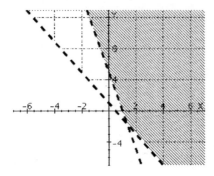

c.

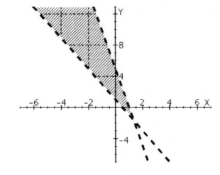

25. Find a system of inequalities whose graph is shown.

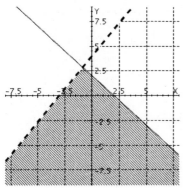

a.
$$\begin{cases} y \leq -x + 2 \\ y < \dfrac{4}{3}x + 4 \end{cases}$$

b.
$$\begin{cases} y \leq -x - 2 \\ y < \dfrac{3}{4}x - 3 \end{cases}$$

c.
$$\begin{cases} y > x + 4 \\ y < -\dfrac{4}{3}x + 2 \end{cases}$$

1. Sketch the graph of the inequality

$y + 5 < x^2$

    a.

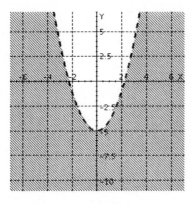

    b.

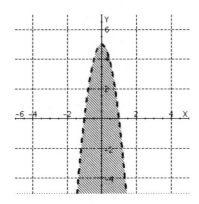

    c.

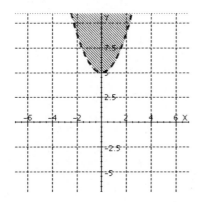

2. Use the method of substitution to solve the system

$$\begin{cases} x + 3y = 30 \\ x^2 + y^2 = 900 \end{cases}$$

   a.   (30, 0)

   b.   (-24, 18)

   c.   no solution

   d.   (30, 0), (-24, 18)

3. Solve the system.

$$\begin{cases} 3x - 13y = 10 \\ -6x + 26y = 18 \end{cases}$$

   a.   (0, 0)

   b.   (0, ∞)

   c.   The system is inconsistent.

   d.   The system is dependent.

4. A silversmith has two alloys, one containing 20% silver and the other 70% silver. How much of each should be melted and combined to obtain 400 grams of an alloy containing 50% silver?

   Select the correct answer(s).
   a.   160 grams

   b.   240 grams

   c.   280 grams

   d.   210 grams

   e.   300 grams

5. *R* is determined by the constraints:

$$x - 2y \geq -8,$$

$$7x - 2y \leq 28,$$
$$x + y \geq 4$$

Find the maximum value of

$$C = 4x - 2y$$

on *R*.

   a.   maximum of 12

   b.   maximum of 0

   c.   maximum of 3

   d.   maximum of 10

6. Use matrices to solve the system.

$$\begin{cases} x - 2y - 2z = -1 \\ 2x + y + z = 8 \\ x + 3y - 3z = 3 \end{cases}$$

   a.   The equations are dependent

   b. $x = -1$, $y = -5$, $z = 1$

   c. $x = 3$, $y = 1$, $z = 1$

   d. $x = 4$, $y = 0$, $z = -1$

   e.   The system is inconsistent

   f. $x = -1$, $y = 3$, $z = 4$

7.

Find -3*B* if: $B = \begin{bmatrix} 3 & 9 \\ -6 & 5 \\ 5 & 9 \end{bmatrix}$

a.

$-3B = \begin{bmatrix} 9 & 27 \\ -18 & 15 \\ 15 & 27 \end{bmatrix}$

b.

$-3B = \begin{bmatrix} -12 & -33 \\ 18 & -15 \\ -18 & -27 \end{bmatrix}$

c.

$-3B = \begin{bmatrix} -9 & -27 \\ 18 & -15 \\ -15 & -27 \end{bmatrix}$

d.

$-3B = \begin{bmatrix} -9 & 33 \\ 18 & -15 \\ 18 & -27 \end{bmatrix}$

e.

$-3B = \begin{bmatrix} -9 & 33 \\ -18 & -15 \\ -15 & -27 \end{bmatrix}$

8.

Let $A = \begin{bmatrix} 1 & -6 & 7 \\ -9 & 4 & 1 \end{bmatrix}$ and $B = \begin{bmatrix} 2 & 1 \\ 0 & 1 \\ -4 & 7 \end{bmatrix}$ Find *AB*.

a.

$AB = \begin{bmatrix} -44 & 26 \\ -7 & 1 \end{bmatrix}$

b.

$AB = \begin{bmatrix} -2 & 22 \\ -26 & 44 \end{bmatrix}$

c.

$AB = \begin{bmatrix} -26 & 44 \\ -22 & 2 \end{bmatrix}$

d.

$AB = \begin{bmatrix} -2 & 1 \\ -9 & 4 \end{bmatrix}$

9.

Find the inverse of the matrix if it exists.
$$\begin{bmatrix} 1 & 2 & 3 \\ -2 & 1 & 0 \\ 3 & -1 & 1 \end{bmatrix}$$

a.
$$\frac{1}{8} \begin{bmatrix} 1 & -2 & 3 \\ 2 & -8 & 2 \\ -1 & 3 & 5 \end{bmatrix}$$

b.
$$\frac{1}{2} \begin{bmatrix} 1 & -5 & -3 \\ 2 & -8 & -6 \\ -1 & 7 & 5 \end{bmatrix}$$

c.   Does not exist

d.
$$\frac{1}{3} \begin{bmatrix} 1 & -8 & 1 \\ -5 & -2 & -6 \\ 0 & 7 & 2 \end{bmatrix}$$

10. Find the determinant of the matrix.
$$\begin{bmatrix} 6 & 4 & -4 \\ 3 & 6 & 2 \\ -4 & 9 & 2 \end{bmatrix}$$

a.   - 296

b.   - 148

c.   - 592

11. Find the determinant of the matrix after introducing zeros.
$$\begin{bmatrix} 2 & 1 & -3 & 3 \\ 3 & 0 & 1 & 9 \\ 0 & 1 & 2 & 4 \\ -1 & 3 & 0 & -2 \end{bmatrix}$$

a.   70

b.   69

c.   67

d.   68

12. Sketch the graph of the system of inequalities

$$\begin{cases} 4x + y < 4 \\ 1 - y < 3x \end{cases}$$

a.

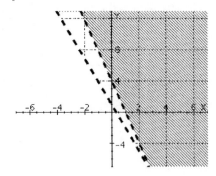

b.

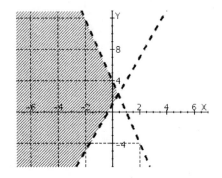

c.

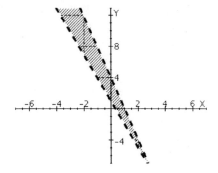

13. Use Cramer's rule to solve the system.

$$\begin{cases} x - 9y - 3z = -8 \\ 9x + y + z = 8 \\ x + 3y - 9z = 34 \end{cases}$$

If the equations of the system are dependent, or if a system is inconsistent, so indicate.

14. Find the maximum and minimum values of the objective function

$$C = 7x + 6y + 9$$

on the region bordered by the polygon in the figure.

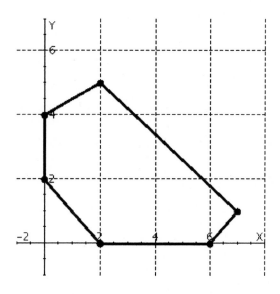

15. Use the method of substitution to solve the system

$$\begin{cases} x + 2y = 25 \\ x^2 + y^2 = 625 \end{cases}$$

16. The price of admission to a high school play was $3 for students and $4 for nonstudents. If 500 tickets were sold for a total of $1822, how many of each kind were purchased?
number of students: _____
number of nonstudents: _____

17. A small furniture company manufactures sofas and recliners. Each sofa requires 10 hours of labor and $45 in materials, while a recliner can be built for $25 in 7 hours. The company has 465 hours of labor available each week and can afford to buy $1800 worth of materials. How many sofas and recliners can be produced if all labor hours and all materials must be used?
_____ sofas
_____ recliners

18. R is determined by the constraints:

$$x - 5y \geq -20,$$

$$7x - 11y \leq 28,$$
$$x + y \geq 4$$

Find the maximum value of

$$C = 4x - 2y$$

on R.

19. Use matrices to solve the system.
$$\begin{cases} 2x - 3y - z = 2 \\ 3x + 2y + z = -3 \\ 5x - 2y - z = 0 \end{cases}$$
If the equations of the system are dependent, or if the system is inconsistent, so indicate.

20. Find -3*B* if:

$$B = \begin{bmatrix} 8 & 1 \\ -7 & 2 \\ 1 & 8 \end{bmatrix}$$

21. Let

$$A = \begin{bmatrix} 3 & -7 & 8 \\ -1 & 2 & 8 \end{bmatrix} \text{ and } B = \begin{bmatrix} 2 & 1 \\ 0 & 1 \\ -4 & 7 \end{bmatrix}$$

Find *AB*.

22. Solve the system

$$\begin{cases} 5x + 4y = 8 \\ 8x + 9y = 5 \end{cases}$$

using the inverse method.

23. Find the determinant of the matrix.

$$\begin{bmatrix} 28 & -12 & 85 \\ -30 & 86 & -35 \\ 51 & 13 & 6 \end{bmatrix}$$

24. Find the partial fraction decomposition.

$$\frac{x + 37}{x^2 - 3x - 28}$$

25. Find a system of inequalities whose graph is shown.

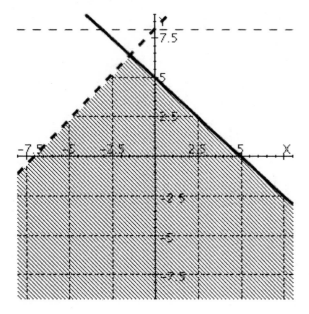

1. Sketch the graph of the inequality

$y + 1 < x^2$

a.

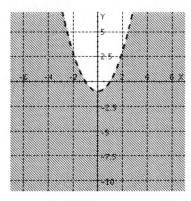

b.

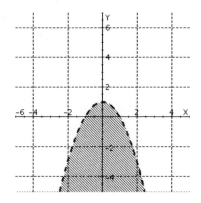

c.

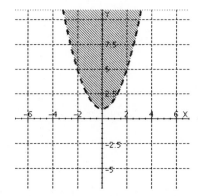

2. Use the method of substitution to solve the system

$$\begin{cases} x + 2y = 25 \\ x^2 + y^2 = 625 \end{cases}$$

a.   no solution

b.   (25, 0)

c.   (25, 0), (-15, 20)

d.   (-15, 20)

3. Solve the system.

$$\begin{cases} 3x - 13y = 8 \\ -6x + 26y = 13 \end{cases}$$

a.   (0, 0)

b.   The system is dependent.

c.   (0, ∞)

d.   The system is inconsistent.

4. A silversmith has two alloys, one containing 30% silver and the other 80% silver. How much of each should be melted and combined to obtain 700 grams of an alloy containing 50% silver?

Select the correct answer(s).

a.   100 grams

b.   560 grams

c.   280 grams

d.   420 grams

e.   390 grams

5. *R* is determined by the constraints:

$$x - 6y \geq -24,$$

$$7x - 14y \leq 28,$$
$$x + y \geq 4$$

Find the maximum value of

$$C = 4x - 2y$$

on *R*.

   a.   maximum of 58

   b.   maximum of 51

   c.   maximum of 60

   d.   maximum of 0

6. Use matrices to solve the system.

$$\begin{cases} x - 2y - 3z = -13 \\ 3x + y + z = 19 \\ x + 3y - 3z = 7 \end{cases}$$

   a.   The equations are dependent

   b. $x = -4$, $y = 4$, $z = 5$

   c. $x = -4$, $y = -7$, $z = 3$

   d. $x = 5$, $y = 3$, $z = -3$

   e.   The system is inconsistent

   f. $x = 4$, $y = 4$, $z = 3$

7. Find -3*B* if:

$$B = \begin{bmatrix} 4 & 8 \\ -9 & 4 \\ 8 & 5 \end{bmatrix}$$

    a.

$$-3B = \begin{bmatrix} -12 & 30 \\ -27 & -12 \\ -24 & -15 \end{bmatrix}$$

    b.

$$-3B = \begin{bmatrix} 12 & 24 \\ -27 & 12 \\ 24 & 15 \end{bmatrix}$$

    c.

$$-3B = \begin{bmatrix} -15 & -30 \\ 27 & -12 \\ -27 & -15 \end{bmatrix}$$

    d.

$$-3B = \begin{bmatrix} -12 & 30 \\ 27 & -12 \\ 27 & -15 \end{bmatrix}$$

    e.

$$-3B = \begin{bmatrix} -12 & -24 \\ 27 & -12 \\ -24 & -15 \end{bmatrix}$$

8. Let

$$A = \begin{bmatrix} 1 & -2 & 9 \\ -5 & 5 & 4 \end{bmatrix} \text{ and } B = \begin{bmatrix} 2 & 1 \\ 0 & 1 \\ -4 & 7 \end{bmatrix}$$

Find AB.

a. $AB = \begin{bmatrix} -62 & 34 \\ -9 & 1 \end{bmatrix}$

b. $AB = \begin{bmatrix} -28 & 26 \\ -34 & 62 \end{bmatrix}$

c. $AB = \begin{bmatrix} -28 & 1 \\ -5 & 5 \end{bmatrix}$

d. $AB = \begin{bmatrix} -34 & 62 \\ -26 & 28 \end{bmatrix}$

9. Find the inverse of the matrix if it exists.

$$\begin{bmatrix} 1 & 5 & 6 \\ -5 & 1 & 0 \\ 6 & -1 & 1 \end{bmatrix}$$

a.

$$\frac{1}{35}\begin{bmatrix} 1 & -20 & 6 \\ 5 & -35 & 5 \\ -1 & 6 & 26 \end{bmatrix}$$

b.

$$\frac{1}{6}\begin{bmatrix} 1 & -35 & 1 \\ -11 & -20 & -30 \\ 0 & 31 & 5 \end{bmatrix}$$

c.   Does not exist

d.

$$\frac{1}{20}\begin{bmatrix} 1 & -11 & -6 \\ 5 & -35 & -30 \\ -1 & 31 & 26 \end{bmatrix}$$

10. Find the determinant of the matrix.

$$\begin{bmatrix} 3 & 6 & -1 \\ 0 & 7 & 5 \\ -3 & 4 & 5 \end{bmatrix}$$

a.   - 264

b.   - 33

c.   - 66

11. Find the determinant of the matrix after introducing zeros.

$$\begin{bmatrix} 4 & 1 & -3 & 3 \\ 3 & 0 & 1 & 8 \\ 0 & 1 & 4 & 6 \\ -1 & 3 & 0 & -4 \end{bmatrix}$$

a.   6

b.   7

c.   4

d.   5

12. Sketch the graph of the system of inequalities

$$\begin{cases} 5x + y < 5 \\ 4 - y < 3x \end{cases}$$

a.

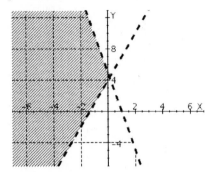

b.

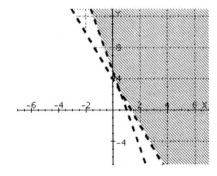

c.

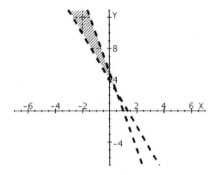

13. Use Cramer's rule to solve the system.

$$\begin{cases} x - 7y - 2z = -9 \\ 7x + y + z = 7 \\ x + 2y - 7z = 19 \end{cases}$$

If the equations of the system are dependent, or if a system is inconsistent, so indicate.

14. Find the maximum and minimum values of the objective function

$$C = 7x + 2y + 7$$

on the region bordered by the polygon in the figure.

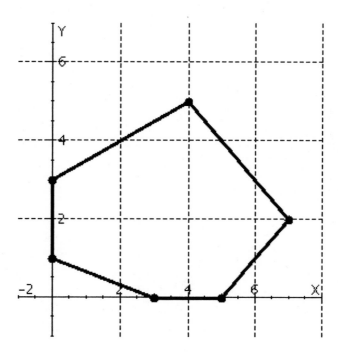

15. Use the method of substitution to solve the system

$$\begin{cases} x + 2y = 15 \\ x^2 + y^2 = 225 \end{cases}$$

16. The price of admission to a high school play was $3 for students and $4 for nonstudents. If 400 tickets were sold for a total of $1418, how many of each kind were purchased?
number of students: _____
number of nonstudents: _____

17. A small furniture company manufactures sofas and recliners. Each sofa requires 12 hours of labor and $65 in materials, while a recliner can be built for $35 in 6 hours. The company has 420 hours of labor available each week and can afford to buy $2400 worth of materials. How many sofas and recliners can be produced if all labor hours and all materials must be used?

_____ sofas
_____ recliners

18. R is determined by the constraints:

$$x - 6y \geq -24,$$

$$5x - 2y \leq 20,$$
$$x + y \geq 4$$

Find the maximum value of

$$C = 4x - 2y$$

on R.

19. Use matrices to solve the system.

$$\begin{cases} 2x - 3y + z = 2 \\ 3x + 2y - z = -3 \\ 5x - 2y + z = 0 \end{cases}$$

If the equations of the system are dependent, or if the system is inconsistent, so indicate.

20. Find $-3B$ if:

$$B = \begin{bmatrix} 6 & 9 \\ -2 & 1 \\ 6 & 7 \end{bmatrix}$$

21. Let

$$A = \begin{bmatrix} 9 & -2 & 3 \\ -8 & 8 & 1 \end{bmatrix} \text{ and } B = \begin{bmatrix} 2 & 1 \\ 0 & 1 \\ -4 & 7 \end{bmatrix}$$

Find *AB*.

22. Solve the system

$$\begin{cases} 9x + 4y = 8 \\ 8x + 5y = 9 \end{cases}$$

using the inverse method.

23. Find the determinant of the matrix.

$$\begin{bmatrix} 21 & -13 & 84 \\ -33 & 93 & -38 \\ 46 & 6 & 8 \end{bmatrix}$$

24. Find the partial fraction decomposition.

$$\frac{x + 29}{x^2 - 5x - 14}$$

25. Find a system of inequalities whose graph is shown.

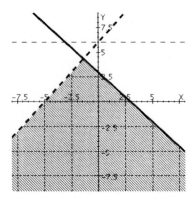

Test Form 8-A

1. $\{2, 5, -9\}$

2. $\dfrac{1}{20} \cdot \begin{bmatrix} 1 & -11 & -6 \\ 5 & -35 & -30 \\ -1 & 31 & 26 \end{bmatrix}$

3. $34, 6$

4. $\{35, 0\}, \{-28, 21\}$

5. $\left(\dfrac{31}{23}, \dfrac{11}{23} \right)$

6. inconsistent

7. $\dfrac{150}{250}$

8. $\dfrac{630}{270}$

9. $\dfrac{20}{30}$

10.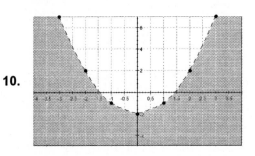

11. 102

12. 3

13. $\left(-\dfrac{5}{8}, -\dfrac{1}{8}, -\dfrac{23}{8} \right)$

14. inconsistent

15. $\begin{bmatrix} -9 & -21 \\ 21 & -18 \\ -24 & -27 \end{bmatrix}$

16. $\begin{bmatrix} -8 & 1 & 2 \\ 5 & -3 & -4 \end{bmatrix}$

17. $\begin{bmatrix} -28 & 62 \\ -26 & 28 \end{bmatrix}$

18. no solution

19. $\left(-\dfrac{6}{19}, \dfrac{65}{19} \right)$

20. -988

21. -290080

22. 92

23. $\dfrac{10}{x-7} - \dfrac{9}{x+1}$

24.

24.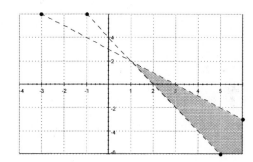

25. $y \leq -x + 4, y < \dfrac{6}{5} \cdot x + 6$

Test Form 8-B

1. $\{1, 4, -5\}$

2. $\dfrac{1}{6} \cdot \begin{bmatrix} 1 & -7 & -4 \\ 3 & -15 & -12 \\ -1 & 13 & 10 \end{bmatrix}$

3. $49, 19$

4. $\{25, 0\}, \{-15, 20\}$

5. $\left(\dfrac{76}{53}, \dfrac{28}{53} \right)$

6. inconsistent

7. $\dfrac{188}{262}$

8. $\dfrac{450}{450}$

9. $\dfrac{25}{35}$

10.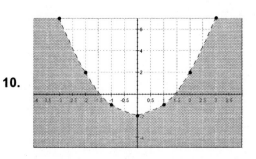

11. 18

12. 3

13. $\left(-\dfrac{7}{8}, -\dfrac{3}{8}, \dfrac{29}{8} \right)$

14. inconsistent

15. $\begin{bmatrix} -18 & -24 \\ 6 & -24 \\ -27 & -18 \end{bmatrix}$

16. $\begin{bmatrix} -5 & -3 & 3 \\ 5 & 7 & -7 \end{bmatrix}$

17. $\begin{bmatrix} -18 & 44 \\ -12 & 20 \end{bmatrix}$

18. no solution

19. $\left(\dfrac{6}{27}, \dfrac{33}{27} \right)$

20. 48

21. -319344

22. -552

23. $\dfrac{5}{x-6} - \dfrac{4}{x+2}$

24.

24.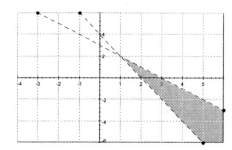

25. $y \le -x + 6, y < \dfrac{8}{7} \cdot x + 8$

Test Form 8-C

1. c	**2.** c	**3.** c	**4.** d	**5.** b	**6.** d	**7.** c,d	**8.** d,e	**9.** a,b
10. a	**11.** a	**12.** b	**13.** d	**14.** a	**15.** d	**16.** d	**17.** c	**18.** c
19. b	**20.** c	**21.** a	**22.** d	**23.** d	**24.** a	**25.** b		

Test Form 8-D

1. b	**2.** b	**3.** c	**4.** c	**5.** c	**6.** a	**7.** a,d	**8.** b,e	**9.** a,b
10. d	**11.** c	**12.** f	**13.** d	**14.** e	**15.** c	**16.** d	**17.** a	**18.** c
19. a	**20.** b	**21.** c	**22.** d	**23.** f	**24.** c	**25.** a		

Test Form 8-E

1. a
2. d
3. c
4. a , b
5. d
6. c
7. c
8. c
9. b
10. a
11. d
12. c

13. $(1,2,-3)$
14. $64,21$
15. $(25,0),(-15,20)$
16. $178,\ 322$
17. $15,\ 45$
18. 46
19. $\left(-\dfrac{3}{8},-\dfrac{7}{8},-\dfrac{1}{8}\right)$
20. $\begin{bmatrix} -24 & -3 \\ 21 & -6 \\ -3 & -24 \end{bmatrix}$

21. $\begin{bmatrix} -26 & 52 \\ -34 & 57 \end{bmatrix}$
22. $\left(\dfrac{52}{13},-\dfrac{39}{13}\right)$
23. -359512
24. $\dfrac{4}{x-7}-\dfrac{3}{x+4}$
25. $y \leq -x+5, y < \dfrac{8}{7}\cdot x+8$

Test Form 8-F

1. a
2. c
3. d
4. c , d
5. a
6. f
7. e
8. d
9. d
10. c
11. d
12. d

13. $(1,2,-2)$
14. $60,9$
15. $(15,0),(-9,12)$
16. $182,\ 218$
17. $10,\ 50$
18. 14
19. $\left(-\dfrac{3}{8},-\dfrac{7}{8},\dfrac{1}{8}\right)$
20. $\begin{bmatrix} -18 & -27 \\ 6 & -3 \\ -18 & -21 \end{bmatrix}$

21. $\begin{bmatrix} 6 & 28 \\ -20 & 7 \end{bmatrix}$
22. $\left(\dfrac{4}{13},\dfrac{17}{13}\right)$
23. -336280
24. $\dfrac{4}{x-7}-\dfrac{3}{x+2}$
25. $y \leq -x+3, y < \dfrac{6}{5}\cdot x+6$

1. Find the third term of the recursively defined infinite sequence

$a_1 = 5$, $\quad a_{k+1} = (k+4) a_k$.

2. Find the fourth term of the sequence of partial sums for the given sequence

$$\left\{ 4 + \frac{3}{2} n \right\}.$$

3. Find the specified term of the arithmetic sequence that has the two given terms.

$a_1 : \quad a_8 = 27, \quad a_9 = 30$

4. Find the sum.

$$\sum_{k=1}^{22} (3n + 2)$$

5. Find the sum.

$$\sum_{k=1}^{20} \left(\frac{3}{2} n + 5 \right)$$

6. Find the fifth term of the geometric sequence :

64, 16, 4, 1,...

7. Find the sum :

$$\sum_{k=1}^{5} 2^{k}$$

8. Find the sum of the infinite geometric series :

$$2401 + 1029 + 441 + 189 + ...$$

9. Find the rational number represented by the repeating decimal :

$$4.\overline{1417}$$

10. The yearly depreciation of a certain machine is 20% of its value at the beginning of the year. If the original cost of the machine is $25000, what is its value after 6 years?

11. If a deposit of $350 is made on the first day of each month into an account that pays 10% interest per year compounded monthly, determine the amount in the account after 15 years.

12. A landfill currently has 3300 tons of waste. During each the year, the tonnage is reduced by 20% due to decomposition. Then, at the end of each year, 3300 new tons are added to the fill. If this process continues forever, what is the maximum tonnage that the landfill can reach?

13. Evaluate the expression: $\dfrac{7!}{6!}$

14. Evaluate the expression: $\begin{pmatrix} 7 \\ 3 \end{pmatrix}$

15. Use the binomial theorem to expand and simplify.

$$(5x - 4y)^4$$

16. Find the number :

$$P(9, 3)$$

17. If six basketball teams are in a tournament, find the number of different ways that first, second, and third place can be decided, assuming ties are not allowed.

18. In how many different ways can seven people be seated in a row?

19. With six different flags, how many different signals can be sent by placing three flags, one above the other, on a flag pole?

20. In how many different ways can three books be selected from a seven-volume set of books?

21. Consider any nine points such that no three are collinear. How many lines are determined?

22. To win a state lottery game, a player must correctly select six numbers from the numbers 1 through 36. Find the total number of selections possible if a player selects only even numbers.

23. A single card is drawn from a 52-card deck. Find the probability that the card is a king, a queen, or a jack.

24. An urn contains five red balls, six green balls, and four white balls. If a single ball is drawn, find the probability that the ball is white.

25. Prove, by mathematical induction, that $6^n - 1$ is divisible by 5 for all natural numbers n.

1. Find the third term of the recursively defined infinite sequence

$$a_1 = 7, \quad a_{k+1} = (k+2)\, a_k .$$

2. Find the fourth term of the sequence of partial sums for the given sequence

$$\left\{ 5 + \frac{3}{2} n \right\} .$$

3. Find the specified term of the arithmetic sequence that has the two given terms.

$$a_1: \quad a_8 = 43, \quad a_9 = 48$$

4. Find the sum.

$$\sum_{k=1}^{20} (4n - 2)$$

5. Find the sum.

$$\sum_{k=1}^{24} \left(\frac{1}{2} n + 4 \right)$$

6. Find the fifth term of the geometric sequence :

$$64,\ 16,\ 4,\ 1, ...$$

7. Find the sum :

$$\sum_{k=1}^{6} 3^k$$

8. Find the sum of the infinite geometric series :

$$1536 + 576 + 216 + 81 + \ldots$$

9. Find the rational number represented by the repeating decimal :

$$1.\overline{3470}$$

10. The yearly depreciation of a certain machine is 10% of its value at the beginning of the year. If the original cost of the machine is $25000, what is its value after 5 years?

11. If a deposit of $450 is made on the first day of each month into an account that pays 6% interest per year compounded monthly, determine the amount in the account after 10 years.

12. A landfill currently has 2600 tons of waste. During each the year, the tonnage is reduced by 10% due to decomposition. Then, at the end of each year, 2600 new tons are added to the fill. If this process continues forever, what is the maximum tonnage that the landfill can reach?

13. Evaluate the expression:

$$\frac{4!}{2!}$$

14. Evaluate the expression: $\begin{pmatrix} 4 \\ 3 \end{pmatrix}$

15. Use the binomial theorem to expand and simplify.

$$(5x - 4y)^4$$

16. Find the number :

$$P(11, 2)$$

17. If seven basketball teams are in a tournament, find the number of different ways that first, second, and third place can be decided, assuming ties are not allowed.

18. In how many different ways can seven people be seated in a row?

19. With eight different flags, how many different signals can be sent by placing four flags, one above the other, on a flag pole?

20. In how many different ways can three books be selected from a ten-volume set of books?

21. Consider any six points such that no three are collinear. How many lines are determined?

22. To win a state lottery game, a player must correctly select six numbers from the numbers 1 through 52. Find the total number of selections possible if a player selects only even numbers.

23. A single card is drawn from a 52-card deck. Find the odds that the card is an ace.

24. An urn contains five red balls, six green balls, and four white balls. If a single ball is drawn, find the probability that the ball is white.

25.
Prove, by mathematical induction, that $S_n = \dfrac{n(5n+1)}{2}$ for $a_n = 5n - 2$.

1. Find the third term of the recursively defined infinite sequence

$a_1 = 4$, $a_{k+1} = (k+3) a_k$.

    a. $a_3 = 90$

    b. $a_3 = 79$

    c. $a_3 = 80$

    d. $a_3 = 77$

2. Find the fourth term of the sequence of partial sums for the given sequence

$$\left\{ 3 + \frac{3}{2} n \right\}.$$

    a. $S_4 = 24$

    b. $S_4 = 33$

    c. $S_4 = 18$

    d. $S_4 = 27$

3. Find the specified term of the arithmetic sequence that has the two given terms.

$$a_1 : \quad a_8 = 34, \quad a_9 = 38$$

    a. $a_1 = 14$

    b. $a_1 = 6$

    c. $a_1 = 1$

    d. $a_1 = 10$

4. Find the sum.

$$\sum_{k=1}^{18} (5n - 3)$$

a. $s = 821$

b. $s = 791$

c. $s = 796$

d. $s = 801$

5. Find the sum.

$$\sum_{k=1}^{28} \left(\frac{5}{2}n + 5 \right)$$

a. $s = 1125$

b. $s = 1165$

c. $s = 1155$

d. $s = 1140$

6. Find the fifth term of the geometric sequence :

64, 16, 4, 1,...

a. $-\dfrac{1}{4}$

b. 4

c. $\dfrac{1}{4}$

d. -4

7. Find the sum :

$$\sum_{k=1}^{5} 3^k$$

    a.   120

    b.   363

    c.   360

    d.   242

8. Find the sum of the infinite geometric series :

$$375 + 225 + 135 + 81 + \ldots$$

    a. $943 \frac{1}{2}$

    b. $932 \frac{1}{2}$

    c. $940 \frac{1}{2}$

    d. $937 \frac{1}{2}$

9. Find the rational number represented by the repeating decimal :

$$5.8\overline{456}$$

a. $\dfrac{58456}{999}$

b. $\dfrac{58451}{9999}$

c. $\dfrac{49995}{9999}$

d. $\dfrac{58456}{9999}$

10. The yearly depreciation of a certain machine is 20% of its value at the beginning of the year. If the original cost of the machine is \$30000, what is its value after 10 years?

a. \$3221.23

b. \$3207.18

c. \$2576.98

d. \$0.00

11. If a deposit of \$500 is made on the first day of each month into an account that pays 8% interest per year compounded monthly, determine the amount in the account after 13 years.

a. \$136460.20

b. \$137369.98

c. \$137369.88

d. \$137369.93

12. A landfill currently has 3700 tons of waste. During each the year, the tonnage is reduced by 10% due to decomposition. Then, at the end of each year, 3700 new tons are added to the fill. If this process continues forever, what is the maximum tonnage that the landfill can reach?

    a.   38250 tons

    b.   41111 tons

    c.   35775 tons

    d.   37000 tons

13. Evaluate the expression:

$$\frac{7!}{6!}$$

    a.   56

    b.   1

    c.   7

14. Evaluate the expression $\begin{pmatrix} 4 \\ 2 \end{pmatrix}$.

    a.   24

    b.   6

    c.   12

    d.   180

15. Use the binomial theorem to expand and simplify.

$$(3x - 3y)^4$$

a. $3x^4 + 324x^3y + 81x^2y^2 + 324xy^3 + 81y^4$

b. $3x^4 - 3x^3y + 81x^2y^2 - 81xy^3 + 324y^4$

c. $81x^4 - 324x^3y + 486x^2y^2 - 324xy^3 + 81y^4$

d. $81x^4 - 324x^3y - 324x^2y^2 - 486xy^3 + 81y^4$

16. Find the number :

$$P(11, 2)$$

a.   110

b.   86

c.   98

d.   90

17. If nine basketball teams are in a tournament, find the number of different ways that first, second, and third place can be decided, assuming ties are not allowed.

a.   5040

b.   6

c.   504

d.   3024

18. In how many different ways can ten people be seated in a row?

  a. 1024

  b. 10000000000

  c. 100

  d. 3628800

19. With six different flags, how many different signals can be sent by placing three flags, one above the other, on a flag pole?

  a. 216

  b. 120

  c. 204

  d. 36

20. In how many different ways can three books be selected from a eight-volume set of books?

  a. 512

  b. 56

  c. 336

  d. 40320

  e. 24

21. Consider any five points such that no three are collinear. How many lines are determined?

    a.   5

    b.   10

    c.   2

22. To win a state lottery game, a player must correctly select six numbers from the numbers 1 through 45.Find the total number of selections possible if a player selects only even numbers.

    a.   132

    b.   4072530

    c.   74613

    d.   977407200

23. A single card is drawn from a 52-card deck. Find the probability that the card is a king, a queen, or a jack.

    a. $\dfrac{4}{13}$

    b. $\dfrac{4}{52}$

    c. $\dfrac{1}{12}$

    d. $\dfrac{3}{13}$

24. An urn contains five red balls, six green balls, and four white balls. If a single ball is drawn, find the probability that the ball is not green.

    a. $\dfrac{5}{15}$

    b. $\dfrac{10}{15}$

    c. $\dfrac{9}{15}$

    d. $\dfrac{6}{15}$

25. Which of the following is the sum formula for the sequence where $a_n = 3n - 5$

    a. $S_n = \dfrac{n(5n+9)}{2}$

    b. $S_n = \dfrac{n(3n+13)}{2}$

    c. $S_n = \dfrac{n(5n-9)}{2}$

    d. $S_n = \dfrac{n(3n-7)}{2}$

1. Find the third term of the recursively defined infinite sequence

    $a_1 = 6$, $a_{k+1} = (k+4) a_k$.

     a. $a_3 = 177$

     b. $a_3 = 168$

     c. $a_3 = 179$

     d. $a_3 = 180$

2. Find the fourth term of the sequence of partial sums for the given sequence

    $$\left\{ 5 + \frac{1}{2} n \right\}.$$

     a. $S_4 = 20$

     b. $S_4 = 25$

     c. $S_4 = 35$

     d. $S_4 = 18$

3. Find the specified term of the arithmetic sequence that has the two given terms.

    $a_1:$ $a_8 = 56$, $a_9 = 63$

     a. $a_1 = 21$

     b. $a_1 = 7$

     c. $a_1 = 1$

     d. $a_1 = 14$

4. Find the sum.

$$\sum_{k=1}^{16} (3n - 1)$$

a. $s = 386$

b. $s = 389$

c. $s = 392$

d. $s = 395$

5. Find the sum.

$$\sum_{k=1}^{20} \left(\frac{5}{2} n + 4 \right)$$

a. $s = 620$

b. $s = 605$

c. $s = 590$

d. $s = 615$

6. Find the fifth term of the geometric sequence :

$$64, 16, 4, 1,...$$

a. $- 4$

b. $- \frac{1}{4}$

c. $\frac{1}{4}$

d. 4

7. Find the sum :

$$\sum_{k=1}^{10} 2^k$$

    a.   1023

    b.   1022

    c.   2044

    d.   2046

8. Find the sum of the infinite geometric series :

$$192 + 144 + 108 + 81 + \dots$$

    a. $771 \frac{3}{4}$

    b. $774 \frac{3}{4}$

    c. $763 \frac{3}{4}$

    d. $768 \frac{3}{4}$

9. Find the rational number represented by the repeating decimal :

$$1.\overline{1417}$$

    a. $\dfrac{11416}{9999}$

    b. $\dfrac{9999}{9999}$

    c. $\dfrac{11417}{999}$

    d. $\dfrac{11417}{9999}$

10. The yearly depreciation of a certain machine is 15% of its value at the beginning of the year. If the original cost of the machine is $40000, what is its value after 9 years?

    a. $0.00

    b. $7874.98

    c. $9264.68

    d. $9250.63

11. If a deposit of $500 is made on the first day of each month into an account that pays 7% interest per year compounded monthly, determine the amount in the account after 10 years.

    a. $87047.28

    b. $87047.23

    c. $86542.40

    d. $87041.18

12. A landfill currently has 2700 tons of waste. During each the year, the tonnage is reduced by 20% due to decomposition. Then, at the end of each year, 2700 new tons are added to the fill. If this process continues forever, what is the maximum tonnage that the landfill can reach?

    a.   14750 tons

    b.   12275 tons

    c.   33750 tons

    d.   13500 tons

13. Evaluate the expression:

$$\frac{8!}{7!}$$

    a.   72

    b.   1

    c.   8

14. Evaluate the expression $\binom{8}{2}$.

    a.   56

    b.   28

    c.   252

    d.   40320

15. Use the binomial theorem to expand and simplify.

$$(2x - 5y)^4$$

a. $2x^4 - 5x^3y + 16x^2y^2 - 625xy^3 + 1000y^4$

b. $16x^4 - 160x^3y + 600x^2y^2 - 1000xy^3 + 625y^4$

c. $2x^4 + 160x^3y + 16x^2y^2 + 1000xy^3 + 625y^4$

d. $16x^4 - 160x^3y - 1000x^2y^2 - 600xy^3 + 625y^4$

16. Find the number :

$$P(9, 3)$$

a.   484

b.   516

c.   504

d.   528

17. If six basketball teams are in a tournament, find the number of different ways that first, second, and third place can be decided, assuming ties are not allowed.

a.   360

b.   6

c.   120

d.   840

18. In how many different ways can nine people be seated in a row?

    a.   362880

    b.   387420489

    c.   512

    d.   81

19. With six different flags, how many different signals can be sent by placing four flags, one above the other, on a flag pole?

    a.   204

    b.   36

    c.   360

    d.   216

20. In how many different ways can four books be selected from a seven-volume set of books?

    a.   343

    b.   28

    c.   210

    d.   840

    e.   5040

21. Consider any four points such that no three are collinear. How many lines are determined?

    a.   2

    b.   4

    c.   6

22. To win a state lottery game, a player must correctly select six numbers from the numbers 1 through 52. Find the total number of selections possible if a player selects only even numbers.

    a.   156

    b.   2443022400

    c.   230230

    d.   10179260

23. A single card is drawn from a 52-card deck. Find the probability that the card is an ace.

    a. $\dfrac{1}{52}$

    b. $\dfrac{1}{12}$

    c. $\dfrac{1}{13}$

    d. $\dfrac{2}{13}$

24. An urn contains five red balls, six green balls, and four white balls. If a single ball is drawn, find the probability that the ball is red.

    a. $\dfrac{5}{15}$

    b. $\dfrac{10}{15}$

    c. $\dfrac{6}{15}$

    d. $\dfrac{9}{15}$

25. Which of the following is the sum formula for the sequence where $a_n = 6n - 3$.

    a. $S_n = 3n^2$

    b. $S_n = n^2$

    c. $S_n = 3n^2 - n$

    d. $S_n = 6n^2$

1. Find the third term of the recursively defined infinite sequence

$a_1 = 3$, $a_{k+1} = (k + 1) a_k$.

    a. $a_3 = 13$

    b. $a_3 = 25$

    c. $a_3 = 28$

    d. $a_3 = 18$

2. Find the specified term of the arithmetic sequence that has the two given terms.

$$a_1 : \quad a_8 = 59, \quad a_9 = 66$$

    a. $a_1 = 10$

    b. $a_1 = 17$

    c. $a_1 = 24$

    d. $a_1 = 1$

3. Find the sum.

$$\sum_{k=1}^{24} \left(\frac{3}{2} n + 8 \right)$$

    a. $s = 630$

    b. $s = 627$

    c. $s = 642$

    d. $s = 639$

4. Find the sum :

$$\sum_{k=1}^{8} 4^{k}$$

    a.   21844

    b.   65535

    c.   87376

    d.   87380

5. Find the rational number represented by the repeating decimal :

$$3.\overline{1417}$$

    a. $\dfrac{31417}{9999}$

    b. $\dfrac{31414}{9999}$

    c. $\dfrac{31417}{999}$

    d. $\dfrac{29997}{9999}$

6. The yearly depreciation of a certain machine is 25% of its value at the beginning of the year. If the original cost of the machine is $10000, what is its value after 9 years?

    a. $563.14

    b. $0.04

    c. $736.80

    d. $750.85

7. Evaluate the expression $\begin{pmatrix} 7 \\ 5 \end{pmatrix}$

    a.   2520

    b.   5040

    c.   21

    d.   168

8. Find the number: $P(9, 3)$

    a.   516

    b.   484

    c.   528

    d.   504

9. In how many different ways can six people be seated in a row?

    a.   64

    b.   720

    c.   36

    d.   46656

10. In how many different ways can three books be selected from a nine-volume set of books?

    a.   729

    b.   72

    c.   362880

    d.   27

    e.   504

11. To win a state lottery game, a player must correctly select six numbers from the numbers 1 through 45. Find the total number of selections possible if a player selects only even numbers.

    a.   4072530

    b.   132

    c.   74613

    d.   977407200

12. An urn contains five red balls, six green balls, and four white balls. If a single ball is drawn, find the probability that the ball is not green.

    a. $\frac{9}{15}$

    b. $\frac{10}{15}$

    c. $\frac{5}{15}$

    d. $\frac{6}{15}$

13. A landfill currently has 4000 tons of waste. During each the year, the tonnage is reduced by 25% due to decomposition. Then, at the end of each year, 4000 new tons are added to the fill. If this process continues forever, what is the maximum tonnage that the landfill can reach?

14. Find the fourth term of the sequence of partial sums for the given sequence

$$\left\{ 3 + \frac{1}{2} n \right\}.$$

15. Find the sum.

$$\sum_{k=1}^{16} (2n + 3)$$

16. Find the seventh term of the geometric sequence :

$$8, 4, 2, 1,...$$

17. Find the sum of the infinite geometric series :

$$1029 + 441 + 189 + 81 + ...$$

18. If a deposit of $250 is made on the first day of each month into an account that pays 7% interest per year compounded monthly, determine the amount in the account after 12 years.

19. Evaluate the expression:

$$\frac{9!}{3!}$$

20. Use the binomial theorem to expand and simplify.

$$(3x - 4y)^4$$

21. If seven basketball teams are in a tournament, find the number of different ways that first, second, and third place can be decided, assuming ties are not allowed.

22. With six different flags, how many different signals can be sent by placing two flags, one above the other, on a flag pole?

23. Consider any six points such that no three are collinear. How many lines are determined?

24. An urn contains five red balls, six green balls, and four white balls. If a single ball is drawn, find the probability that the ball is not green.

25. Prove, by mathematical induction, that $S_n = 4n^2$ for $a_n = 8n - 4$.

1. Find the third term of the recursively defined infinite sequence

    $a_1 = 7$, $a_{k+1} = (k+4)a_k$.
    a. $a_3 = 198$

    b. $a_3 = 209$

    c. $a_3 = 205$

    d. $a_3 = 210$

2. Find the specified term of the arithmetic sequence that has the two given terms.

    $$a_1 : \quad a_8 = 31, \quad a_9 = 35$$

    a. $a_1 = 11$

    b. $a_1 = 7$

    c. $a_1 = 3$

    d. $a_1 = 1$

3. Find the sum.

    $$\sum_{k=1}^{28} \left(\frac{5}{2}n + 5 \right)$$

    a. $s = 1155$

    b. $s = 1150$

    c. $s = 1140$

    d. $s = 1125$

4. Find the sum :

$$\sum_{k=1}^{5} 3^{k}$$

    a.   360

    b.   242

    c.   120

    d.   363

5. Find the rational number represented by the repeating decimal :

$$3.\overline{6251}$$

    a. $\dfrac{36251}{9999}$

    b. $\dfrac{36248}{9999}$

    c. $\dfrac{36251}{999}$

    d. $\dfrac{29997}{9999}$

6. The yearly depreciation of a certain machine is 25% of its value at the beginning of the year. If the original cost of the machine is $5000, what is its value after 5 years?

    a. $889.89

    b. $4.88

    c. $1186.52

    d. $1172.47

7. Evaluate the expression. $\begin{pmatrix} 6 \\ 2 \end{pmatrix}$

    a.   840

    b.   720

    c.   30

    d.   15

8. Find the number :

$$P(9, 3)$$

    a.   484

    b.   516

    c.   528

    d.   504

9. In how many different ways can five people be seated in a row?

    a.   3125

    b.   25

    c.   120

    d.   32

10. In how many different ways can two books be selected from a five-volume set of books?

    a.   5

    b.   120

    c.   125

    d.   20

    e.   10

11. To win a state lottery game, a player must correctly select six numbers from the numbers 1 through 36. Find the total number of selections possible if a player selects only even numbers.

    a.   108

    b.   973896

    c.   18564

    d.   233735040

12. An urn contains five red balls, six green balls, and four white balls. If a single ball is drawn, find the probability that the ball is white.

    a. $\dfrac{4}{15}$

    b. $\dfrac{10}{15}$

    c. $\dfrac{11}{15}$

    d. $\dfrac{5}{15}$

13. A landfill currently has 4600 tons of waste. During each the year, the tonnage is reduced by 20% due to decomposition. Then, at the end of each year, 4600 new tons are added to the fill. If this process continues forever, what is the maximum tonnage that the landfill can reach?

14. Find the fourth term of the sequence of partial sums for the given sequence

$$\left\{\, 4 + \frac{3}{2} n \,\right\}.$$

15. Find the sum.

$$\sum_{k=1}^{26} (4n - 1)$$

16. Find the seventh term of the geometric sequence :

27, 9, 3, 1,...

17. Find the sum of the infinite geometric series :

2401 + 1029 + 441 + 189 + ...

18. If a deposit of $300 is made on the first day of each month into an account that pays 10% interest per year compounded monthly, determine the amount in the account after 11 years.

19. Evaluate the expression:

$$\frac{6!}{3!}$$

20. Use the binomial theorem to expand and simplify.

$$(5x - 4y)^4$$

21. If eleven basketball teams are in a tournament, find the number of different ways that first, second, and third place can be decided, assuming ties are not allowed.

22. With seven different flags, how many different signals can be sent by placing three flags, one above the other, on a flag pole?

23. Consider any four points such that no three are collinear. How many lines are determined?

24. An urn contains five red balls, six green balls, and four white balls. If a single ball is drawn, find the probability that the ball is red or white.

25. Prove, by mathematical induction, that $4^n + 8$ is divisible by 3 for all natural numbers n.

Test Form 9-A

1. 150
2. 31
3. 6
4. 803
5. 415
6. $\dfrac{1}{4}$
7. 62
8. 4201.75
9. $\dfrac{41413}{9999}$
10. 6553.60
11. 146273.49
12. 16500 tons
13. 7
14. 35
15. $625x^4 - 2000x^3 \cdot y + 2400x^2 \cdot y^2 - 1280x \cdot y^3 + 256y^4$
16. 504
17. 120
18. 5040
19. 120
20. 210
21. 36
22. 18564
23. $\dfrac{12}{52}$
24. $\dfrac{4}{15}$

25. **Part 1:** We need to show that $6^n - 1$ is divisible by 5 when n = 1.
    When n = 1, $6^1 - 1 = 5$ and 5 is divisible by 5 (ie. 5/5 does not have a remainder).

    Part 2: Now we assume $6^n - 1$ is divisible by 5 when n = k and we need to show that
    $6^n - 1$ is divisible by 5 when n = k + 1. That is, we need to show that $6^k - 1 = 5x$ for some integer x.

    $6^k - 1 = 5x \rightarrow 6^k = 5x + 1$. Now, multiply both sides by 6 and we have

    $6(6^k) = 6(5x + 1) \rightarrow 6^{k+1} = 30x + 6$. Next, subtract 1 from both sides to get

    $6^{k+1} - 1 = 30x + 5 \rightarrow 6^{k+1} - 1 = 30x + 5 \rightarrow 6^{k+1} - 1 = 5(6x + 1)\ldots$

Test Form 9-B

1. 84
2. 35
3. 8
4. 800
5. 246
6. $\dfrac{1}{4}$
7. 1092
8. 2457.6
9. $\dfrac{13469}{9999}$
10. 14762.25
11. 74114.43
12. 26000 tons
13. 12
14. 4

15. $625x^4 - 2000x^3 \cdot y + 2400x^2 \cdot y^2 - 1280x \cdot y^3 + 256y^4$

16. 110
17. 210
18. 5040
19. 1680
20. 720
21. 15
22. 230230
23. 1, 12
24. $\dfrac{4}{15}$

25.

Part 1: We need to show that S_n is true when n = 1.

$$S_1 = \frac{1(5 \cdot 1 + 1)}{2} = 3 \text{ and since } a_1 = 3, \text{ the sum formula holds true for } n = 1.$$

Part 2: We assume that the sum formula holds true for n = k and show that it will be true for n = k +1; that is, we need to prove that

$$S_{k+1} = \frac{(k+1)(5(k+1)+1)}{2} \text{ or } S_{k+1} = \frac{(k+1)(5k+6)}{2}$$

$$S_{k+1} = S_k + a_{k+1} \rightarrow S_{k+1} = \frac{k(5k+1)}{2} + 5(k+1) - 2 \rightarrow S_{k+1} = \frac{k(5k+1)}{2} + 5k + 3 \rightarrow$$

$$S_{k+1} = \frac{5k^2 + k + 10k + 6}{2} \rightarrow S_{k+1} = \frac{5k^2 + 11k + 6}{2} \rightarrow S_{k+1} = \frac{(k+1)(5k+6)}{2}$$

Test Form 9-C

1. c	**2.** d	**3.** b	**4.** d	**5.** c	**6.** c	**7.** b	**8.** d
9. b	**10.** a	**11.** d	**12.** d	**13.** c	**14.** b	**15.** c	**16.** a
17. c	**18.** d	**19.** b	**20.** c	**21.** b	**22.** c	**23.** d	**24.** c
25. d							

Test Form 9-D

1. d	**2.** b	**3.** b	**4.** c	**5.** b	**6.** c	**7.** d	**8.** d
9. a	**10.** c	**11.** b	**12.** d	**13.** c	**14.** b	**15.** b	**16.** c
17. c	**18.** a	**19.** c	**20.** d	**21.** c	**22.** c	**23.** c	**24.** a
25. a							

Test Form 9-E

1. d
2. a
3. c
4. d
5. b
6. d
7. c
8. d
9. b
10. e
11. c
12. a
13. 16000 tons
14. 17
15. 320
16. $\dfrac{1}{8}$
17. 1800.75
18. 56501.43
19. 120
20. $81x^4 - 432x^3 \cdot y + 864x^2 \cdot y^2 - 768x \cdot y^3 + 256y^4$
21. 210
22. 30
23. 15
24. $\dfrac{9}{15}$

25. **Part 1**: We need to show that S_n is true when $n = 1$.

$S_1 = 4(1)^2 = 4$ and since $a_1 = 4$, the sum formula holds true for $n = 1$.

   Part 2: We assume that the sum formula holds true for $n = k$ and show that it will be true for $n = k + 1$; that is, we need to prove that $S_{k+1} = 4(k+1)^2$

$S_{k+1} = S_k + a_{k+1} \rightarrow S_{k+1} = 4k^2 + 8(k + 1) - 4 \rightarrow S_{k+1} = 4k^2 + 8k + 4 \rightarrow$

$S_{k+1} = 4(k^2 + 2k + 1) \rightarrow S_{k+1} = 4(k + 1)^2 \ldots$

Test Form 9-F

1. d
2. c
3. a
4. d
5. b
6. c
7. d
8. d
9. c
10. d
11. c
12. a
13. 23000 tons
14. 31
15. 1378
16. $\dfrac{1}{27}$
17. 4201.75
18. 72255.30
19. 120
20. $625x^4 - 2000x^3 \cdot y + 2400x^2 \cdot y^2 - 1280x \cdot y^3 + 256y^4$
21. 990
22. 210
23. 6
24. $\dfrac{9}{15}$
25. **Part 1**: We need to show that $4^n + 8$ is divisible by 3 when n = 1.
    When n = 1, $4^1 + 8 = 12$ and 12 is divisible by 3 (ie. 12/3 does not have a remainder).

    Part 2: Now we assume $4^n + 8$ is divisible by 3 when n = k and we need to show that
    $4^n + 8$ is divisible by 3 when n = k + 1. That is, we need to show that $4^{k+1} + 8 = 3x$ for some integer x.

    $4^k + 8 = 3x \rightarrow 4^k = 3x - 8$. Now, multiply both sides by 4 and we have

    $4(4^k) = 4(3x - 8) \rightarrow 4^{k+1} = 12x - 32$. Next, add 8 to both sides to get

    $4^{k+1} + 8 = 12x - 24 \rightarrow 4^{k+1} + 8 = 3(4x - 8) \ldots$

1. Find the focus of the parabola: $4y = x^2$

2. Find the vertex of the parabola: $(x + 4)^2 = -4(y - 9)$

3. Find the directrix of the parabola: $(y + 10)^2 = -16(x + 5)$

4. Find an equation of the parabola that satisfies the condition.

Vertex $V(-3, 6)$, directrix $y = 5$

5. Find an equation for the parabola that has a vertical axis and passes through the given points.

$P(2, 1), Q(-2, -11), R(3, -6)$

6. Find an equation of the parabola that satisfies the condition.

Vertex $V(-6, 7)$, directrix $y = 2$

7. Find an equation for the ellipse that has its center at the origin and satisfies the conditions:

Vertices $V(\pm 10, 0)$, Foci $F(\pm 4, 0)$

8. Find an equation for the ellipse that has its center at the origin and satisfies the conditions :

horizontal major axis of length 12, minor axis of length 4 .

9. Assume that the length of the major axis of Earth's orbit is 185000000 miles and that the eccentricity is 0.017. Approximate, to the nearest 1000 miles, the minimum distance between Earth and the sun.

10. Find the vertices of the hyperbola: $\dfrac{y^2}{16} - \dfrac{x^2}{9} = 1$

11. Find the equations of the asymptotes of the hyperbola: $\dfrac{(x-4)^2}{49} - \dfrac{(y-1)^2}{9} = 1$

12. Find the equations of the asymptotes of the hyperbola: $y^2 - 4x^2 - 12y - 16x + 19 = 0$

13. Find an equation in x and y whose graph contains the points on the curve C.
$$x = 8 \sin t, \ y = 6 \cos t; \ 0 \le t \le 2\pi$$

14. The parametric equations specify the position of a moving point $P(x, y)$ at time t. Sketch the graph, and indicate the motion of P as t increases.
$$x = \sin t, \ y = \cos t; \ 0 \le t \le \pi$$

15. The parametric equations specify the position of a moving point $P(x, y)$ at time t. Sketch the graph, and indicate the motion of P as t increases.

$$x = \cos^2 t,\ y = \sin^2 t;\quad 0 \le t \le 2\pi$$

16. Change the polar coordinates $(3,\ \pi/3)$ to rectangular coordinates.
Enter the exact answer in the form (x, y). Use *sqr(x)* to enter the square root of a number x.

17. Change the rectangular coordinates $(-5\sqrt{3},\ -5)$ to polar coordinates with $r > 0$ and $0 \le \theta \le 2\pi$.

18. Find a polar equation in r and θ that has the same graph as the equation $x^2 + y^2 = 100$.

19. Find a polar equation in r and θ that has the same graph as the equation $x + y = 5$.

20. Find a polar equation in r and θ that has the same graph as the equation $6y = -x$.

21. Find a polar equation in r and θ that has the same graph as the equation $(x - 7)^2 + y^2 = 49$.

22. Sketch the graph of the polar equation $r = 2 + 4\sin\theta$.

23. Sketch the graph of the polar equation $r = 2 + 2\sec\theta$

24. Find an equation in x and y that has the same graph as the polar equation.

$$r = \frac{8}{\cos\theta - 4}$$

25. Sketch the graph of the polar equation: $r = \frac{12}{2 + 6\cos\theta}$

1. Find the equations of the asymptotes of the hyperbola: $y^2 - 4x^2 - 12y - 16x + 11 = 0$

2. Find an equation in x and y that has the same graph as the polar equation.

$$r = \frac{10}{\cos \theta - 6}$$

3. Find the focus of the parabola.

$$8\,y = x^2$$

4. Find the vertex of the parabola.

$$(x + 6)^2 = -8(y - 7)$$

5. Find the directrix of the parabola.

$$(y + 8)^2 = -8(x + 9)$$

6. Find an equation of the parabola that satisfies the condition.

Vertex $V(-6, 7)$, directrix $y = 2$

7. Find an equation for the parabola that has a vertical axis and passes through the given points.

$P(3, -9)$, $Q(-3, -39)$, $R(2, 1)$

8. Sketch the graph of the ellipse, showing the foci: $y^2 + 9x^2 = 9$.

9. Find an equation for the ellipse that has its center at the origin and satisfies the conditions :

$$\text{vertices } V(\pm 7, 0), \quad \text{foci } F(\pm 4, 0).$$

10. Find an equation for the ellipse that has its center at the origin and satisfies the conditions :

horizontal major axis of length 8, minor axis of length 4 .

11. Assume that the length of the major axis of Earth's orbit is 186000000 miles and that the eccentricity is 0.017. Approximate, to the nearest 1000 miles, the minimum distance between Earth and the sun.

12. Find the equations of the asymptotes of the hyperbola

$$\frac{(x-4)^2}{25} - \frac{(y-1)^2}{9} = 1$$

13. Find an equation in x and y whose graph contains the points on the curve C. Sketch the graph of C, and indicate the orientation.

$$x = 4t^2 - 5, \ y = 2t + 3; \ t \text{ in } \mathbb{R}$$

14. The parametric equations specify the position of a moving point $P(x, y)$ at time t. Sketch the graph, and indicate the motion of P as t increases.
$$x = \sin t, \, y = \cos t; \; 0 \le t \le \pi$$

15. The parametric equations specify the position of a moving point $P(x, y)$ at time t. Sketch the graph, and indicate the motion of P as t increases.
$$x = \cos^2 t, \, y = \sin^2 t; \; 0 \le t \le 2\pi$$

16. Change the polar coordinates $(5, \, \pi/6)$ to rectangular coordinates.
Enter the exact answer in the form (x, y). Use $sqr(x)$ to enter the square root of a number x.

17. Change the rectangular coordinates $(3\sqrt{3}, \, 3)$ to polar coordinates with $r > 0$ and $0 \le \theta \le 2\pi$.

18. Find a polar equation in r and θ that has the same graph as the equation $x^2 + y^2 = 81$.

19. Find a polar equation in r and θ that has the same graph as the equation $x + y = 3$.

20. Find a polar equation in r and θ that has the same graph as the equation $5y = -x$.

21. Find a polar equation in r and θ that has the same graph as the equation $(x - 3)^2 + y^2 = 9$.

22. Sketch the graph of the polar equation $r = 2 + 4\sin\theta$.

23. Sketch the graph of the polar equation $r = 2 + 2\sec\theta$

24. Sketch the graph of the polar equation: $r = \dfrac{12}{2 + 6\cos\theta}$

25.
Find the vertices of the hyperbola: $\dfrac{y^2}{9} - \dfrac{x^2}{81} = 1$

1. Find the equations of the asymptotes of the hyperbola:

$$y^2 - 4x^2 - 12y - 16x + 19 = 0$$

   a. $y - 3 = 9(x + 7) , y - 3 = - 9(x + 7)$

   b. $y - 6 = 2(x + 2) , y - 6 = -2(x + 2)$

   c. $y - 7 = 3(x + 9) , y - 7 = - 3(x + 9)$

2. Find the vertices of the hyperbola

$$\frac{y^2}{9} - \frac{x^2}{4} = 1$$

   a. $V(0 , 7) , V(0 , - 7)$

   b. $V(0 , 2) , V(0 , - 2)$

   c. $V(0 , 3) , V(0 , - 3)$

3. Sketch the graph of the polar equation: $r = 3 + 6 \sin \theta$

a.

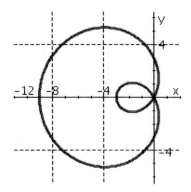

b.

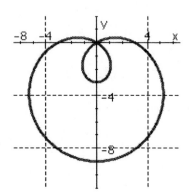

c.

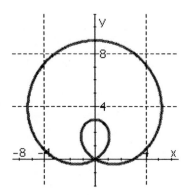

4. Sketch the graph of the ellipse.

$$y^2 + 16\,x^2 = 16.$$

a.

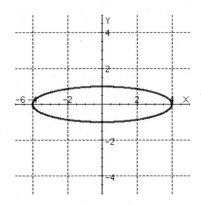

b.

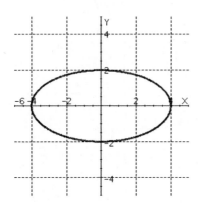

c.

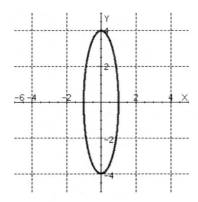

5. Sketch the graph of the ellipse, showing the foci .

$$4x^2 + y^2 = 4y - 3.$$

a.

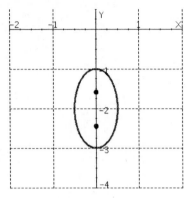

b.

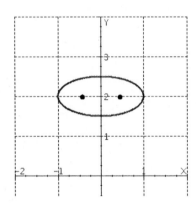

c.

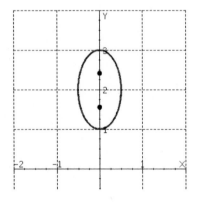

6. The parametric equations specify the position of a moving point $P(x, y)$ at time t. Sketch the graph.

$$x = 2 \sin t, \, y = 2 \cos t; \, 0 \leq t \leq \pi$$

a.

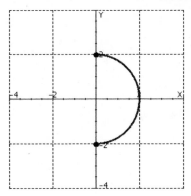

b.

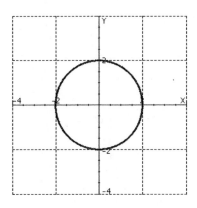

c.

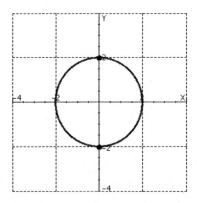

7. The parametric equations specify the position of a moving point $P(x, y)$ at time t. Sketch the graph.
$$x = 7\cos^2 t, \; y = 7\sin^2 t; \quad 0 \le t \le 2\pi$$

a.

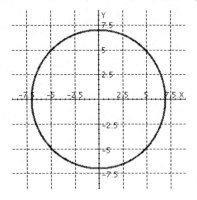

b.

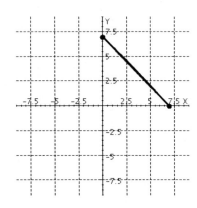

c.

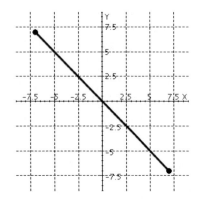

8. Find the focus of the parabola.

$$20\,y = x^2$$

    a. $F\,(1,5)$

    b. $F\,(0,20)$

    c. $F\,(2,5)$

    d. $F\,(0,5)$

9. Find the vertex of the parabola.

$$(x + 8)^2 = -8(y - 5)$$

    a. $V\,(8,5)$

    b. $V\,(-5,8)$

    c. $V\,(-8,5)$

    d. $V\,(8,8)$

10. Find the directrix of the parabola.

$$(y + 8)^2 = -12(x + 9)$$

    a. $x = 9$

    b. $x = -7$

    c. $x = -8$

    d. $x = -6$

11. Find an equation of the parabola that satisfies the condition.

Vertex $V(-1, 7)$, directrix $y = 4$

    a. $(y + 1)^2 = 12(y - 7)$

    b. $(x + 1)^2 = 12(y - 7)$

    c. $(x + 1)^2 = (y - 7)$

    d. $(x - 1)^2 = 12(y + 7)$

12. Find an equation for the parabola that has a vertical axis and passes through the given points.

$P(4, -37), Q(-3, -30), R(5, -62)$

    a. $y = -3x^2 + 2x + 3$

    b. $y = 3x^2 - 2x - 3$

    c. $y = -3x^2 + 2x - 3$

    d. $y = 2x^2 + 3x + 3$

13. Find an equation for the ellipse that has its center at the origin and satisfies the conditions :

vertices $V(\pm 10, 0)$,   foci $F(\pm 4, 0)$.

a. $\dfrac{x^2}{84} + \dfrac{y^2}{100} = 1$

b. $\dfrac{x^2}{116} + \dfrac{y^2}{84} = 1$

c. $\dfrac{x^2}{100} + \dfrac{y^2}{116} = 1$

d. $\dfrac{x^2}{100} + \dfrac{y^2}{84} = 1$

14. Find an equation for the ellipse that has its center at the origin and satisfies the conditions :

horizontal major axis of length 12, minor axis of length 8 .

a. $\dfrac{x^2}{16} + \dfrac{y^2}{36} = 1$

b. $\dfrac{x^2}{40} + \dfrac{y^2}{36} = 1$

c. $\dfrac{x^2}{36} + \dfrac{y^2}{16} = 1$

d. $\dfrac{x^2}{44} + \dfrac{y^2}{16} = 1$

15. Assume that the length of the major axis of Earth's orbit is 185000000 miles and that the eccentricity is 0.017. Approximate, to the nearest 1000 miles, the minimum distance between Earth and the sun.

     a.   90929000 mi

     b.   90931000 mi

     c.   90928000 mi

     d.   90926000 mi

16. Find the equations of the asymptotes of the hyperbola

$$\frac{(x-4)^2}{49} - \frac{(y-2)^2}{4} = 1$$

     a. $(y-4) = -\frac{2}{7}(x-2), (y-4) = \frac{2}{7}(x-2)$

     b. $(y-2) = -\frac{7}{2}(x-4), (y-2) = \frac{7}{2}(x-4)$

     c. $(y-2) = -\frac{2}{7}(x-4), (y-2) = \frac{2}{7}(x-4)$

17. Find an equation in x and y whose graph contains the points on the curve C.

$$x = 6 \sin t,\ y = 7 \cos t;\ 0 \le t \le 2\pi$$

a. $\dfrac{x^2}{49} - \dfrac{y^2}{36} = 1$

b. $\dfrac{x^2}{36} - \dfrac{y^2}{49} = 1$

c. $\dfrac{x^2}{36} + \dfrac{y^2}{49} = 1$

d. $\dfrac{x^2}{49} + \dfrac{y^2}{36} = 1$

18. Change the polar coordinates $(5,\ \pi/4)$ to rectangular coordinates.

a. $\left(\dfrac{5\sqrt{2}}{4},\ \dfrac{5\sqrt{2}}{4} \right)$

b. $\left(\dfrac{5\sqrt{2}}{2},\ \dfrac{5\sqrt{2}}{2} \right)$

c. $\left(-\dfrac{5\sqrt{2}}{2},\ \dfrac{5\sqrt{2}}{4} \right)$

19. Change the rectangular coordinates $(2\sqrt{3},\ -2)$ to polar coordinates with $r > 0$ and $0 \le \theta \le 2\pi$.

a. $\left(2\sqrt{2},\ \dfrac{11\pi}{6} \right)$

b. $\left(4,\ \dfrac{11\pi}{6} \right)$

c. $\left(4,\ \dfrac{\pi}{6} \right)$

20. Find a polar equation in r and θ that has the same graph as the equation $x^2 + y^2 = 64$.

    a. $r = 64$

    b. $\theta = 7$

    c. $r = 8\cos\theta$

    d. $r = 8$

    e. $r = -8$

21. Find a polar equation in r and θ that has the same graph as the equation $x + y = 7$.

    a. $r = 7(\cos\theta + \sin\theta)$

    b. $r = \dfrac{7}{\sin\theta}$

    c. $r = \dfrac{7}{\cos\theta}$

    d. $r = \dfrac{7}{\cos\theta + \sin\theta}$

22. Find a polar equation in r and θ that has the same graph as the equation $10\,y = -x$.

    a. $\theta = \tan 10$

    b. $r = \dfrac{10}{\sin\theta}$

    c. $r = \dfrac{10}{\cos\theta}$

    d. $\theta = \arctan\left(-\dfrac{1}{10}\right)$

23. Find a polar equation in r and θ that has the same graph as the equation $(x - 2)^2 + y^2 = 4$.

    a. $r = 4\sin\theta$

    b. $r = \cos 4\theta$

    c. $r = 4\sec\theta$

    d. $r = 4\cos\theta$

24. Find an equation in x and y that has the same graph as the polar equation

$$r = \frac{10}{\cos\theta - 6}$$

    a. $35x^2 + 36y^2 + 20x - 100 = 0$

    b. $37x^2 + 36y^2 + 21x - 98 = 0$

    c. $35x^2 + 33y^2 + 18x - 100 = 0$

    d. $35x^2 + 6y^2 + 20x + 100 = 0$

25. Sketch the graph of the polar equation

$$r = \frac{8}{2 + 4\cos\theta}$$

a.
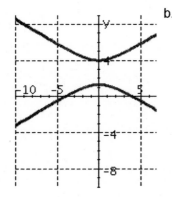

b.
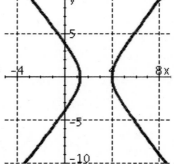

c.
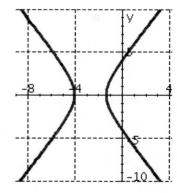

1. Find the equations of the asymptotes of the hyperbola:

$$y^2 - 4x^2 - 12y - 16x + 11 = 0$$

    a. $y - 6 = 2(x + 2)$, $y - 6 = -2(x + 2)$

    b. $y - 1 = 3(x + 7)$, $y - 1 = -3(x + 7)$

    c. $y - 3 = 7(x + 1)$, $y - 3 = -7(x + 1)$

2. Find the vertices of the hyperbola

$$\frac{y^2}{4} - \frac{x^2}{16} = 1$$

    a. $V(0, 8)$, $V'(0, -8)$

    b. $V(0, 4)$, $V'(0, -4)$

    c. $V(0, 2)$, $V'(0, -2)$

3. Sketch the graph of the polar equation: $r = 3 + 6\sin\theta$

    a.

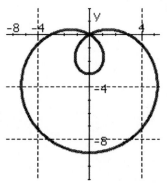

    b.

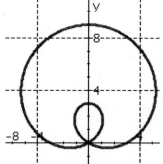

    c.

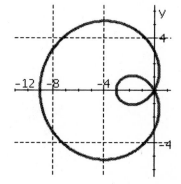

4. Sketch the graph of the ellipse.

$$y^2 + 16\,x^2 = 16.$$

a.

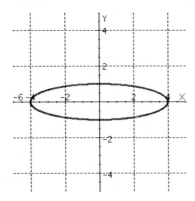

b.

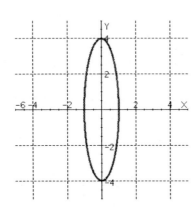

c.

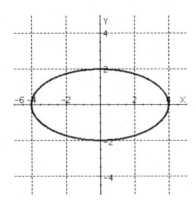

5. Sketch the graph of the ellipse, showing the foci .
$$4x^2 + y^2 = 6y - 8.$$

a.

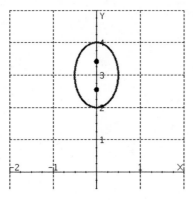

b.

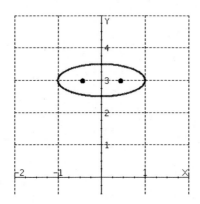

c.

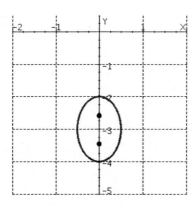

6. The parametric equations specify the position of a moving point $P(x, y)$ at time t. Sketch the graph.

$$x = 8 \sin t, \ y = 8 \cos t; \ 0 \leq t \leq \pi$$

a.

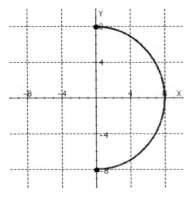

b.

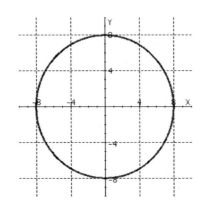

c.

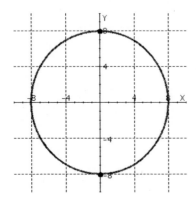

7. The parametric equations specify the position of a moving point $P(x, y)$ at time t. Sketch the graph.
$$x = 3\cos^2 t,\; y = 3\sin^2 t;\quad 0 \leq t \leq 2\pi$$

a.

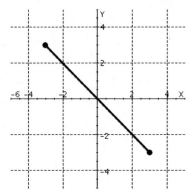

b.

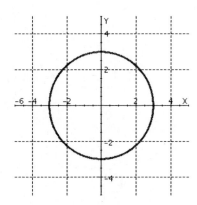

c.

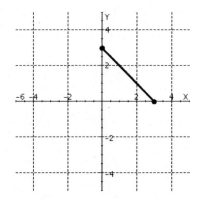

8. Find the focus of the parabola.

$$20\,y = x^2$$

    a. $F\,(0,20)$

    b. $F\,(0,5)$

    c. $F\,(2,5)$

    d. $F\,(1,5)$

9. Find the vertex of the parabola.

$$(\,x + 10\,)^2 = -\,8(\,y - 3\,)$$

    a. $V\,(-10,3)$

    b. $V\,(10,3)$

    c. $V\,(-3,8)$

    d. $V\,(10,8)$

10. Find the directrix of the parabola.

$$(\,y + 2\,)^2 = -\,12(\,x + 7\,)$$

    a. $x = -2$

    b. $x = -4$

    c. $x = -5$

    d. $x = 7$

11. Find an equation of the parabola that satisfies the condition.

Vertex $V(-5, 6)$, directrix $y = 5$

    a. $(y + 5)^2 = 4(y - 6)$

    b. $(x + 5)^2 = 4(y - 6)$

    c. $(x + 5)^2 = (y - 6)$

    d. $(x - 5)^2 = 4(y + 6)$

12. Find an equation for the parabola that has a vertical axis and passes through the given points.

$P(3, 1)$, $Q(-3, -29)$, $R(4, -8)$

    a. $y = -4x^2 + 5x - 2$

    b. $y = 5x^2 + 4x + 2$

    c. $y = 2x^2 - 5x - 4$

    d. $y = -2x^2 + 5x + 4$

13. Find an equation for the ellipse that has its center at the origin and satisfies the conditions :

vertices $V(\pm 10, 0)$, foci $F(\pm 3, 0)$.

a. $\dfrac{x^2}{91} + \dfrac{y^2}{100} = 1$

b. $\dfrac{x^2}{109} + \dfrac{y^2}{91} = 1$

c. $\dfrac{x^2}{100} + \dfrac{y^2}{109} = 1$

d. $\dfrac{x^2}{100} + \dfrac{y^2}{91} = 1$

14. Find an equation for the ellipse that has its center at the origin and satisfies the conditions :

horizontal major axis of length 10, minor axis of length 8 .

a. $\dfrac{x^2}{25} + \dfrac{y^2}{16} = 1$

b. $\dfrac{x^2}{33} + \dfrac{y^2}{16} = 1$

c. $\dfrac{x^2}{16} + \dfrac{y^2}{25} = 1$

d. $\dfrac{x^2}{29} + \dfrac{y^2}{25} = 1$

15. Assume that the length of the major axis of Earth's orbit is 186000000 miles and that the eccentricity is 0.017. Approximate, to the nearest 1000 miles, the minimum distance between Earth and the sun.

    a.   91420000 mi

    b.   91419000 mi

    c.   91422000 mi

    d.   91421000 mi

16. Find the equations of the asymptotes of the hyperbola

$$\frac{(x-2)^2}{9} - \frac{(y-4)^2}{25} = 1$$

    a. $(y-4) = -\frac{5}{3}(x-2), (y-4) = \frac{5}{3}(x-2)$

    b. $(y-2) = -\frac{5}{3}(x-4), (y-2) = \frac{5}{3}(x-4)$

    c. $(y-4) = -\frac{3}{5}(x-2), (y-4) = \frac{3}{5}(x-2)$

17. Find an equation in x and y whose graph contains the points on the curve C.

$$x = 4\sin t, \; y = 5\cos t; \; 0 \le t \le 2\pi$$

    a. $\dfrac{x^2}{25} - \dfrac{y^2}{16} = 1$

    b. $\dfrac{x^2}{16} + \dfrac{y^2}{25} = 1$

    c. $\dfrac{x^2}{25} + \dfrac{y^2}{16} = 1$

    d. $\dfrac{x^2}{16} - \dfrac{y^2}{25} = 1$

18. Change the polar coordinates $(7, \pi/3)$ to rectangular coordinates.

 a. $\left(-\dfrac{7}{2}, \dfrac{7\sqrt{3}}{4} \right)$

 b. $\left(\dfrac{7}{4}, \dfrac{7\sqrt{3}}{4} \right)$

 c. $\left(\dfrac{7}{2}, \dfrac{7\sqrt{3}}{2} \right)$

19. Change the rectangular coordinates $(7\sqrt{3}, 7)$ to polar coordinates with $r > 0$ and $0 \le \theta \le 2\pi$.

 a. $\left(14, \dfrac{\pi}{6} \right)$

 b. $\left(7\sqrt{2}, \dfrac{\pi}{6} \right)$

 c. $\left(14, \dfrac{11\pi}{6} \right)$

20. Find a polar equation in r and θ that has the same graph as the equation $x^2 + y^2 = 36$.

 a. $r = 36$

 b. $r = 6 \cos \theta$

 c. $\theta = \pi$

 d. $r = 6$

 e. $r = -6$

21. Find a polar equation in r and θ that has the same graph as the equation $x + y = 7$.

     a. $r = 7(\cos\theta + \sin\theta)$

     b. $r = \dfrac{7}{\sin\theta}$

     c. $r = \dfrac{7}{\cos\theta + \sin\theta}$

     d. $r = \dfrac{7}{\cos\theta}$

22. Find a polar equation in r and θ that has the same graph as the equation $9\,y = -x$.

     a. $\theta = \tan 9$

     b. $r = \dfrac{9}{\sin\theta}$

     c. $\theta = \arctan\left(-\dfrac{1}{9}\right)$

     d. $r = \dfrac{9}{\cos\theta}$

23. Find a polar equation in r and θ that has the same graph as the equation $(x - 9)^2 + y^2 = 81$.

     a. $r = 18\sin\theta$

     b. $r = 18\cos\theta$

     c. $r = \cos 18\theta$

     d. $r = 81\sec\theta$

24. Find an equation in x and y that has the same graph as the polar equation

$$r = \frac{6}{\cos \theta - 4}$$

    a. $15x^2 + 16y^2 + 12x - 36 = 0$

    b. $15x^2 + 4y^2 + 12x + 36 = 0$

    c. $15x^2 + 15y^2 + 11x - 36 = 0$

    d. $19x^2 + 16y^2 + 10x - 47 = 0$

25. Sketch the graph of the polar equation

$$r = \frac{32}{4 + 8 \cos \theta}$$

    a.

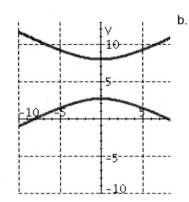

    b.   c.

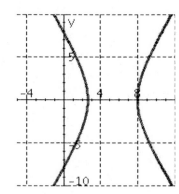

1. Find the equations of the asymptotes of the hyperbola:

$$y^2 - 4x^2 - 12y - 16x + 11 = 0$$

   a. $y - 3 = 7(x + 8)$, $y - 3 = - 7(x + 8)$

   b. $y - 7 = 8(x + 3)$, $y - 7 = - 8(x + 3)$

   c. $y - 6 = 2(x + 2)$, $y - 6 = -2(x + 2)$

2. Find the vertices of the hyperbola

$$\frac{y^2}{4} - \frac{x^2}{25} = 1$$

   a. $V(0 , 5)$, $V(0 , - 5)$

   b. $V(0 , 2)$, $V(0 , - 2)$

   c. $V(0 , 3)$, $V(0 , - 3)$

3. Find an equation in x and y whose graph contains the points on the curve C. Sketch the graph of C.

$$x = 4t^2 - 3, \ y = 2t + 3; \ t \text{ in } \mathbb{R}$$

  a. 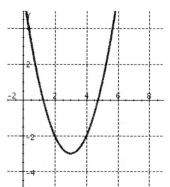   b. 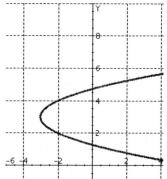   c.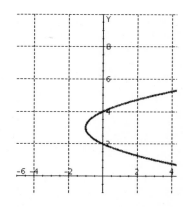

4. Sketch the graph of the ellipse, showing the foci .

$$4x^2 + y^2 = 6y - 8.$$

a.

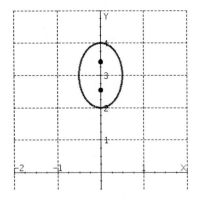

b.

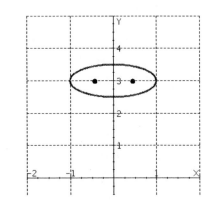

c.

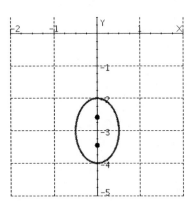

5. The parametric equations specify the position of a moving point $P(x, y)$ at time t. Sketch the graph.

$$x = 8 \cos^2 t,\ y = 8 \sin^2 t;\quad 0 \leq t \leq 2\pi$$

a.

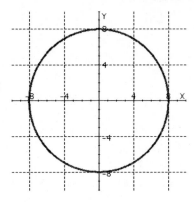

b.

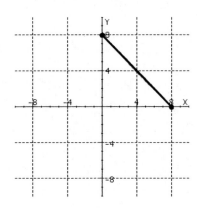

c.

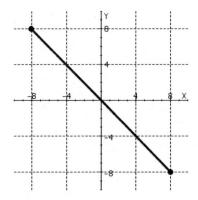

6. Find the focus of the parabola.

$$12\,y = x^2$$

    a.　　$F\,(1,3)$

    b.　　$F\,(0,12)$

    c.　　$F\,(2,3)$

    d.　　$F\,(0,3)$

7. Find the vertex of the parabola.

$$(x+4)^2 = -8(y-9)$$

    a.　　$V\,(4,9)$

    b.　　$V\,(-4,9)$

    c.　　$V\,(4,8)$

    d.　　$V\,(-9,8)$

8. Find the directrix of the parabola.

$$(y+12)^2 = -8(x+9)$$

    a.　　$x = -7$

    b.　　$x = -12$

    c.　　$x = -6$

    d.　　$x = 9$

9. Find an equation for the ellipse that has its center at the origin and satisfies the conditions :

horizontal major axis of length 12, minor axis of length 4 .

a. $$\frac{x^2}{36} + \frac{y^2}{4} = 1$$

b. $$\frac{x^2}{44} + \frac{y^2}{4} = 1$$

c. $$\frac{x^2}{4} + \frac{y^2}{36} = 1$$

d. $$\frac{x^2}{40} + \frac{y^2}{36} = 1$$

10. Find the equations of the asymptotes of the hyperbola

$$\frac{(x-4)^2}{9} - \frac{(y-2)^2}{4} = 1$$

a. $(y-4) = -\frac{2}{3}(x-2) , (y-4) = \frac{2}{3}(x-2)$

b. $(y-2) = -\frac{3}{2}(x-4) , (y-2) = \frac{3}{2}(x-4)$

c. $(y-2) = -\frac{2}{3}(x-4) , (y-2) = \frac{2}{3}(x-4)$

11. Change the polar coordinates $(7, \pi/3)$ to rectangular coordinates.

a. $\left(\dfrac{7}{4}, \dfrac{7\sqrt{3}}{4} \right)$

b. $\left(\dfrac{7}{2}, \dfrac{7\sqrt{3}}{2} \right)$

c. $\left(-\dfrac{7}{2}, \dfrac{7\sqrt{3}}{4} \right)$

12. Change the rectangular coordinates $(7\sqrt{3}, 7)$ to polar coordinates with $r > 0$ and $0 \le \theta \le 2\pi$.

a. $\left(14, \dfrac{11\pi}{6} \right)$

b. $\left(14, \dfrac{\pi}{6} \right)$

c. $\left(7\sqrt{2}, \dfrac{\pi}{6} \right)$

13. Find an equation in x and y that has the same graph as the polar equation.

$r = \dfrac{8}{\cos\theta - 4}$

14. Find an equation of the parabola that satisfies the condition.

Vertex V (- 4, 4), directrix $y = 2$

15. Find an equation for the parabola that has a vertical axis and passes through the given points.

$P (3, - 14), Q (- 2, - 14), R (4, - 32)$

16. Find an equation for the ellipse that has its center at the origin and satisfies the conditions :

$$\text{vertices } V(\pm 8, 0), \quad \text{foci } F(\pm 4, 0).$$

17. Assume that the length of the major axis of Earth's orbit is 187000000 miles and that the eccentricity is 0.017. Approximate, to the nearest 1000 miles, the minimum distance between Earth and the sun.

18. Find an equation in x and y whose graph contains the points on the curve C.
$$x = 6 \sin t, \ y = 5 \cos t; \ 0 \le t \le 2\pi$$

19. Find a polar equation in r and θ that has the same graph as the equation $x^2 + y^2 = 9$.

_____

20. Find a polar equation in r and θ that has the same graph as the equation $x + y = 3$.

21. Find a polar equation in r and θ that has the same graph as the equation $2y = -x$.

22. Find a polar equation in r and θ that has the same graph as the equation $(x - 5)^2 + y^2 = 25$.

23. Sketch the graph of the polar equation $r = 2 + 4 \sin \theta$.

24. Sketch the graph of the polar equation $r = 2 + 2 \sec \theta$

25. Sketch the graph of the polar equation.

$$r = \frac{12}{2 + 6 \cos \theta}$$

1. Find the equations of the asymptotes of the hyperbola:

$$y^2 - 4x^2 - 12y - 16x + 16 = 0$$

   a. $y - 7 = 8(x + 1)$, $y - 7 = - 8(x + 1)$

   b. $y - 1 = 7(x + 8)$, $y - 1 = - 7(x + 8)$

   c. $y - 6 = 2(x + 2)$, $y - 6 = -2(x + 2)$

2. Find the vertices of the hyperbola

$$\frac{y^2}{81} - \frac{x^2}{4} = 1$$

   a. $V(0 , 2)$, $V'(0 , - 2)$

   b. $V(0 , 9)$, $V'(0 , - 9)$

   c. $V(0 , 8)$, $V'(0 , - 8)$

3. Find an equation in x and y whose graph contains the points on the curve C. Sketch the graph of C.

$$x = 4t^2 - 5,\ y = 2t + 3;\ t \text{ in } \mathbb{R}$$

   a.

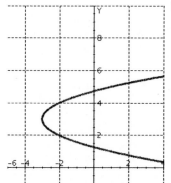

   b.

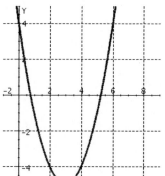

   c.

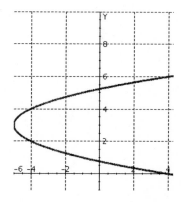

4. Sketch the graph of the ellipse, showing the foci .
$$4x^2 + y^2 = 8y - 15.$$

a.

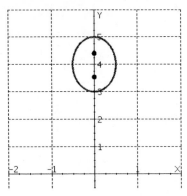

b.

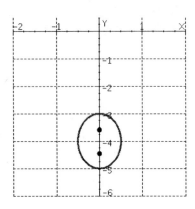

c.

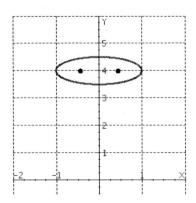

5. The parametric equations specify the position of a moving point $P(x, y)$ at time t. Sketch the graph.

$$x = 2 \cos^2 t, \; y = 2 \sin^2 t; \quad 0 \leq t \leq 2\pi$$

a.

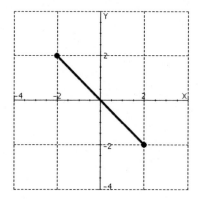

b.

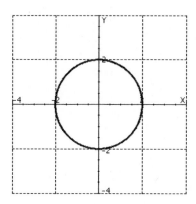

c.

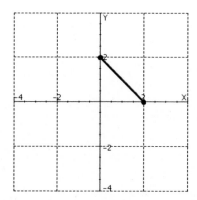

6. Find the focus of the parabola.

$$12\,y = x^2$$

   a. $F\,(0,12)$

   b. $F\,(2,3)$

   c. $F\,(0,3)$

   d. $F\,(1,3)$

7. Find the vertex of the parabola.

$$(x + 10)^2 = -16(y - 3)$$

   a. $V\,(-3,16)$

   b. $V\,(10,3)$

   c. $V\,(10,16)$

   d. $V\,(-10,3)$

8. Find the directrix of the parabola.

$$(y + 9)^2 = -16(x + 1)$$

   a. $x = 3$

   b. $x = 1$

   c. $x = 4$

   d. $x = -9$

9. Find an equation for the ellipse that has its center at the origin and satisfies the conditions :

horizontal major axis of length 14, minor axis of length 8 .

a. $\dfrac{x^2}{16} + \dfrac{y^2}{49} = 1$

b. $\dfrac{x^2}{53} + \dfrac{y^2}{49} = 1$

c. $\dfrac{x^2}{49} + \dfrac{y^2}{16} = 1$

d. $\dfrac{x^2}{57} + \dfrac{y^2}{16} = 1$

10. Find the equations of the asymptotes of the hyperbola

$$\dfrac{(x - 3)^2}{4} - \dfrac{(y - 2)^2}{49} = 1$$

a. $(y - 3) = -\dfrac{7}{2}(x - 2) , (y - 3) = \dfrac{7}{2}(x - 2)$

b. $(y - 2) = -\dfrac{7}{2}(x - 3) , (y - 2) = \dfrac{7}{2}(x - 3)$

c. $(y - 2) = -\dfrac{2}{7}(x - 3) , (y - 2) = \dfrac{2}{7}(x - 3)$

11. Change the polar coordinates $(\,7,\ \pi/4\,)$ to rectangular coordinates.

a. $\left(\dfrac{7\sqrt{2}}{4},\ \dfrac{7\sqrt{2}}{4}\right)$

b. $\left(\dfrac{7\sqrt{2}}{2},\ \dfrac{7\sqrt{2}}{2}\right)$

c. $\left(-\dfrac{7\sqrt{2}}{2},\ \dfrac{7\sqrt{2}}{4}\right)$

12. Change the rectangular coordinates $(-\,3\sqrt{3},\ 3)$ to polar coordinates with $r > 0$ and $0 \leq \theta \leq 2\pi$.

a. $\left(6,\ \dfrac{5\pi}{6}\right)$

b. $\left(3\sqrt{2},\ \dfrac{5\pi}{6}\right)$

c. $\left(6,\ \dfrac{7\pi}{6}\right)$

13. Find an equation in x and y that has the same graph as the polar equation.

$$r = \frac{8}{\cos\theta - 6}$$

14. Find an equation of the parabola that satisfies the condition.

Vertex $V\,(-\,2,\,4)$, directrix $y = 2$

15. Find an equation for the parabola that has a vertical axis and passes through the given points.

$P(2, -4), Q(-2, -20), R(3, -20)$

16. Find an equation for the ellipse that has its center at the origin and satisfies the conditions :

vertices $V(\pm 6, 0)$, foci $F(\pm 3, 0)$.

17. Assume that the length of the major axis of Earth's orbit is 187000000 miles and that the eccentricity is 0.017. Approximate, to the nearest 1000 miles, the minimum distance between Earth and the sun.

18. Find an equation in x and y whose graph contains the points on the curve C.
$$x = 8 \sin t, \, y = 2 \cos t; \, 0 \le t \le 2\pi$$

19. Find a polar equation in r and θ that has the same graph as the equation $x^2 + y^2 = 25$.

_____

20. Find a polar equation in r and θ that has the same graph as the equation $x + y = 5$.

21. Find a polar equation in r and θ that has the same graph as the equation $5y = -x$.

22. Find a polar equation in r and θ that has the same graph as the equation $(x - 4)^2 + y^2 = 16$.

23. Sketch the graph of the polar equation $r = 2 + 4 \sin \theta$.

24. Sketch the graph of the polar equation $r = 2 + 2 \sec \theta$

25. Sketch the graph of the polar equation.

$$r = \frac{12}{2 + 6 \cos \theta}$$

Test Form 10-A

1. $(0, 1)$
2. $(-4, 9)$
3. $x = -1$
4. $(x+3)^2 = -4(y-6)$
5. $y = -2x^2 + 3x + 3$
6. $(x+6)^2 = 20(y-7)$

15.

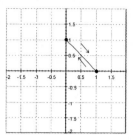

16. $\left(\dfrac{3}{2}, \dfrac{3\sqrt{3}}{2} \right)$

17. $\left(10, \dfrac{7\pi}{6} \right)$

18. $r = 10$

7. $\dfrac{x^2}{100} + \dfrac{y^2}{84} = 1$

19. $r = \dfrac{5}{(\cos(\theta) + \sin(\theta))}$

8. $\dfrac{x^2}{36} + \dfrac{y^2}{4} = 1$

20. $\theta = \arctan\left(-\dfrac{1}{6} \right)$

21. $r = 14\cos(\theta)$

9. 90928000

10. $(0,4),(0,-4)$

22.

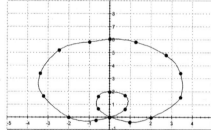

11. $(y-1) = -\dfrac{3}{7} \cdot (x-4), (y-1) = \dfrac{3}{7} \cdot (x-4)$

12. $(y-6) = 2(x+2), (y-6) = -2(x+2)$

13. $\dfrac{x^2}{64} + \dfrac{y^2}{36} = 1$

23.

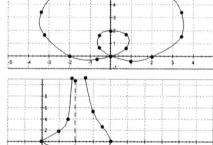

14.

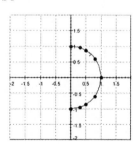

24. $15x^2 + 16y^2 + 16x - 64 = 0$

25.

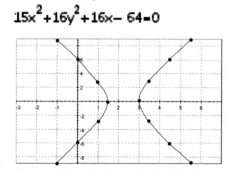

Test Form 10-B

1. $(y-6)=2(x+2), (y-6)=-2(x+2)$
2. $35x^2+36y^2+20x-100=0$
3. $(0,2)$
4. $(-6,7)$
5. $x=-7$
6. $(x+6)^2=20(y-7)$
7. $y=-3x^2+5x+3$

8.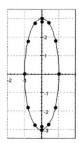

9. $\dfrac{x^2}{49}+\dfrac{y^2}{33}=1$

10. $\dfrac{x^2}{16}+\dfrac{y^2}{4}=1$

11. $914\,19000$

12. $(y-1)=-\dfrac{3}{5}\cdot(x-4), (y-1)=\dfrac{3}{5}\cdot(x-4)$

13.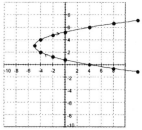

14.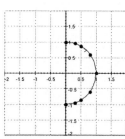

15.

16. $\left(\dfrac{5\sqrt{3}}{2},\dfrac{5}{2}\right)$

17. $\left(6,\dfrac{\pi}{6}\right)$

18. $r=9$

19. $r=\dfrac{3}{(\cos(\theta)+\sin(\theta))}$

20. $\theta=\arctan\left(-\dfrac{1}{5}\right)$

21. $r=6\cos(\theta)$

22.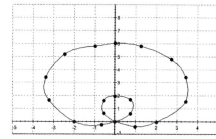

23.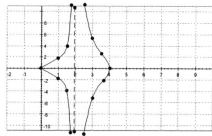

24.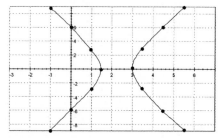

25. $(0,3),(0,-3)$

Test Form 10-C

1. b	**2.** c	**3.** c	**4.** c	**5.** c	**6.** a	**7.** b	**8.** d	**9.** c
10. d	**11.** b	**12.** a	**13.** d	**14.** c	**15.** c	**16.** c	**17.** c	**18.** b
19. b	**20.** d	**21.** d	**22.** d	**23.** d	**24.** a	**25.** b		

Test Form 10-D

1. a	**2.** c	**3.** b	**4.** b	**5.** a	**6.** a	**7.** c	**8.** b	**9.** a
10. b	**11.** b	**12.** d	**13.** d	**14.** a	**15.** b	**16.** a	**17.** b	**18.** c
19. a	**20.** d	**21.** c	**22.** c	**23.** b	**24.** a	**25.** c		

Test Form 10-E

1.   c
2.   b
3.   b
4.   a
5.   b
6.   d
7.   b
8.   a
9.   a
10.   c
11.   b
12.   b
13. $$15x^2 + 16y^2 + 16x - 64 = 0$$
14. $$(x+4)^2 = 8(y-4)$$
15. $$y = -3x^2 + 3x + 4$$
16. $$\frac{x^2}{64} + \frac{y^2}{48} = 1$$
17.   91911000

18. $$\frac{x^2}{36} + \frac{y^2}{25} = 1$$
19. $r = 3$
20. $$r = \frac{3}{(\cos(\theta) + \sin(\theta))}$$
21. $$\theta = \arctan\left(-\frac{1}{2}\right)$$
22. $r = 10\cos(\theta)$
23.
24.
25.

Test Form 10-F

1.   c
2.   b
3.   c
4.   a
5.   c
6.   c
7.   d
8.   a
9.   c
10.   b
11.   b
12.   a
13. $35x^2 + 36y^2 + 16x - 64 = 0$

14. $(x+2)^2 = 8(y-4)$

15. $y = -4x^2 + 4x + 4$

16. $\dfrac{x^2}{36} + \dfrac{y^2}{27} = 1$

17.   91911000

18. $\dfrac{x^2}{64} + \dfrac{y^2}{4} = 1$

19. $r = 5$

20. $r = \dfrac{5}{(\cos(\theta) + \sin(\theta))}$

21. $\theta = \arctan\left(-\dfrac{1}{5}\right)$

22. $r = 8\cos(\theta)$

23.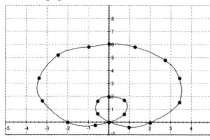

24.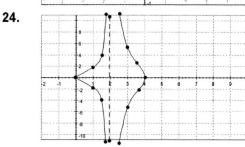

25.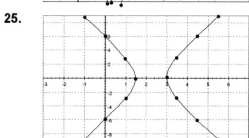

1. As $x \to 0^{+}$, $f(x) \to L$ for some real number L. Use the graph to predict L

$$f(x) = \frac{5 - 5\cos x}{x}$$

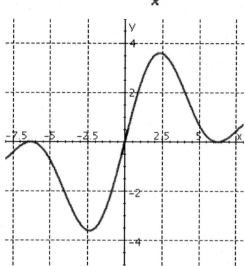

2. Find the inverse of the matrix if it exists.

$$\begin{bmatrix} 1 & 5 & 6 \\ -5 & 1 & 0 \\ 6 & -1 & 1 \end{bmatrix}$$

3. A landfill currently has 2500 tons of waste. During each the year, the tonnage is reduced by 20% due to decomposition. Then, at the end of each year, 2500 new tons are added to the fill. If this process continues forever, what is the maximum tonnage that the landfill can reach?

4. Prove, by mathematical induction, that $6^{n} - 1$ is divisible by 5 for all natural numbers n.

5. Two surveyors with two-way radios leave the same point at 9:00 A.M., one walking due south at 4 mi/hr and the other due west at 3 mi/hr. How long can they communicate with one another if each radio has a maximum range of 1.67 miles?

6. Find the solutions of the equation

$$5 x^2 - 30 x + 90 = 0$$

7. Solve the equation

$$x^{3/4} = 8$$

8. Solve the inequality :

$$| 13x + 4 | < 6$$

9. A construction firm is trying to decide which of two models of a crane to purchase. Model A costs $50000 and requires $3500 per year to maintain. Model B has an initial cost of $39500 and a maintenance cost of $5000 per year. For how many years must model A be used before it becomes more economical than B?

10. Solve the inequality

$$x^2 - x - 90 < 0$$

Express the answer in terms of intervals, if possible.

11. Find an equation of the circle that satisfies the conditions:

endpoints of the diameter A (6, - 17) and B (- 2, 19)

12. Find the domain of f: $f(x) = \dfrac{\sqrt{5x - 2}}{x^2 - 4}$

13. Simplify the difference quotient $\dfrac{f(x + h) - f(x)}{h}$, $h \neq 0$ if

$$f(x) = x^2 + 4$$

14. If a linear function f satisfies the conditions : $f(-3) = -2$ and $f(3) = 16$, find $f(x)$.

15. Express the function

$$f(x) = -\frac{3}{4}x^2 + 15x - 20$$

in the form $a(x - h)^2 + k$.

16. Sketch the graph of the function: $f(x) = 2x^2 - 4x - 5$

17. Sketch the graph of f for the indicated value of a: $f(x) = ax^3 + 2, \quad a = -\frac{1}{3}$

18. Find all values of x such that $f(x) > 0$: $f(x) = \frac{1}{2}(x + 1)(x - 1)(x - 4)$

19. Use synthetic division to find $f(c)$

$$f(x) = 3x^3 + 4x^2 - 2x + 2$$
$$c = 2$$

20. A storage tank for propane gas is to be constructed in the shape of a right circular cylinder with a hemisphere attached to the top. If the total height of the structure is 35 feet, determine the radius of the cylinder that results in a total volume of $1188 \div ft^3$.

21. For a particular salmon population, the relationship between the number S of spawners and the number R of offspring that survive to maturity is given by the formula

$$R = \frac{4200S}{S + 480}$$

Find the number of spawners that would yield 60% of the greatest possible number of offspring that survive to maturity.

22. In 1974, Johnny Miller won 8 tournaments on the PGA tour and accumulated $308164 in official season earnings. In 1999, Tiger Woods accumulated $6565306 with a similar record. Find the annual interest rate needed for Miller's winnings to be equivalent in value to Woods's winnings.

23. Solve the equation.

$$\log_2(2x-4) = \log_2(16) - \log_2(4)$$

24. Solve the equation.

$$\log_6(x+7) + \log_6(x+12) = 1$$

25. Pareto's law for capitalist countries states that the relationship between annual income y and the number p of individuals whose income exceeds y is where c and q are positive constants. Solve this equation for p.

$$\log p = \log c - q \log y$$

26. Use the compound interest formula to determine how long it will take for a sum of money to double if it is invested at a rate of 8% per year compounded monthly.

27. The central angle θ subtended by the arc of length $s = 9$ cm on a circle of radius $r = 3$ cm. Find to the nearest tenth the area of the sector determined by θ.

28. Simplify the expression.

$$\frac{\sin^3 \theta + \cos^3 \theta}{\sin \theta + \cos \theta}$$

29. Refer to the graph of $y = \cos x$ to find the exact values of x in the interval $[0, \ 4\pi]$ that satisfy the equation.

$$\cos x = \frac{\sqrt{3}}{2}$$

30. Estimate the horizontal asymptote.

$$y = \frac{1 - \cos^2\left(\frac{2}{x}\right)}{\sin\left(\frac{5}{x}\right)}$$

31. Find an equation using the tangent function that has the same graph as $y = \cot x$. Translate the function as little as possible.

32. Find the solutions of the equation that are in the interval $[0, \ 2\pi)$.

$$\tan^2 \theta - \tan \theta = 0$$

33. Find the solutions of the equation that are in the interval $[0, \ 2\pi)$.

$$2 \sin v \sec v - \sec v = 4 \sin v - 2$$

34. Find the exact values of $\sin 2\theta$, $\cos 2\theta$, and $\tan 2\theta$ for the given values of θ.

$$\cos \theta = \frac{8}{17} \; ; \; 0° < \theta < 90°$$

35. Use half-angle formulas to find the exact value: $\tan \dfrac{\pi}{8}$

36. Use sum-to-product formulas to find the solutions of the equation.

$$\sin 6x - \sin 2x = 2\cos 4x$$

37. A triangular field has sides of lengths a, b, and c (in yards). Approximate the number of acres in the field (1 acre = 4840 yd^2).

$$a = 285 \, , \, b = 350 \, , \, c = 500$$

Round the answer to the nearest hundredth.

38. Find the angle between the two vectors $\langle -5, \, 9 \rangle$ and $\langle -6, \, 7 \rangle$.

39. Determine m such that the two vectors are orthogonal.

$$3\mathbf{i} - 2\mathbf{j} \text{ and } 7\mathbf{i} + 8m\mathbf{j}$$

40. Solve the system.

$$\begin{cases} 2x + 8y = 7 \\ 3x - 5y = 4 \end{cases}$$

41. Solve the system

$$\begin{cases} 9x + 2y = 4 \\ 4x + 5y = 9 \end{cases}$$

using the inverse method.

42. Find the determinant of the matrix.

$$\begin{bmatrix} 29 & -14 & 87 \\ -34 & 93 & -31 \\ 51 & 12 & 9 \end{bmatrix}$$

43. Find the third term of the recursively defined infinite sequence

$$a_1 = 8, \quad a_{k+1} = (k+4)\,a_k.$$

44. With seven different flags, how many different signals can be sent by placing four flags, one above the other, on a flag pole?

45. Find the vertex of the parabola.

$$(x+6)^2 = -12(y-3)$$

46. Find an equation for the ellipse that has its center at the origin and satisfies the conditions :

horizontal major axis of length 14, minor axis of length 6 .

47. Find an equation in x and y whose graph contains the points on the curve C. Sketch the graph of C, and indicate the orientation.

$$x = 4t^2 - 5, \, y = 2t + 3; \, t \text{ in } \mathbb{R}$$

48. The parametric equations specify the position of a moving point $P(x, y)$ at time t. Sketch the graph, and indicate the motion of P as t increases.

$$x = \cos^2 t, \, y = \sin^2 t; \quad 0 \leq t \leq 2\pi$$

49. Find a polar equation in r and θ that has the same graph as the equation $9 \, y = - x$.

50. Find the exact values of $\sin 2\theta$, $\cos 2\theta$, and $\tan 2\theta$ for the given values of θ

$$\sec \theta = - \, 4; \; 90^\circ < \theta < 180^\circ$$

1. Express in the form $a + bi$, where a and b are real numbers.

$$8\left(\cos \frac{\pi}{4} + i \sin \frac{\pi}{4}\right)$$

a. $4\sqrt{3} + 4i$

b. $8\sqrt{2} + 8\sqrt{2}\,i$

c. $4\sqrt{2} - 4\sqrt{2}\,i$

d. $4\sqrt{2} + 4\sqrt{2}\,i$

2. Find a factored form with integer coefficients of the polynomial f shown in the figure.

$$f(x) = 10\,x^5 - 41\,x^4 + 52\,x^3 - 17\,x^2 - 8\,x + 4$$

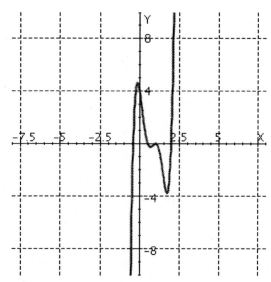

a. $(2x + 5)(2x - 1)(x - 1)^2(x - 2)$

b. $(5x + 2)(2x - 1)(x - 1)^2(x - 2)$

c. $(2x + 5)(x^2 - 2)(x - 1)(x - 2)$

d. $x(5x + 2)(2x - 1)(x - 1)(x - 2)$

3. Find the exact value.

$$\cos \frac{\pi}{3} + \cos \frac{\pi}{4}$$

    a. $\dfrac{1 + \sqrt{2}}{2}$

    b. $\dfrac{\sqrt{5}}{3}$

    c. $\sqrt{5} - \sqrt{2}$

    d.   2

4. Find the exact value of the expression.

$$\arccos(\cos 0)$$

    a. $\dfrac{5\pi}{6}$

    b.   0

    c. $\dfrac{\pi}{3}$

5. Find the period of the equation.

$$y = -2\sec\left(\frac{1}{2}x - \frac{\pi}{2}\right)$$

    a. 2π

    b. 4π

    c. $\dfrac{\pi}{2}$

    d. π

    e. $\dfrac{\pi}{4}$

6. The graph of an equation is shown in the figure. Find the period.

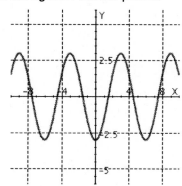

    a.   3

    b.   4

    c.   5

    d.   6

7. Sketch the graph of the polar equation

$$r = \frac{60}{6 + 10\cos\theta}$$

a.

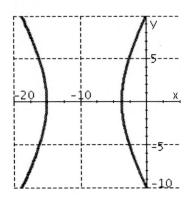

b.

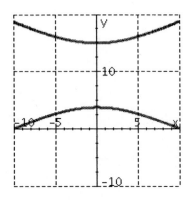

c.

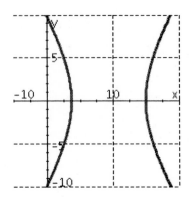

8. Sketch the graph of *f*.

$$f(x) = \frac{-2x}{x+2}$$

a.

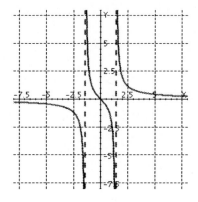

b.

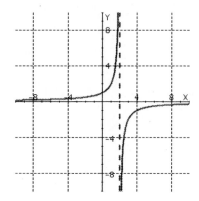

c.

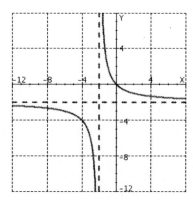

9. Sketch the graph of the equation.

$$y = 2\sin\left(x - \frac{\pi}{3}\right)$$

a.

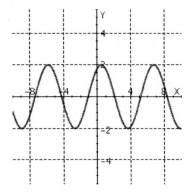

b.

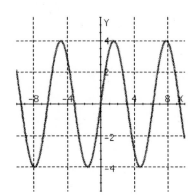

c.

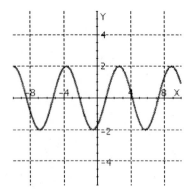

10. Sketch the graph of *f* if:

$$f(x) = 4^{x-3}$$

a.
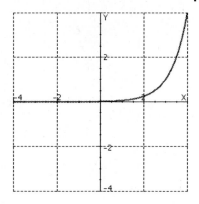

b.
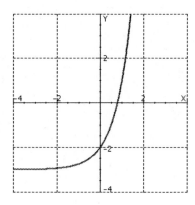

c.
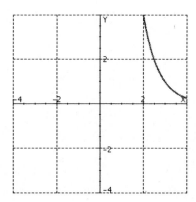

11. Use inverse trigonometric functions to find the solutions of the equation that are in the given interval, and approximate the solutions to four decimal places.

$$6\sin^3\theta + 18\sin^2\theta - 5\sin\theta - 15 = 0; \qquad \left(-\frac{\pi}{2}, \frac{\pi}{2}\right)$$

a.　$\theta = 1.1503, \theta = -1.1503$

b.　$\theta = 1.0503, \theta = -1.0503$

c.　$\theta = 1.4503, \theta = -1.4503$

d.　$\theta = 1.3503, \theta = -0.9503$

12. Solve the formula for p .

$$S = \frac{c}{p + c(1 - p)}$$

Select the correct answer.

a.　$p = \dfrac{c(1 + S)}{S(1 + c)}$

b.　$p = \dfrac{c(1 - S)}{S(1 + c)}$

c.　$p = \dfrac{c(1 + S)}{S(1 - c)}$

d.　$p = \dfrac{c(1 - S)}{S(1 - c)}$

13. A runner starts at the beginning of a runners' path and runs at a constant rate of 8 mi/hr. Five minutes later a second runner begins at the same point, running at a rate of 10 mi/hr and following the same course. How long will it take the second runner to reach the first?

Select the correct answer.
- a.   25 minutes

- b.   29 minutes

- c.   30 minutes

- d.   22 minutes

14. Solve the equation by factoring.

$$\frac{x}{x-6} + \frac{7}{x+6} - \frac{72}{x^2-36}$$

Select the correct answer.
- a. $x = -6$

- b. $x = 36$

- c. $x = -19, x = 6$

- d. $x = -19$

15. Two surveyors with two-way radios leave the same point at 9:00 A.M., one walking due south at 2 mi/hr and the other due west at 4 mi/hr. How long can they communicate with one another if each radio has a maximum range of 2.24 miles? Round the answer to the nearest minute.
- a.   21 minutes

- b.   63 minutes

- c.   30 minutes

- d.   87 minutes

16. Write the expression $(1 - 2i)(1 + 2i)$ in the form $a + bi$, where a and b are real numbers.

    a. $1 + 4i$

    b.   -3

    c. $1 - 4i$

    d.   5

17. Solve the equation: $\sqrt{37 - x} = x - 7$

    a.   1, 12

    b.   No solution

    c.   12

    d.   1

18. Solve the equation: $x^{3/4} = 125$

    a. $x = 25$

    b. $x = 5$

    c. $x = 125$

    d. $x = 625$

19. Solve the inequality $x^2 - x - 6 < 0$ and express the solution in terms of intervals.

    a. $(-\infty, -2) \cup (3, \infty)$

    b. $(-\infty, -2)$

    c.   (-2, 3)

    d. $(3, \infty)$

20. Sketch the graph of the equation:

$(x + 1)^2 + (y - 3)^2 = 9$

a.

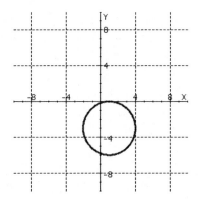

b.

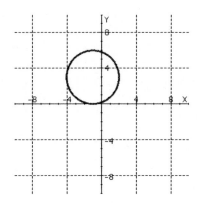

c.

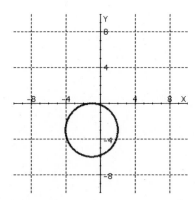

21. Find the equation of the circle that satisfies the conditions:

center C (4, - 9), tangent to the y-axis

    a. $(x + 4)^2 + (y - 9)^2 = 4$

    b. $(x + 4)^2 - (y + 9)^2 = 16$

    c. $(x + 4)^2 + (y + 9)^2 = 4$

    d. $(x - 4)^2 + (y + 9)^2 = 4$

    e. $(x - 4)^2 + (y + 9)^2 = 16$

22. The growth of a fetus more than 12 weeks old can be approximated by the formula $L = 1.53t - 6.7$, where L is the length (in centimeters) and t is the age (in weeks). Prenatal length can be determined by ultrasound. Approximate the age of a fetus whose length is 31.55 centimeters.

    a.   25 weeks

    b.   30 weeks

    c.   22 weeks

23. Sketch the graph of the function $f(x) = 5x^2 - 10x - 5$

    a.

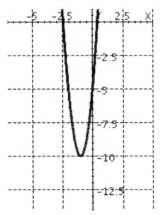

    b.

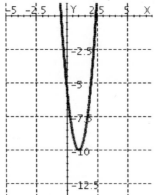

    c.

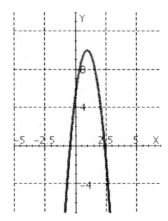

24. Find all values of x such that $f(x) < 0$.

$$f(x) = x^4 - 30\,x^2 + 125$$

a. $(-125, -\sqrt{125}\,) \cup (\sqrt{125}, 125)$

b. $(-5, -\sqrt{5}\,) \cup (\sqrt{5}, 5)$

c. $(-\infty, -30) \cup (30, \infty)$

25. Use synthetic division to decide whether c is a zero of

$$f(x) = 6\,x^4 + 9\,x^3 - 12\,x^2 - 13\,x + 3$$
$$c = -1$$

a. c is a zero

b. c is not a zero

26. The pressure P acting at a point in a liquid is directly proportional to the distance d from the surface of the liquid to the point. Express P as a function of d by means of a formula that involves a constant of proportionality k. In a certain oil tank, the pressure at a depth of 6 feet is 354. Find the pressure at a depth of 10 feet for the oil tank.

a. $p = 567$

b. $p = 623$

c. $p = 578$

d. $p = 590$

27. The speed V at which an automobile was traveling before the brakes were applied can sometimes be estimated from the length L of the skid marks. Assume that V is directly proportional to the square root of L. Express V as a function of L by means of a formula that involves a constant of proportionality k. For a certain automobile on a dry surface, $L = 55$ ft when $V = 30$ mi/hr . Estimate the initial speed of the automobile if the skid marks are 102 feet long.

    a. $v = 36.07$ mi/hr

    b. $v = 32.49$ mi/hr

    c. $v = 40.85$ mi/hr

    d. $v = 29.42$ mi/hr

28. Find the inverse function of

$$f(x) = \frac{11x + 5}{5x - 7}$$

    a. $f^{-1}(x) = \dfrac{7 + 5x}{5x - 11}$

    b. $f^{-1}(x) = \dfrac{11 + 5x}{11x - 7}$

    c. $f^{-1}(x) = \dfrac{5 + 7x}{5x - 11}$

    d. $f^{-1}(x) = \dfrac{5 + 7x}{11x - 5}$

29. An investment of $1055 increased to $5225 in 20 years. If the interest was compounded continuously, find the interest rate.

    a.   5%

    b.   8%

    c.   10%

    d.   16%

30. A tire for a compact car is 24 inches in diameter. If the car is travelling at a speed of 60 mi/hr, find the number of revolutions the tire makes per minute.

    a.   840 rev/min

    b.   819 rev/min

    c.   827 rev/min

    d.   829 rev/min

31. Approximate the acute angle θ to the nearest $0.01°$.

$\tan \theta = 4.91$

    a. $\theta = 77.29°$

    b. $\theta = 79.59°$

    c. $\theta = 79.92°$

    d. $\theta = 78.49°$

32. Find the magnitude of the vector **a**.

$$\mathbf{a} = -4\,\mathbf{i} + 5\,\mathbf{j}$$

    a. $\sqrt{40}$

    b. $\sqrt{44}$

    c. $\sqrt{39}$

    d. $\sqrt{41}$

33. Find a vector that has the opposite direction of 3 **i** - 9 **j** and four times the magnitude.

    a.   − **15i** + **39j**

    b.   − **11i** + **35j**

    c.   − **12i** + **36j**

    d.   − **14i** + **38j**

34. If forces $\mathbf{F}_1$, $\mathbf{F}_2$,..., $\mathbf{F}_n$ act at a point P, the net (or resultant) force **F** is the sum $\mathbf{F}_1 + \mathbf{F}_2 + \cdots + \mathbf{F}_n$.
If **F** = 0 the forces are said to be in equilibrium. The given forces act at the origin O of an xy-plane. Find an additional force **G** such that equilibrium occurs.

$$\mathbf{F}_1 = \langle 9, 4 \rangle, \ \mathbf{F}_2 = \langle -9, -3 \rangle, \ \mathbf{F}_3 = \langle 4, 4 \rangle$$

    a. $\langle -3, -4 \rangle$

    b. $\langle -4, -5 \rangle$

    c. $\langle -6, -7 \rangle$

    d. $\langle -1, -2 \rangle$

35. Find the solutions of the equation.
$$x^6 + 729 = 0$$

    a. $3i, \ -3i, \ \dfrac{3}{2} + \dfrac{3\sqrt{3}\,i}{2}, \ \dfrac{3}{2} - \dfrac{3\sqrt{3}\,i}{2}, \ -\dfrac{3}{2} + \dfrac{3\sqrt{3}\,i}{2}, \ -\dfrac{3}{2} - \dfrac{3\sqrt{3}\,i}{2}$

    b. $6i, \ -6i, \ 3 + 3\sqrt{3}\,i, \ 3 - 3\sqrt{3}\,i, \ -3 + 3\sqrt{3}\,i, \ -3 - 3\sqrt{3}\,i$

    c. $3i, \ -3i, \ \dfrac{3\sqrt{3}}{2} + \dfrac{3i}{2}, \ \dfrac{3\sqrt{3}}{2} - \dfrac{3i}{2}, \ -\dfrac{3\sqrt{3}}{2} + \dfrac{3i}{2}, \ -\dfrac{3\sqrt{3}}{2} - \dfrac{3i}{2}$

    d. $6i, \ -6i, \ 3\sqrt{3} + 3i, \ 3\sqrt{3} - 3i, \ -3\sqrt{3} + 3i, \ -3\sqrt{3} - 3i$

36. A silversmith has two alloys, one containing 35% silver and the other 85% silver. How much of each should be melted and combined to obtain 500 grams of an alloy containing 50% silver?

    a.   150 grams

    b.   350 grams

    c.   425 grams

    d.   380 grams

    e.   100 grams

37. *R* is determined by the constraints:

$$x - 5y \geq -20,$$
$$9x - 21y \leq 36,$$
$$x + y \geq 4$$

Find the maximum value of

$$C = 4x - 2y$$

on *R*.

    a.   maximum of 82

    b.   maximum of 0

    c.   maximum of 84

    d.   maximum of 75

38. Use matrices to solve the system.

$$\begin{cases} x - 3y - 3z = -17 \\ 2x + y + z = 15 \\ x + 3y - 3z = 7 \end{cases}$$

a.   The system is inconsistent

b.   The equations are dependent

c. $x = -4$, $y = 4$, $z = 5$

d. $x = 5$, $y = 3$, $z = -3$

e. $x = -4$, $y = -7$, $z = 3$

f. $x = 4$, $y = 4$, $z = 3$

39. Find the inverse of the matrix if it exists.

$$\begin{bmatrix} 1 & 4 & 5 \\ -4 & 1 & 0 \\ 5 & -1 & 1 \end{bmatrix}$$

a. $\dfrac{1}{5} \begin{bmatrix} 1 & -24 & 1 \\ -9 & -12 & -20 \\ 0 & 21 & 4 \end{bmatrix}$

b.   Does not exist

c. $\dfrac{1}{12} \begin{bmatrix} 1 & -9 & -5 \\ 4 & -24 & -20 \\ -1 & 21 & 17 \end{bmatrix}$

d. $\dfrac{1}{24} \begin{bmatrix} 1 & -12 & 5 \\ 4 & -24 & 4 \\ -1 & 5 & 17 \end{bmatrix}$

40. Find the determinant of the matrix.

$$\begin{bmatrix} 37 & -14 & 95 \\ -35 & 87 & -32 \\ 49 & 6 & 14 \end{bmatrix}$$

a.   - 715346

b.   - 178837

c.   - 357673

41. Use Cramer's rule to solve the system.

$$\begin{cases} x - 8y - 5z = -33 \\ 8x + y + z = 34 \\ x + 5y - 8z = 105 \end{cases}$$

a.   The system is inconsistent.

b.   (4 , 9 , - 7)

c.   (6 , 8 , - 10)

d.   (3 , 11 , - 9)

e.   The equations are dependent.

f.   (5 , 10 , - 8)

42. Find the sum.

$$\sum_{k=1}^{26} (2n + 4)$$

a. $s = 812$

b. $s = 808$

c. $s = 806$

d. $s = 804$

43. If six basketball teams are in a tournament, find the number of different ways that first, second, and third place can be decided, assuming ties are not allowed.

    a.   6

    b.   360

    c.   120

    d.   840

44. An urn contains five red balls, six green balls, and four white balls. If a single ball is drawn, find the probability that the ball is red or white.

    a. $\dfrac{9}{15}$

    b. $\dfrac{6}{15}$

    c. $\dfrac{5}{15}$

    d. $\dfrac{10}{15}$

45. Find an equation for the ellipse that has its center at the origin and satisfies the conditions :

$$\text{vertices } V(\pm 10, 0), \quad \text{foci } F(\pm 3, 0).$$

    a. $\dfrac{x^2}{109} + \dfrac{y^2}{91} = 1$

    b. $\dfrac{x^2}{91} + \dfrac{y^2}{100} = 1$

    c. $\dfrac{x^2}{100} + \dfrac{y^2}{109} = 1$

    d. $\dfrac{x^2}{100} + \dfrac{y^2}{91} = 1$

46. Find an equation in x and y whose graph contains the points on the curve C.

$$x = 8 \sin t, \; y = 2 \cos t; \; 0 \leq t \leq 2\pi$$

a. $\dfrac{x^2}{4} - \dfrac{y^2}{64} = 1$

b. $\dfrac{x^2}{64} - \dfrac{y^2}{4} = 1$

c. $\dfrac{x^2}{64} + \dfrac{y^2}{4} = 1$

d. $\dfrac{x^2}{4} + \dfrac{y^2}{64} = 1$

47. If the following expression is equated to one of the expressions below, the resulting equation is an identity.

$$\frac{\sec^2 3\theta}{2 - \sec^2 3\theta}$$

a. $2 \cos 6\theta$

b. $2 \csc 6\theta$

c. $\sec 6\theta$

d. $\cot 6\theta$

48. Simplify the expression.

$$\frac{\cot^2 \theta - 4}{\cot^2 \theta - \cot \theta - 6}$$

a. $1 - \sin \theta \cos \theta$

b. $\dfrac{\cot \theta - 2}{\cot \theta - 3}$

c. $\sin \theta$

d. $\cos \theta$

49. Use fundamental identities to find the values of the trigonometric functions for the given conditions.

$\sin \theta = \frac{4}{7}$ and $\cos \theta < 0$

a.

$$\sin \theta = \frac{4}{7}, \quad \cos \theta = \frac{\sqrt{33}}{7}, \quad \tan \theta = \frac{4}{\sqrt{33}}$$

$$\cot \theta = \frac{\sqrt{33}}{4}, \quad \sec \theta = \frac{7}{\sqrt{33}}, \quad \csc \theta = -\frac{7}{4}$$

b.

$$\sin \theta = \frac{1}{7}, \quad \cos \theta = \frac{\sqrt{7}}{4}, \quad \tan \theta = \frac{1}{\sqrt{7}}$$

$$\cot \theta = \sqrt{7}, \quad \sec \theta = \frac{7}{\sqrt{7}}, \quad \csc \theta = 1$$

c.

$$\sin \theta = \frac{4}{7}, \quad \cos \theta = -\frac{\sqrt{33}}{7}, \quad \tan \theta = -\frac{4}{\sqrt{33}}$$

$$\cot \theta = \frac{\sqrt{33}}{4}, \quad \sec \theta = \frac{7}{\sqrt{33}}, \quad \csc \theta = \frac{7}{4}$$

d.

$$\sin \theta = \frac{1}{4}, \quad \cos \theta = -\frac{\sqrt{7}}{4}, \quad \tan \theta = \frac{1}{\sqrt{33}}$$

$$\cot \theta = \sqrt{7}, \quad \sec \theta = \frac{33}{\sqrt{7}}, \quad \csc \theta = -4$$

50. Verify the identity.

$$\frac{\sin \theta + \sin 17\theta}{\cos \theta + \cos 17\theta} = \tan 9\theta$$

a.   Not identical

b.   Identical

1. Use inverse trigonometric functions to find the solutions of the equation that are in the given interval, and approximate the solutions to four decimal places.

$$6\sin^3\theta + 18\sin^2\theta - 5\sin\theta - 15 = 0; \qquad \left(-\frac{\pi}{2}, \frac{\pi}{2}\right)$$

   a. $\theta = 1.0503, \theta = -1.0503$

   b. $\theta = 1.4503, \theta = -0.8503$

   c. $\theta = 1.3503, \theta = -1.3503$

   d. $\theta = 1.1503, \theta = -1.1503$

2. Solve the equation

$$\frac{-5}{x+4} + \frac{-5x+31}{x^2-16}$$

   a. $x = 7$

   b. $x = -6$

   c. $x = 9$

   d. $x = 4$

3. Solve the formula for q.

$$S = \frac{c}{q + c(1-q)}$$

   a. $q = \dfrac{c(1+S)}{S(1-c)}$

   b. $q = \dfrac{c(1-S)}{S(1+c)}$

   c. $q = \dfrac{c(1-S)}{S(1-c)}$

   d. $q = \dfrac{c(1+S)}{S(1+c)}$

4. It takes a boy 75 minutes to mow the lawn, but his sister can mow it in 50 minutes. How long would it take them to mow the lawn if they worked together, using two lawn mowers?

    a.   22 minutes

    b.   15 minutes

    c.   30 minutes

    d.   34 minutes

5. Solve the inequality : $|13x + 1| < 2$

    a. $\left(-\dfrac{2}{13}, \dfrac{2}{13}\right)$

    b. $\left(-\infty, -\dfrac{3}{13}\right) \cup \left(\dfrac{1}{13}, \infty\right)$

    c. $\left(-\infty, -\dfrac{2}{13}\right) \cup \left(\dfrac{2}{13}, \infty\right)$

    d. $\left(-\dfrac{3}{13}, \dfrac{1}{13}\right)$

6. Simplify the difference quotient $\dfrac{f(x + h) - f(x)}{h}$, $h \neq 0$ if

$$f(x) = x^2 + 2$$

    a. $\dfrac{f(x + h) - f(x)}{h} = 2x$

    b. $\dfrac{f(x + h) - f(x)}{h} = 2x + h + 4$

    c. $\dfrac{f(x + h) - f(x)}{h} = 2x + h$

    d. $\dfrac{f(x + h) - f(x)}{h} = x + h$

7. Find all solutions of the equation.

$$x^4 + 3x^3 - 30x^2 - 6x + 56 = 0$$

a. $\quad -7,\ -\sqrt{7},\ \sqrt{7},\ 4$

b. $\quad -7,\ -\sqrt{2},\ \sqrt{2},\ 4$

c. $\quad -3,\ -\sqrt{7},\ \sqrt{2},\ 4$

d. $\quad 7,\ -\sqrt{2},\ \sqrt{2},\ 4$

8. Find an equation of a rational function f that satisfies the conditions:
vertical asymptotes: $x = -1,\ x = 0$
horizontal asymptote: $y = 0$
x-intercept: 2; $f(3) = 1$

a. $\quad f(x) = \dfrac{1 - x^2}{x^2 + 12x - 2}$

b. $\quad f(x) = \dfrac{12x - 2}{x^2 + 24x}$

c. $\quad f(x) = \dfrac{12x - 24}{x^2 + 1x}$

9. The pressure P acting at a point in a liquid is directly proportional to the distance d from the surface of the liquid to the point. Express P as a function of d by means of a formula that involves a constant of proportionality k. In a certain oil tank, the pressure at a depth of 8 feet is 472. Find the pressure at a depth of 13 feet for the oil tank.

a. $\quad p = 767$

b. $\quad p = 800$

c. $\quad p = 744$

d. $\quad p = 755$

10. The 1980 population of the United States was approximately 227 million, and the population has been growing continuously at a rate of 0.7% per year. Predict the population in the year 2020 if this growth trend continues.

    a.   900 million people

    b.   600 million people

    c.   300 million people

    d.   100 million people

11. Solve the equation.

$$\log_6(x+4) + \log_6(x+9) = 1$$

    a. $x = -7$

    b. $x = 7$

    c. $x = 3$

    d. $x = -3$

12. Solve the equation.

$$\ln x = 1 - \ln(x+2)$$

    a. $x = -2 - \sqrt{4+e}$

    b. $x = -1 - \sqrt{1+e}$

    c. $x = -1 + \sqrt{1+e}$

    d. $x = -2 + \sqrt{4+e}$

13. If a circular arc of the length $s = 20$ cm subtends the central angle $\theta = 2$ on a circle, find the radius of the circle.

    a.   11 cm

    b.   10.5 cm

    c.   11.5 cm

    d.   10 cm

14. A builder wishes to construct a ramp 29 feet long that rises to a height of 3.5 feet above level ground. Approximate the angle that the ramp should make with the horizontal. Round the answer to the nearest degree.

    a. 9^0

    b. 4^0

    c. 7^0

    d. 8^0

15. An airplane flying at a speed of 300 mi/hr flies from a point A in the direction $150°$ for 45 minutes and then flies in the direction $240°$ for 30 minutes. Approximate, to the nearest mile, the distance from the airplane to A.

    a.   375 mi

    b.   150 mi

    c.   168 mi

    d.   270 mi

16. Express as a product.

$$\cos 12\,x - \cos 4\,x$$

    a. $- 2\sin(8x)\sin(4x)$

    b. $2\cos(9x)\sin(3x)$

    c. $- 2\sin(9x)\cos(3x)$

    d. $2\cos(8x)\cos(4x)$

17. Given that $\mathbf{a} = \langle 4, -4 \rangle$, $\mathbf{b} = \langle 5, 4 \rangle$, and $\mathbf{c} = \langle -1, 2 \rangle$, find the number $(\mathbf{a} - \mathbf{b}) \cdot (\mathbf{b} + \mathbf{c})$.

    a.   44

    b.   -52

    c.   42

    d.   -12

18. If **c** represents a constant force, find the work done if the point of application of **c** moves along the line segment from P to Q.

$$\mathbf{c} = 2\,\mathbf{i} + 3\,\mathbf{j} \text{ and } P(0, 0),\ Q(5, -1)$$

    a.   7

    b.   1

    c.   -13

    d.   13

19. Let

$$A = \begin{bmatrix} 2 & -5 & 3 \\ -3 & 8 & 1 \end{bmatrix} \text{ and } B = \begin{bmatrix} 2 & 1 \\ 0 & 1 \\ -4 & 7 \end{bmatrix}$$

Find *AB*.

a.

$$AB = \begin{bmatrix} -18 & 8 \\ -3 & 2 \end{bmatrix}$$

b.

$$AB = \begin{bmatrix} -8 & 18 \\ -10 & 12 \end{bmatrix}$$

c.

$$AB = \begin{bmatrix} -12 & 10 \\ -8 & 18 \end{bmatrix}$$

d.

$$AB = \begin{bmatrix} -12 & 2 \\ -3 & 8 \end{bmatrix}$$

20. Solve the system

$$\begin{cases} 3x + 4y = 34 \\ 8x + 7y = 65 \end{cases}$$

using the inverse method.

a. $x = -6, y = 5$

b. $x = -2, y = 5$

c. $x = 2, y = 7$

d.   The equations are dependent

e.   The system is inconsistent

21. Find the determinant of the matrix.

$$\begin{bmatrix} 3 & 9 & -5 \\ 5 & 9 & 3 \\ -5 & 7 & 1 \end{bmatrix}$$

    a.   - 616

    b.   - 1848

    c.   - 308

22. Use Cramer's rule to solve the system.

$$\begin{cases} x - 4y - 3z = -1 \\ 4x + y + z = 37 \\ x + 3y - 4z = 54 \end{cases}$$

    a.   The system is inconsistent.

    b.   (11 , 6 , - 9)

    c.   (8 , 9 , - 8)

    d.   The equations are dependent.

    e.   (9 , 7 , - 6)

    f.   (10 , 8 , - 7)

23. In how many different ways can four books be selected from a six-volume set of books?

    a.   120

    b.   216

    c.   360

    d.   24

    e.   720

24. Find a polar equation in r and θ that has the same graph as the equation $(x - 4)^2 + y^2 = 16$.

    a. $r = 8 \sin \theta$

    b. $r = 16 \sec \theta$

    c. $r = 8 \cos \theta$

    d. $r = \cos 8\theta$

25. Find a system of inequalities whose graph is shown.

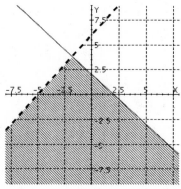

    a. $\begin{cases} y \le -x + 2 \\ y < \dfrac{6}{5}x + 6 \end{cases}$

    b. $\begin{cases} y \le -x - 2 \\ y < \dfrac{5}{6}x - 5 \end{cases}$

    c. $\begin{cases} y > x + 6 \\ y < -\dfrac{6}{5}x + 2 \end{cases}$

26. Use fundamental identities to find the values of the trigonometric functions for the given conditions.

$\csc \theta = 8$ and $\cot \theta < 0$

27. Find an equation in x and y that has the same graph as the polar equation.

$$r = \frac{6}{\cos \theta - 2}$$

28. Solve the equation

$$\frac{3}{4} + \frac{-4}{12x + 4} - \frac{11}{3x + 1}$$

29. Solve for t.

$$s = \frac{1}{2} g t^2 + v_0 t \qquad \text{(distance an object falls)}$$

30. Two surveyors with two-way radios leave the same point at 9:00 A.M., one walking due south at 2 mi/hr and the other due west at 3 mi/hr. How long can they communicate with one another if each radio has a maximum range of 1.80 miles?

31. Solve the equation

$$\sqrt{19 - x} = x - 7$$

32. Solve the equation

$$2\sqrt{x} \ - \ \sqrt{x \ - \ 2} \ = \ \sqrt{x \ + \ 5}$$

33. The braking distance d (in feet) of a certain car traveling v mi/hr is given by the equation $d = v + (v^2/20)$. Determine the velocities that result in braking distances of less than 40 feet. Express the answer in terms of intervals, if possible.

34. Find an equation of the circle that satisfies the conditions:

center C (7, - 5), radius 1

35. If a linear function f satisfies the conditions : f (-3) = - 16 and f (3) = 20 , find f (x).

36. A polynomial f (x) with real coefficients and leading coefficient 1 has the given zeros and degree. Express f (x) as a product of linear and quadratic polynomials with real coefficients that are irreducible over **R**.

$$7 + 4\,i\,,\,-\,1 + i\,;\,\text{degree 4}$$

37. Find all solutions of the equation.

$$66\,x^5 + 751\,x^4 + 269\,x^3 - 66\,x^2 = 0$$

38. Find an equation of a rational function f that satisfies the conditions:
vertical asymptotes: $x = -4$, $x = 1$
horizontal asymptote: $y = 0$
x-intercept: -2; $f(0) = -2$
hole at $x = 3$

39. Refer to the graph of $y = \cos x$ to find the exact values of x in the interval $[0, \ 4\pi]$ that satisfy the equation.

$$\cos x = -\frac{\sqrt{2}}{2}$$

40. Is the following equation an identity?

$$\frac{\tan u - \tan v}{1 + \cot u \tan v} = \frac{\cot v - \cot u}{\cot u \cot v + 1}$$

41. If $\tan \alpha = -\frac{7}{24}$ and $\cot \beta = \frac{3}{4}$ for a second-quadrant angle α and a third-quadrant angle β, find

$$\sin(\alpha - \beta)$$

42. Use sum-to-product formulas to find the solutions of the equation.
$$\sin 5t + \sin 3t = 0$$

43. Solve $\triangle ABC$

$$a = 2.0, \ b = 3.0, \ c = 4.0$$

angle α: _____ °
angle β: _____ °
angle γ: _____ °

44. A triangular field has sides of lengths a, b, and c (in yards). Approximate the number of acres in the field (1 acre = 4840 yd^2).

$$a = 305 , b = 350 , c = 500$$

Round the answer to the nearest hundredth.

45. A quarterback releases a football with a speed of 40 ft/sec at an angle of $30°$ with the horizontal. Approximate the horizontal component of the vector that is described. Round the answer to the nearest hundredth.

46. Determine m such that the two vectors are orthogonal.

$$3i - 2j \text{ and } 9i + 4mj$$

47. Use De Moivre's theorem to change the given complex number to the form $a + bi$, where a and b are real numbers.

$$(\sqrt{3} + i)^{11}$$

48. Region R is determined by the constraints:

$$y \geq 0,$$

$$3x + y \geq 3,$$
$$x + 5y \leq 15,$$
$$2x + y \leq 12$$

Find the minimum value of

$$C = 4x + y$$

on R.

49. Find the sum of the infinite geometric series :

$$192 + 144 + 108 + 81 + \ldots$$

50. Find a polar equation in r and θ that has the same graph as the equation $x^2 + y^2 = 16$.

Final Exam-Form A

1. 0
2. $\dfrac{1}{20}\cdot\begin{bmatrix} 1 & -11 & -6 \\ 5 & -35 & -30 \\ -1 & 31 & 26 \end{bmatrix}$

3. 12500 tons
4. Proof by Induction
5. 20
6. $3+3i, 3-3i$
7. 16
8. $\left(-\dfrac{10}{13},\dfrac{2}{13}\right)$
9. 7
10. $(-9,10)$
11. $(x-2)^2+(y-1)^2=340$
12. $x\in\left[\dfrac{2}{5},2\right)\cup(2,\infty)$
13. $\dfrac{f(x+h)-f(x)}{h}=2x+h$
14. $f(x)=3x+7$
15. $f(x)=-\dfrac{3}{4}\cdot(x-10)^2+55$

16.

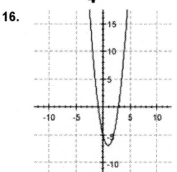

17.

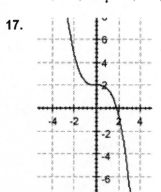

18. $(-1,1)\cup(4,\infty)$
19. 38   **20.**   6

21. $S=720$
22. 13.02
23. 4
24. $x=-6$
25. $p=\dfrac{c}{y^q}$

26. 8.69
27. 13.5
28. $1-\sin(\theta)\cdot\cos(\theta)$
29. $\dfrac{\pi}{6},\dfrac{11\pi}{6},\dfrac{13\pi}{6},\dfrac{23\pi}{6}$
30. $y=0$
31. $y=-\tan\left(x+\dfrac{\pi}{2}\right)$
32. $0,\dfrac{\pi}{4},\pi,\dfrac{5\pi}{4}$
33. $\dfrac{\pi}{6},\dfrac{\pi}{3},\dfrac{5\pi}{6},\dfrac{5\pi}{3}$
34. $\dfrac{240}{289};-\dfrac{161}{289};-\dfrac{240}{161}$
35. $\sqrt{2}-1$
36. $\dfrac{\pi}{8}+\dfrac{\pi}{4}\cdot n,\dfrac{\pi}{4}+\pi\cdot n$
37. 10.02
38. 11, 33
39. $\dfrac{21}{16}$
40. $\left(\dfrac{67}{34},\dfrac{13}{34}\right)$
41. $\left(\dfrac{2}{37},\dfrac{65}{37}\right)$
42. -395226
43. 240
44. 840
45. $(-6,3)$
46. $\dfrac{x^2}{49}+\dfrac{y^2}{9}=1$

47.

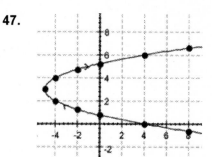

48.

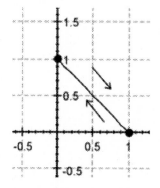

49. $\theta=\arctan\left(-\dfrac{1}{9}\right)$

50. $-\dfrac{\sqrt{15}}{8};-\dfrac{7}{8};\dfrac{\sqrt{15}}{7}$

Final Exam-Form B

1.	d	26.	d
2.	b	27.	c
3.	a	28.	c
4.	b	29.	b
5.	b	30.	a
6.	d	31.	d
7.	c	32.	d
8.	c	33.	c
9.	c	34.	b
10.	a	35.	c
11.	a	36.	a b
12.	d	37.	a
13.	a	38.	f
14.	d	39.	c
15.	c	40.	c
16.	d	41.	b
17.	c	42.	c
18.	d	43.	c
19.	c	44.	a
20.	b	45.	d
21.	e	46.	c
22.	a	47.	c
23.	b	48.	b
24.	b	49.	c
25.	b	50.	b

Final Exam-Form C

1. d
2. a
3. c
4. c
5. d
6. c
7. b
8. c
9. a
10. c
11. d
12. c
13. d
14. c
15. d
16. a
17. b
18. a
19. b
20. c
21. a
22. e
23. c
24. c
25. a

26. $\dfrac{1}{8}, -\dfrac{\sqrt{63}}{8}, -\dfrac{1}{\sqrt{63}}, -\sqrt{63}, -\dfrac{8}{\sqrt{63}}, 8$

27. $3x^2 + 4y^2 + 12x - 36 = 0$

28. $x = -5$

29. $t = \dfrac{\sqrt{v_0^2 + 2s \cdot g} - v_0}{g}$

30. 30
31. $x = 10$
32. $\dfrac{49}{24}$
33. $(0, 20)$
34. $(x - 7)^2 + (y + 5)^2 = 1^2$
35. $f(x) = 6x + 2$

36. $\left(x^2 - 14x + 65\right) \cdot \left(x^2 + 2x + 2\right)$

37. $-11, -\dfrac{6}{11}, \dfrac{1}{6}, 0, 0$

38. $f(x) = \dfrac{4x^2 - 4x - 24}{x^3 - 13x + 12}$

39. $\dfrac{3\pi}{4}, \dfrac{5\pi}{4}, \dfrac{11\pi}{4}, \dfrac{13\pi}{4}$

40. no

41. $-\dfrac{117}{125}$

42. $\dfrac{\pi}{4} \cdot n$

43. $29°, 47°, 104°$

44. 10.88

45. 34.64

46. $\dfrac{27}{8}$

47. $1024\sqrt{3} - 1024i$

48. 3

49. 768

50. $r = 4$